Study Guide and Solutions Book

Organic Chemistry

Fifth Edition

Study Guide and Solutions Book

Organic Chemistry
A Short Course

Fifth Edition

HAROLD HART   *Michigan State University*

ROBERT D. SCHUETZ   *Late of Michigan State University*

HOUGHTON MIFFLIN COMPANY   BOSTON

Dallas   Geneva, Illinois   Hopewell, New Jersey   Palo Alto   London

ISBN: 0-395-25162-1

Contents

Introduction for the Student

This study guide and answer book has been written to help you master the subject matter of the text. The principles and facts of organic chemistry are not easily learned by simply reading them, even repeatedly. Formulas, equations, and molecular structures are best mastered by *written* practice. So to help you become thoroughly familiar with and understand the material, we have included many questions at the end of each chapter in the text.

It is our experience that such questions are not put to their best use unless correct answers are also available. Indeed, answers alone are not enough. If you know how to work a problem, and find that your answer agrees with the correct one, fine; your ego is boosted, and you go on to the next problem with some confidence. But what if you work conscientiously and yet cannot solve the problem? You then succumb to temptation, look up the answer, and encounter another quandary—how in the world did the authors get *that* answer?

This book has been designed with this difficulty in mind. For many of the problems, all the reasoning involved in getting the correct answer is spelled out in detail. Almost all the answers also include cross-references to the text. Such cross-references pertain not only to the chapter where the problem occurs but to earlier chapters as well, thus helping you to review continuously. If you cannot solve a particular problem, these references will also guide you to parts of the text that you should review.

When studying a new subject, it is always helpful to know what is expected of you. To help you, we have included in this study guide a list of objectives for each chapter—that is, a list of what you should be able to do after you have read and studied each chapter. Your instructor may want to delete from these lists of objectives or add to them. However, we believe that if you have mastered these objectives—and the problems are designed to help you do so—you should have no difficulty with examinations in this course. Furthermore, you should be very well prepared for future courses that require this course as a prerequisite.

Finally, we offer you a brief word of advice about how to master the many reactions you will study during this course. First, learn the nomenclature systems thoroughly for each new class of compounds you encounter. Then, rather than memorize the particular example of a reaction that may be given in the text, study reactions as typical of the class of compounds. For example, if you are asked how compound A would react with compound B, proceed in the following way. First ask yourself, To what class of compounds does A belong? How does this class of compounds react with B (or with compounds of the general class to which B belongs)? Then proceed from the general reaction to the specific case at hand. This approach will probably help you to eliminate a great deal of the memory work often associated with organic chemistry courses.

We have prepared a study review (located at the end of this book) that organizes the reactions studied during the course as preparative methods for the various classes of compounds. It also summarizes the various types of reaction mechanisms. We hope that this review will help you to check your knowledge of the subject.

We urge you to study regularly, and we hope that this study guide and answer book will make it easier for you to do so.

A NOTE TO THE INSTRUCTOR

Swelling enrollments in our colleges and universities have had many conse-quences for both professor and student. One of these consequences, an increase in student-to-faculty ratio, has necessarily resulted in a decline in the number of small recitation sections where individual student difficulties can be handled. A greater burden for self-education has been placed on the student's shoulders. We have written this book to help ease this burden.

Before giving the answers to the set of problems that appears at the end of each chapter in the text, we have presented a "List of Objectives" for each chapter—a list of what the student might reasonably be expected to do after reading and studying the material in each chapter. We hope these lists of objectives will help the student distinguish between material that *must* be learned and material that is for enrichment only. The objectives that we have listed may not coincide precisely with your own. In this case we suggest that you add to, delete from, or amend the list as you see fit.

Great effort has been expended to ensure the accuracy of the answers in this book. It is easy for errors to creep in, however, and we will be particularly grate-ful to those who call them to our attention. Suggestions for improving this book will also be welcomed. Send them to Harold Hart in care of the publisher.

H. H.

1. Introduction

OBJECTIVES

1. Know the meaning of electronegative; electropositive; single and multiple bonds; isomerism; molecular and structural formulas; acyclic, carbocyclic, and heterocyclic; functional group.

2. Given a periodic table, determine* the number of valence electrons of an element and write its electron-dot formula.

3. Given an abbreviated structural formula of a compound, write its electron-dot formula.

4. Given a molecular formula, draw the structural formulas for all possible structural isomers.

5. Given a structural formula abbreviated on one line of type, write the complete structure and clearly show the arrangement of atoms in the molecule.

6. Given a line formula, such as ⌒⌒ (pentane), write the complete structure and clearly show the arrangement of atoms in the molecule. Tell how many hydrogens are attached to each carbon, what the molecular formula is, and what the functional groups are.

7. Given a series of structural formulas, recognize compounds that belong to the same class (same functional group).

8. Begin to recognize the important functional groups: alcohol, ether, aldehyde, ketone, carboxylic acid, and amine.

ANSWERS TO THE EXERCISES AND PROBLEMS

1.1. The number of valence electrons is the same as the number in the group of the periodic table (Table 1.1) to which the element belongs.

---

* Although the objectives are often worded in the form of imperatives (i.e., determine . . . , write . . . , draw . . .), these verbs are all to be preceded by the phrase "be able to. . . ." We have omitted this politeness to avoid repetition and to save space.

a. ·Ċ·

d. ·Ḃ

b. :F̈·

e. ·S̈·

c. ·S̈i·

f. ·P̈·

1.2 a. CH_3Cl: Carbon contributes 4 valence electrons, each hydrogen contributes 1, and the chlorine contributes 7. Therefore 14 valence electrons are available to bind the 5 atoms together. This must be done in such a way that the carbon and chlorine have 8 electrons around them, and each hydrogen has 2. Hence

```
      H    ..
H : C : Cl :
      H    ..
```

b. C_3H_8: There are 20 valence electrons (3 × 4 from carbon and 8 × 1 from hydrogen).

```
      H  H  H
H : C : C : C : H
      H  H  H
```

c. C_2H_5F: Again, 20 valence electrons (2 × 4 for carbon, 5 × 1 for hydrogen, and 1 × 7 for fluorine). Halogens (F, Cl, Br, I) usually have three unshared electron pairs.

```
      H  H   ..
H : C : C : F :
      H  H   ..
```

d. CH_3NH_2: The order of attachment is as shown. There is one unshared electron pair remaining on the nitrogen.

```
      H   ..
H : C : N : H
      H  H
```

e. C_2H_5OH: Twenty electrons are available (8 from the two carbons, 6 from the hydrogens, and 6 from the oxygen). The oxygen ends up with two unshared pairs.

```
      H  H   ..
H : C : C : O : H
      H  H   ..
```

f. CH_2O: There are 12 valence electrons altogether (C = 4, H = 1 and O = 6). A double bond between C and O is necessary to put 8 electrons around each of these atoms.

```
      H    ..
H : C : : O :
```

1.3. a.

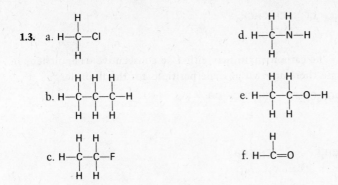

1.4. The four carbons can be arranged in a consecutive chain, or they may be arranged in a chain of three with a branch at the middle carbon.

These compounds are **isomers** (same molecular formula, C_4H_{10}, but different structural formulas). The formulas can be abbreviated to

$$CH_3CH_2CH_2CH_3 \quad \text{and} \quad \underset{\underset{CH_3}{|}}{CH_3CHCH_3}$$

1.5. a. C_3H_8: $CH_3CH_2CH_3$

b. C_3H_8O: The oxygen, which is divalent, can be attached to two carbons, or to a carbon and a hydrogen.

$$CH_3-O-CH_2CH_3 \quad CH_3CH_2CH_2OH \quad \underset{\underset{OH}{|}}{CH_3CHCH_3}$$

c. $C_2H_4Cl_2$: The chlorines can either be attached to the same carbon or to different carbons.

$$CH_3CHCl_2 \quad ClCH_2-CH_2Cl$$

d. C_3H_6: There are two fewer hydrogens than in part a. Therefore there must be either a double bond or a ring.

$$CH_3CH{=}CH_2 \quad \underset{\underset{CH_2}{\diagdown\diagup}}{CH_2-CH_2}$$

e. C_3H_7Cl: Compare with part a. The chlorine can replace one of the hydrogens on an end carbon, or one of the hydrogens on the middle carbon.

$CH_3CH_2CH_2Cl$ CH_3CHCH_3
                        |
                        Cl

f. C_4H_9F: The carbon chain may either be consecutive or branched; in each case there are two possible positions for the fluorine.

$CH_3CH_2CH_2CH_2F$ $CH_3CHCH_2CH_3$
                          |
                          F

                              F
                              |
CH_3CHCH_2F CH_3CCH_3
      | |
      CH_3 CH_3

1.6. C_6H_{14}: The problem should be approached systematically. Consider first a chain of six carbons, then a chain of five carbons with a one-carbon branch, and so on.

$CH_3CH_2CH_2CH_2CH_2CH_3$

$CH_3CHCH_2CH_2CH_3$
      |
      CH_3

$CH_3CH_2CHCH_2CH_3$
          |
          CH_3

            CH_3
            |
$CH_3-C-CH_2-CH_3$
            |
            CH_3

$CH_3CH-CHCH_3$
      | |
      CH_3 CH_3

1.7 a. $CH_3CH_2CH_2CH_2CH_2CH_3$

          CH_3
          |
  b. $CH_3-C-CH_2CH_3$
          |
          CH_3

  c. CH_3CHCH_3
          |
          OH

  d. $CH_3CH_2SCH_2CH_3$

  e. CH_2-CH_2
      | |
      Cl   OH

          CH_3
          |
  f. $CH_3-N-CH_2CH_3$

1.8. See Section 1.5 for examples of what these "stick" formulas mean.

  a. $CH_2=CH-CH_2CH_3$

          CH_2
        /   \
  b. CH_2 CH
        | ‖
        CH_2-CH

      CH_3 CH_3
        \   /
  c.   CH-CH
        /   \
      CH_3 CH_3

  d. $CH_3CH_2CHCH_2CHCH_2CH_3$
              | |
              CH_3 CH_2CH_3

  e. $CH_3CH_2OCH_2CH_3$

        CH_3 CH_3
        | |
  f. $CH_3-C-C-CH_3$
        | |
        CH_3 CH_3

1.9. See Section 1.5 for the meaning of these formulas.

  a. 10

  b. $C_{10}H_{18}O$

$$\text{c. } (CH_3)_2C{=}CHCH_2CH_2\overset{\overset{\displaystyle CH_3}{|}}{C}{=}CHCH_2OH$$

d. Two double bonds and one hydroxyl group. Geraniol is an unsaturated alcohol.

1.10. First count the carbons, then the hydrogens, and last the remaining atoms.

a. $C_{16}H_{30}O$

b. C_6H_6

c. $C_{19}H_{28}O_2$

d. $C_{10}H_{14}N_2$

1.11. Many correct answers are possible. Here are a few.

a. $CH_3CH_2\overset{\overset{\displaystyle O}{\|}}{C}CH_2CH_3$

$$CH_2{=}CH{-}\underset{\underset{\displaystyle OH}{|}}{CH}{-}CH_2CH_3$$

b.
$$\begin{array}{c}
CH_2{-}CH_2 \\
\diagup \qquad \diagdown \\
CH_2 \qquad\quad CH_2 \\
\diagdown \qquad \diagup \\
CH \\
| \\
OH
\end{array}$$

$$\begin{array}{l}
CH_2{-}CH{-}CH_2OH \\
\,| \qquad\;\; | \\
CH_2{-}CH_2
\end{array}$$

c. $\overset{\displaystyle O}{\overset{\diagup\!\diagdown}{CH_2{-}CH}}CH_2CH_2CH_3$

$$\begin{array}{c}
\quad O \\
\diagup\;\diagdown \\
CH_2 \qquad CH_2 \\
|\qquad\qquad | \\
CH_2 \qquad CH_2 \\
\diagdown \qquad \diagup \\
CH_2
\end{array}$$

1.12. *a*, *c*, *e*, and *g* all have hydroxyl groups and belong to the class of compounds called alcohols. *b*, *h*, and *i* are ethers; they all have a C—O—C bond. *d* and *f* are both hydrocarbons.

1.13. The common functional groups are described in Section 1.6b. Sometimes more than one answer is possible.

a. $CH_3CH_2CH_2CH_2OH$, $CH_3CH(OH)CH_2CH_3$, $(CH_3)_2CHCH_2OH$, and $(CH_3)_3COH$

b. $CH_3OCH_2CH_2CH_3$, $CH_3OCH(CH_3)_2$, and $CH_3CH_2OCH_2CH_3$

c. $CH_3CH_2\overset{\overset{\displaystyle O}{\|}}{C}H$ (only correct answer)

d. $CH_3\overset{\overset{\displaystyle O}{\|}}{C}CH_3$ (only correct answer)

e. $CH_3\overset{\overset{\displaystyle O}{\|}}{C}{-}OH$ (only correct answer)

f. $CH_3\overset{\overset{\displaystyle O}{\|}}{C}{-}O{-}CH_2CH_3$ or any of the answers shown in part g.

g. $CH_3CH_2\overset{\overset{\displaystyle O}{\|}}{C}{-}O{-}CH_3$, $H{-}\overset{\overset{\displaystyle O}{\|}}{C}{-}OCH_2CH_2CH_3$, and $H{-}\overset{\overset{\displaystyle O}{\|}}{C}{-}OCH(CH_3)_2$

h. $CH_3CH_2NH_2$ or CH_3NHCH_3

2. Bonding in Organic Compounds

OBJECTIVES

1. Know the meaning of: ionic and covalent bonds; formal charge; resonance and resonance hybrid; atomic and molecular orbitals; hybrid orbitals; sigma (σ) bonds; and the tetrahedral geometry of sp^3 hybrid orbitals.

2. Given the formula of a compound and a periodic table, classify the compound as ionic or covalent.

3. Given a covalent bond, tell whether it is polar. If it is, predict the direction of bond polarity from the electronegativities of the atoms.

4. Given a simple molecular formula, draw the electron-dot formula and determine whether each atom in the structure carries a formal charge.

5. Draw electron-dot formulas that show all important contributors to a resonance hybrid.

6. Construct diagrams, such as Figure 2.4, that show the electron distributions in orbitals of first-row elements (especially C, N, and O) before and after hybridization.

7. Predict the geometry of bonds around an atom, knowing the electron distribution in the orbitals.

8. Construct the orbital pictures of methane and ethane showing orbital overlap, as in Figure 2.8.

9. Draw in three dimensions the tetrahedral bonding around sp^3-hybridized carbon atoms.

ANSWERS TO THE EXERCISES AND PROBLEMS

2.1. In sodium chloride, Cl is present as chloride ion (Cl^-); Cl^- reacts with Ag^+ to give AgCl, a white precipitate. The C—Cl bonds in CCl_4 are covalent; no Cl^- is present to react with the Ag^+.

2.2. Ionic compounds are formed from elements that differ widely in their electronegativity: NaF, $MgCl_2$, and LiCl. Covalent compounds are formed from elements with identical or similar electronegativities: F_2, P_2S_5, and S_2Cl_2.

2.3. a. 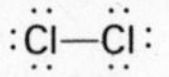 :Cl—Cl: Since the bond is between identical atoms, it is pure covalent (nonpolar).

b. 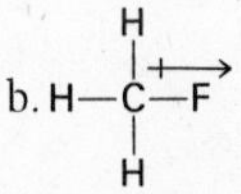 H—C—F with H above and below   Fluorine is more electronegative than carbon.

c. 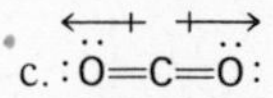 :O=C=O: The C=O bond is polar, and the oxygen is more electronegative than carbon. However, since the CO_2 molecule is linear, the bond dipole moments act in equal and opposite directions and thus cancel each other. Therefore the whole molecule is nonpolar.

d. 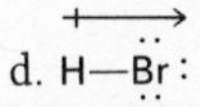 H—Br: The halogens are more electronegative than hydrogen.

e. 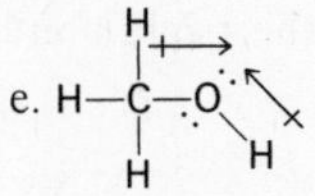 H—C—O—H with H above and below   Both the C—O and H—O bonds are polar, and the oxygen is more eletronegative than either carbon or hydrogen.

f. 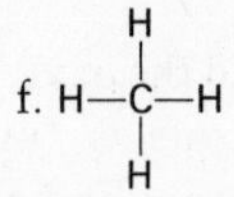 H—C—H with H above and below   Carbon and hydrogen have nearly identical electronegativities, and the bonds are essentially nonpolar.

2.4. Oxygen is much more electronegative than carbon; therefore the O—H hydrogen is more acidic than the CH_3 hydrogens. The reaction of acetic acid with sodium is similar to the reaction of methyl alcohol with sodium (Eq. 2.3).

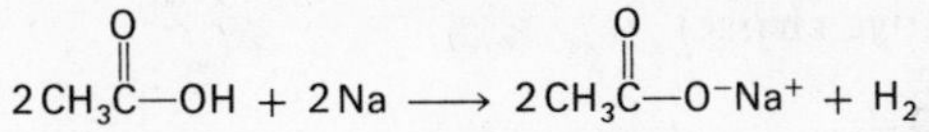

$$2\,CH_3\overset{O}{\overset{\|}{C}}-OH + 2\,Na \longrightarrow 2\,CH_3\overset{O}{\overset{\|}{C}}-O^-Na^+ + H_2$$

2.5. a. HONO   First determine the total number of valence electrons; H = 1, O = 2 × 6 = 12, N = 5, for a total of 18. These must be arranged in pairs so that the hydrogen has two and the other atoms have eight electrons around them.

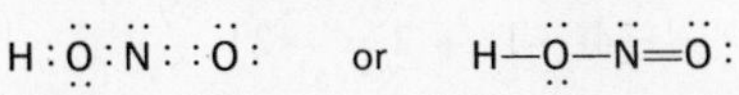

         H:O:N::O: or   H—O—N=O:

Review Section 2.2a for guidance in evaluating formal charge. None of the atoms in nitrous acid has a formal charge. For example, if we use the formula:

formal charge = periodic group − (covalent bonds + unshared elecrons)

we get for N: 5 − (3 + 2) = 0.

b. $HONO_2$

$$H : \overset{..}{O} : \overset{..}{N} : \overset{:\overset{..}{O}: \leftarrow (-)}{\underset{\zeta \; :\overset{..}{O}.}{}}$$ (24 valence electrons)

(+)

The nitrogen has a $+1$ formal charge, and the singly bound oxygen has a -1 formal charge. The whole molecule is neutral.

c. H_2CO

$$H : \overset{H}{\underset{}{C}} : : \overset{..}{O} :$$ No formal charges.

d. $NH_4{}^+$

$$H : \overset{H}{\underset{H}{N}} : H \; (+)$$ The nitrogen has a $+1$ formal charge.

e. CN^-

There are a total of 10 valence electrons ($C = 4, N = 5$ plus one more because of the negative charge).

$$\overset{\ominus}{} : C : : : N :$$

The carbon has a -1 formal charge (one unshared electron pair $+3$ electrons from the triple bond).

f. CO

There are 10 valence electrons.

$$: C : : : O :$$

The carbon has a -1 formal charge, and the oxygen has a $+1$ formal charge. Carbon monoxide is "isoelectronic" with cyanide ion but has no net charge ($-1 + 1 = 0$).

g. $SO_4{}^{2-}$

There are 32 valence electrons (six each from the sulfur and oxygens, plus two more because of the double negative charge).

$$: \overset{..}{O} : \\ : \overset{..}{O} : \overset{..}{S} : \overset{..}{O} : \\ : \overset{..}{O} :$$

Each oxygen has a formal charge of -1; the sulfur has a formal charge of $+2$. The net charge is therefore -2 $[4(-1) + 2 = -2]$.

h. BF_3

There are 24 valence electrons ($B = 3, F = 7$). The structure is usually written with only six electrons around the boron.

$$: \overset{..}{F} : \\ \overset{}{B} : \overset{..}{F} : \\ : \overset{..}{F} :$$

In this case, there are no formal charges. This structure shows that BF_3 is a Lewis acid, anxious to accept an electron pair to complete the octet around the boron.

2.6. $H-\overset{..}{\underset{..}{O}}: ^- + H \overset{\overset{H}{|}}{\underset{\underset{H}{|}}{-N}} -H \rightleftharpoons H-\overset{..}{\underset{..}{O}}-H + :\overset{\overset{H}{|}}{\underset{\underset{H}{|}}{N}}-H$

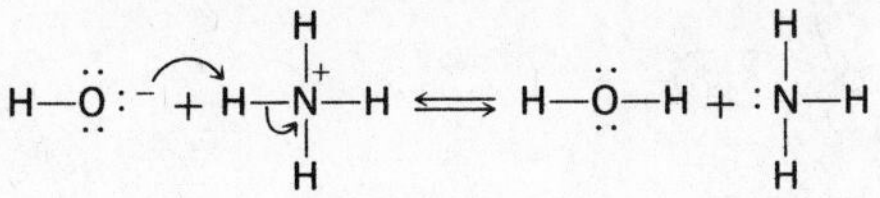

2.7. There are 24 valence electrons in nitrate ion; to arrange these with 8 electrons around each atom we must have one double bond. There are three such equivalent structures.

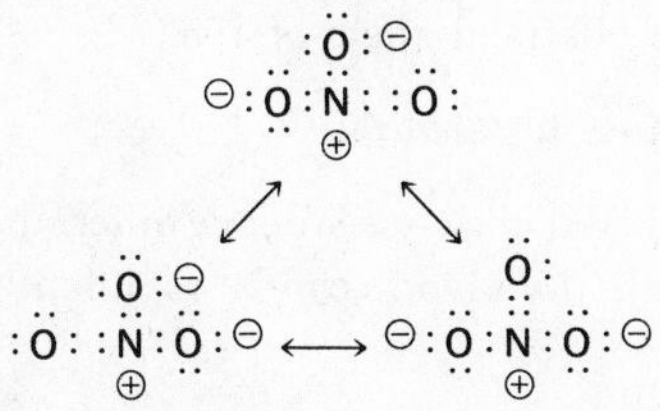

$$:\overset{..}{\underset{..}{O}}:^{\ominus}$$
$$^{\ominus}:\overset{..}{\underset{..}{O}}:\underset{\oplus}{N}::\overset{..}{\underset{..}{O}}:$$

$$:\overset{..}{\underset{..}{O}}:^{\ominus} \qquad \overset{..}{\underset{..}{O}}:$$
$$:\overset{..}{\underset{..}{O}}::\underset{\oplus}{N}:\overset{..}{\underset{..}{O}}:^{\ominus} \longleftrightarrow {}^{\ominus}:\overset{..}{\underset{..}{O}}:\underset{\oplus}{N}:\overset{..}{\underset{..}{O}}:^{\ominus}$$

In each structure, the nitrogen has a formal charge of $+1$, and the two singly bound oxygens each carry a formal charge of -1, for a net -1 charge on the ion. If we use lines for the bonds, the structures can be drawn as below; the curved arrows then show the relationship between the structures.

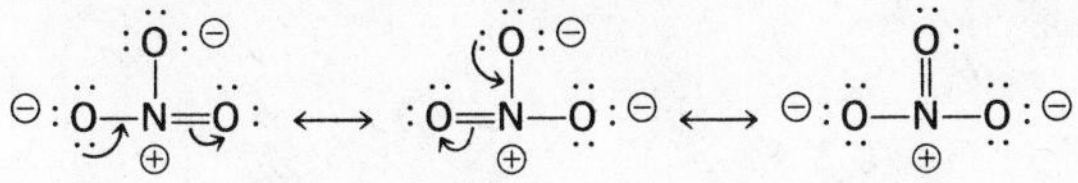

$$:\overset{..}{\underset{..}{O}}:^{\ominus} \qquad \overset{..}{O}:^{\ominus} \qquad \overset{..}{O}:$$
$$^{\ominus}:\overset{..}{\underset{..}{O}}\underset{\oplus}{N}=\overset{..}{\underset{..}{O}}: \longleftrightarrow :\overset{..}{O}=\underset{\oplus}{N}-\overset{..}{\underset{..}{O}}:^{\ominus} \longleftrightarrow {}^{\ominus}:\overset{..}{\underset{..}{O}}-\underset{\oplus}{N}-\overset{..}{\underset{..}{O}}:^{\ominus}$$

2.8. If the s and p orbitals were hybridized sp^3, two electrons would go into one

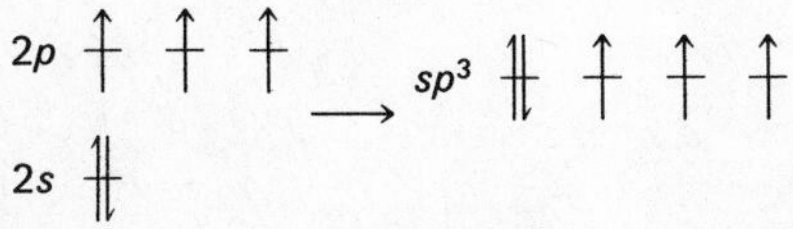

$$2p \; \uparrow \; \uparrow \; \uparrow \qquad \underset{\longrightarrow}{} \qquad sp^3 \; \uparrow\downarrow \; \uparrow \; \uparrow \; \uparrow$$
$$2s \; \uparrow\downarrow$$

of these orbitals and one electron would go into each of the remaining three orbitals. The predicted geometry of ammonia would then be tetrahedral, with one hydrogen at each of three corners, and the unshared pair at the fourth corner. In fact, ammonia has a pyramidal shape—a somewhat flattened tetrahedron. The bond angle is $107°$ rather than $109° \, 28'$.

2.9. The ammonium ion is in fact isoelectronic (has the same arrangement of electrons) with methane, and consequently has the same geometry. Four sp^3 orbitals of nitrogen each contain one electron (see the answer to Question 2.8); these orbitals then overlap with the $1s$ hydrogen orbitals, as in Figure 2.8.

2.10. If the oxygen nucleus is at the origin of a coordinate system, as shown on p. 10, then it has one electron in each of two mutually perpendicular p orbitals. These overlap, then, with $1s$ hydrogen orbitals to produce a water molecule with a $90°$ H—O—H angle (the two unshared electron pairs on oxygen would be in a $2s$ and a $2p$ orbital, not shown). Actually, water is isoelectronic with methane and ammonia, and it is therefore nearly tetrahedral. The unshared electron pairs take up somewhat more space than the bonds to the hydrogen atoms do. Therefore the H—O—H angle is compressed, from 109° 28′ to the observed angle of 105°.

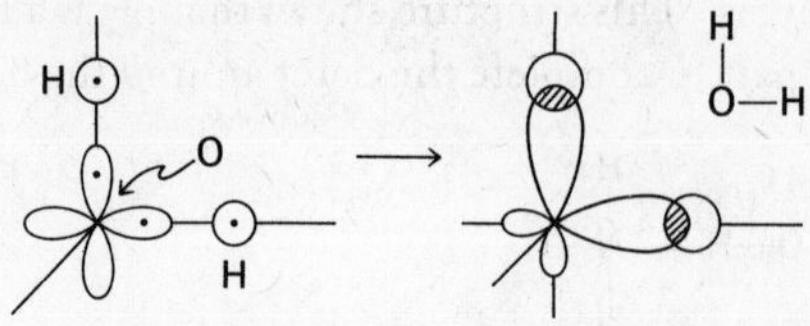

2.11. The bonding is exactly as in methane: tetrahedral.

2.12. The rings must be mutually perpendicular as a consequence of tetrahedral bonding at the spiro carbon (see Figure 2.9). β-Vetivone can be represented by the following three-dimensional structure:

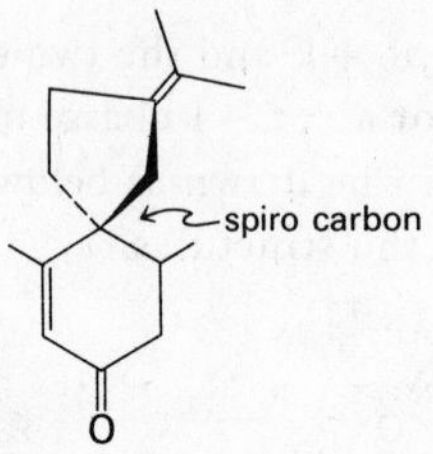

3. Saturated Hydrocarbons; Geometric and Conformational Isomerism

OBJECTIVES

1. Know the meaning of: saturated hydrocarbon or alkane; IUPAC nomenclature; homologous series; methylene and alkyl groups; carbanion, carbocation, and free radical; electrophile and nucleophile; substitution and halogenation; chain reaction; combustion; cycloalkane; geometric or cis-trans isomerism; conformation; staggered and eclipsed; Newman projection formula; chair conformation of cyclohexane; axial and equatorial bonds.

2. Given the IUPAC name of an alkane or cycloalkane, or a halogen-substituted alkane or cycloalkane, draw its structural formula.

3. The converse of Objective 2. (Given the structure, supply the IUPAC name.)

4. Know the common names of the alkyl groups, cycloalkyl groups, methylene halides, and haloforms.

5. Tell whether two hydrogens in a particular structure are identical or different from one another, by determining whether they give the same or different products by monosubstitution with some group X.

6. Know the relationship between boiling points of alkanes and (a) their molecular weights, and (b) the extent of chain branching.

7. Write all the steps in the free-radical chain reaction between a halogen and an alkane, and identify the catalyst, initiation, propagation, and termination steps.

8. Write a balanced equation for the complete combustion of an alkane or cycloalkane.

9. Draw, using sawhorse or Newman projection formulas, the important conformations of ethane, propane, butane, and various halogenated derivatives of these alkanes.

10. Recognize, draw, and name cis-trans isomers of substituted cycloalkanes.

11. Draw the chair conformation of cyclohexane, clearly showing the distinction between axial and equatorial bonds.

12. Identify the more stable conformation of a monosubstituted cyclohexane; also, identify substituents as axial or equatorial when the structure is "flipped" from one chair conformation to another.

ANSWERS TO THE EXERCISES AND PROBLEMS

3.1. a. 3-Methylpentane: first, locate the root of the name (in this case, *pent*), write down and number the carbon chain.

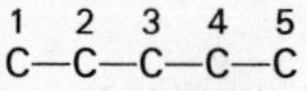

$$
\begin{array}{ccccc}
1 & 2 & 3 & 4 & 5 \\
C{-}C{-}C{-}C{-}C
\end{array}
$$

Next, locate the substituents (3-methyl)

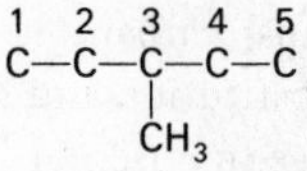

$$
\begin{array}{ccccc}
1 & 2 & 3 & 4 & 5 \\
C{-}C{-}C{-}C{-}C \\
 & & | & & \\
 & & CH_3 & &
\end{array}
$$

Finally, fill in the remaining hydrogens.

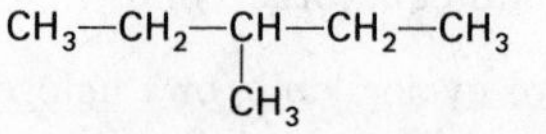

$$CH_3{-}CH_2{-}\underset{\underset{CH_3}{|}}{CH}{-}CH_2{-}CH_3$$

b. 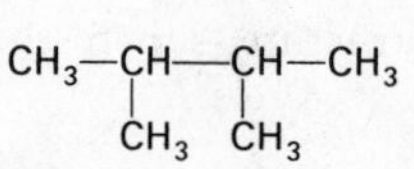 $CH_3{-}\underset{\underset{CH_3}{|}}{CH}{-}\underset{\underset{CH_3}{|}}{CH}{-}CH_3$

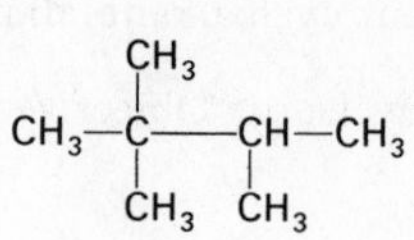

c. 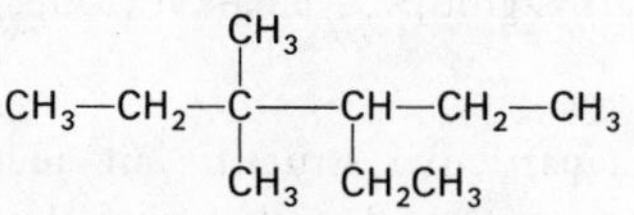 $CH_3{-}CH_2{-}\overset{\overset{CH_3}{|}}{\underset{\underset{CH_3}{|}}{C}}{-}\underset{\underset{CH_2CH_3}{|}}{CH}{-}CH_2{-}CH_3$

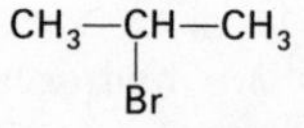

d. 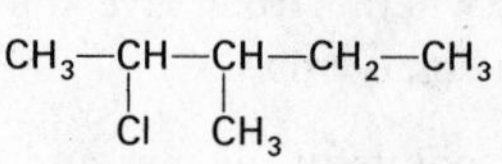 $CH_3{-}\underset{\underset{Cl}{|}}{CH}{-}\underset{\underset{CH_3}{|}}{CH}{-}CH_2{-}CH_3$

e. $CH_3{-}\overset{\overset{CH_3}{|}}{\underset{\underset{CH_3}{|}}{C}}{-}\underset{\underset{CH_3}{|}}{CH}{-}CH_3$

f. $CH_3{-}\underset{\underset{Br}{|}}{CH}{-}CH_3$

g. 1,1-Dichlorocyclopropane: The root *prop* indicates three carbons; the prefix *cyclo* designates that they form a ring:

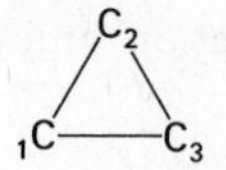

The substituents are placed:

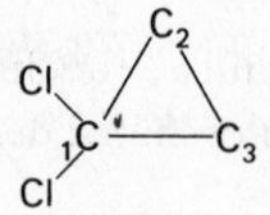

And the hydrogens are filled in:

$$Cl-\underset{\underset{Cl}{|}}{C}\overset{\overset{CH_2}{\diagup\diagdown}}{\diagdown}CH_2$$

h. $\underset{\overset{|}{Cl}}{Cl-CH}-CH_2-\underset{\overset{|}{Cl}}{CH}-Cl$ or $CHCl_2CH_2CHCl_2$

3.2. a. $CH_3CH_2CH_2CH_2CH_3$

pentane

b. $\overset{1}{CH_3}\underset{\underset{CH_3}{|}}{\overset{2}{CH}}\overset{3}{CH_2}\overset{4}{CH_3}$

2-methylbutane

c. $CH_3CH_2\underset{\underset{CH_3}{|}}{\overset{\overset{CH_3}{|}}{C}}CH_2CH_3$

3,3-dimethylpentane

d. $CH_3CH_2CH_2\underset{\underset{CH_3}{|}}{\overset{\overset{CH_3}{|}}{C}}CH_3$

2,2-dimethylpentane

e. $CH_3CH_2\underset{\overset{|}{Br}}{CH}CH_3$

2-bromobutane

f. $CH_3\underset{\overset{|}{Cl}}{\overset{\overset{Cl}{|}}{C}}-\underset{\overset{|}{Br}}{\overset{\overset{Br}{|}}{C}}-Br$

1,1,1-tribromo-2,2-dichloropropane

The placement of commas and hyphens is important; the answer to this question shows clearly how these punctuation marks are to be used.

g. $CH_3CH_2\underset{\underset{CH_2CH_3}{|}}{\overset{\overset{CH_2CH_3}{|}}{C}}CH_2CH_3$

3,3-diethylpentane

h. $\underset{\overset{|}{Cl}}{\overset{2}{CH_2}}-\underset{\overset{|}{Br}}{\overset{1}{CH_2}}$

1-bromo-2-chloroethane

The priority of the halogens follows alphabetical order.

i. $\underset{\overset{|}{Br}}{\overset{1}{CH_2}}-\underset{\overset{|}{CH_3}}{\overset{2}{CH}}-\underset{\overset{|}{CH_3}}{\overset{3}{CH}}-\overset{4}{CH_3}$

1-bromo-2,3-dimethylbutane

We use the longest chain that contains the most distinctive substituent (in this case, Br).

j. $\underset{CH_2-CH_2}{CH_2\overset{\overset{CH_2}{\diagup\diagdown}}{}CH_2}$

cyclopentane

3.3.   *Common*   *IUPAC*

      a. Methyl iodide   Iodomethane

      b. Ethyl chloride   Chloroethane

      c. Methylene chloride   Dichloromethane
         (CH_2 = methylene)

      d. Bromoform   Tribromomethane

      e. *n*-Propyl chloride   1-Chloropropane

      f. Isopropyl bromide   2-Bromopropane

      g. Chloroform   Trichloromethane

      h. Cyclobutyl chloride   Chlorocyclobutane

3.4   a.
$$\overset{1}{C}H_3-\overset{2}{C}H_2-\overset{3}{C}H_2-\overset{4}{C}H-\overset{5}{C}H_3 \qquad \text{4-methylpentane}$$
$$\underset{\displaystyle CH_3}{\mid}$$

The chain should be numbered from the other end, to give the methyl substituent the lowest possible number:

$$\overset{5}{C}H_3-\overset{4}{C}H_2-\overset{3}{C}H_2-\overset{2}{C}H-\overset{1}{C}H_3 \qquad \text{2-methylpentane}$$
$$\underset{\displaystyle CH_3}{\mid}$$

      b.
$$\overset{1}{C}H_3-\overset{2}{C}H-\overset{3}{C}H_2-\overset{4}{C}H_3 \qquad \text{2-ethylbutane}$$
$$\underset{\displaystyle CH_2}{\mid}$$
$$\underset{\displaystyle CH_3}{\mid}$$

The longest chain was not selected. The correct numbering is

$$\overset{3}{C}H_3-\overset{4}{C}H-\overset{5}{C}H_2-\overset{5}{C}H_3 \qquad \text{3-methylpentane}$$
$$\underset{\displaystyle 2CH_2}{\mid}$$
$$\underset{\displaystyle 1CH_3}{\mid}$$

      c. Numbering started at the wrong end. The name should be 1,2-dichloropropane.

$$\overset{1}{C}-\overset{2}{C}-\overset{3}{C}$$
$$\underset{\displaystyle Cl}{\mid}\;\underset{\displaystyle Cl}{\mid}$$

      d. The ring was numbered the wrong way around to give the lowest substituent numbers. The correct name is 1,2-dimethylcyclobutane.

$$\begin{array}{c} C\;\underset{1}{\diagdown}\;\underset{2}{\diagup}\;C \\ C-C \\ \underset{4}{\mid}\quad\underset{3}{\mid} \\ C-C \end{array}$$

e. The longest chain was not selected. The correct name is 2-methylpentane.

```
1
C
|2  3  4
C—C—C
|     |5
C     C
```

f. 1-Bromo-2-methylpropane (use the lower number)

```
      C
3    |2  1
C—C—C
     |
     Br
```

3.5. Approach each problem systematically. Start with the longest possible carbon chain and shorten it one carbon at a time until no further isomers are possible. To conserve space, the formulas below are written in condensed form, but you should write them out using expanded formulas.

a. $CH_3(CH_2)_2CH_3$ butane
    $(CH_3)_3CH$ 2-methylpropane

b. $CH_3CH_2CH_2CH_2Br$ 1-bromobutane
    $CH_3CHBrCH_2CH_3$ 2-bromobutane
    $(CH_3)_2CHCH_2Br$ 1-bromo-2-methylpropane
    $(CH_3)_3CBr$ 2-bromo-2-methylpropane

c. $CH_3(CH_2)_4CH_3$ hexane
    $CH_3CH(CH_3)CH_2CH_2CH_3$ 2-methylpentane
    $CH_3CH_2CH(CH_3)CH_2CH_3$ 3-methylpentane
    $CH_3CH(CH_3)CH(CH_3)CH_3$ 2,3-dimethylbutane
    $CH_3C(CH_3)_2CH_2CH_3$ 2,2-dimethylbutane

d. $CH_3CH_2CHBr_2$ 1,1-dibromopropane
    $CH_3CHBrCH_2Br$ 1,2-dibromopropane
    $CH_2BrCH_2CH_2Br$ 1,3-dibromopropane
    $CH_3CBr_2CH_3$ 2,2-dibromopropane

3.6. The less chain branching and the higher the molecular weight, the higher the boiling point. On these grounds, the order should be, from lowest to highest, *e, d, c, a, b*. The actual boiling points are as follows: 2-methylpentane (60°), hexane (69°), 3,3-dimethylpentane (86°), 2-methylhexane (90°), heptane (98.4°).

3.7. For definitions of these species, see Section 3.6a.

```
        H
        |
a.  H—C+
        |
        H
```

```
        H  H
        |  |
b.  H—C—C·
        |  |
        H  H
```

c. 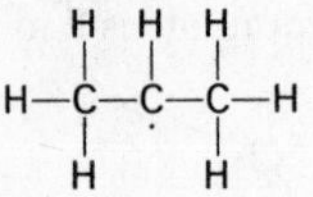 $H-\overset{\overset{\displaystyle H}{|}}{\underset{\underset{\displaystyle H}{|}}{C}}-\overset{\overset{\displaystyle H}{|}}{\underset{\underset{\displaystyle H}{|}}{C}}-\overset{\overset{\displaystyle H}{|}}{C}-H$

d. 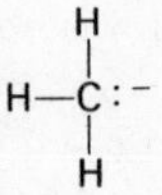 $H-\overset{\overset{\displaystyle H}{|}}{\underset{\underset{\displaystyle H}{|}}{C}}:^{-}$

3.8. The equations follow the same pattern as Eq. 3.5 through Eq. 3.10.

$Cl_2 \xrightarrow[\text{sunlight}]{\text{heat or}} 2:\ddot{C}l\cdot$ initiation

$CH_3CH_3 + Cl\cdot \longrightarrow CH_3CH_2\cdot + HCl$

$CH_3CH_2\cdot + Cl_2 \longrightarrow CH_3CH_2Cl + Cl\cdot$ } propagation

$CH_3CH_2\cdot + :\ddot{C}l\cdot \longrightarrow CH_3CH_2Cl$

$2:\ddot{C}l\cdot \longrightarrow Cl_2$ } termination

$2\ CH_3CH_2\cdot \longrightarrow CH_3CH_2CH_2CH_3$

3.9. Methyl radicals are produced as reactive fragments during the chlorination of methane (Eq. 3.6). If two such radicals were to combine, one would obtain ethane (Eq. 3.9), which could be further chlorinated. This observation, then, tends to support the mechanism. The amount of ethane produced should be small, since its formation requires collision between two fragments that are present in low concentration. It is much more likely that a mehyl radical will encounter a methane or chlorine molecule than another methyl radical.

3.10. The four possible structures are

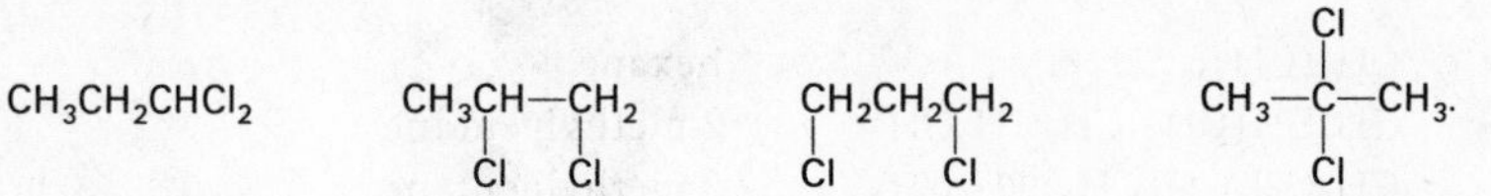

$CH_3CH_2CHCl_2$　　　$CH_3\underset{\underset{\displaystyle Cl}{|}}{C}H-\underset{\underset{\displaystyle Cl}{|}}{C}H_2$　　　$\underset{\underset{\displaystyle Cl}{|}}{C}H_2CH_2\underset{\underset{\displaystyle Cl}{|}}{C}H_2$　　　$CH_3-\overset{\overset{\displaystyle Cl}{|}}{\underset{\underset{\displaystyle Cl}{|}}{C}}-CH_3.$

1,1-dichloropropane　　1,2-dichloropropane　　1,3-dichloropropane　　2,2-dichloropropane

Only the last of these has all hydrogens equivalent and can give only *one* trichloro compound. This must therefore be C:

$CH_3CCl_2CH_3 \xrightarrow{Cl_2} CH_3CCl_2CH_2Cl$

1,3-Dichloropropane has only two different "kinds" of hydrogen. It must be D:

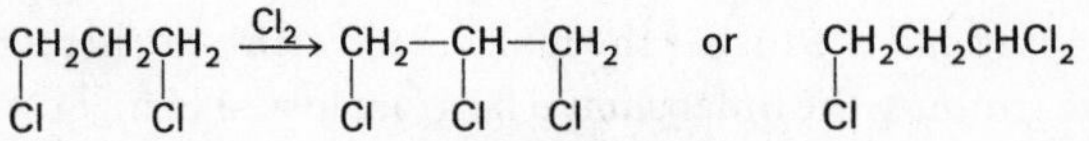

$\underset{\underset{\displaystyle Cl}{|}}{C}H_2CH_2\underset{\underset{\displaystyle Cl}{|}}{C}H_2 \xrightarrow{Cl_2} \underset{\underset{\displaystyle Cl}{|}}{C}H_2-\underset{\underset{\displaystyle Cl}{|}}{C}H-\underset{\underset{\displaystyle Cl}{|}}{C}H_2$　or　$\underset{\underset{\displaystyle Cl}{|}}{C}H_2CH_2CHCl_2$

　　Next, A must be capable of giving 1,2,2-trichloropropane (the product from C). This is not possible for the 1,1-isomer, since it already has two chlorines on carbon 1. Therefore A must be

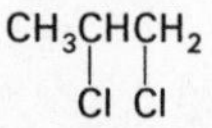

$CH_3\underset{\underset{\displaystyle Cl}{|}}{C}H\underset{\underset{\displaystyle Cl}{|}}{C}H_2$

since it can give the 1,2,2-trichloro product (as well as 1,1,2- and 1,2,3-).
　　By elimination, B is $CH_3CH_2CHCl_2$.

3.11. a. $CH_3CH_2CH_2CH_2CH_3 + 8\,O_2 \longrightarrow 5\,CO_2 + 6\,H_2O$

b. 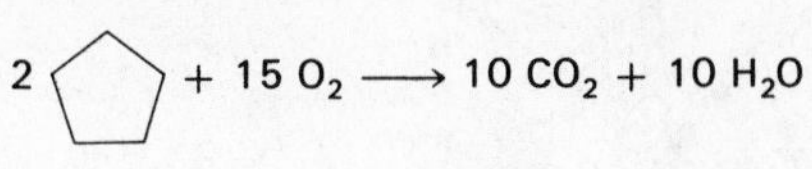 2 $+ 15\,O_2 \longrightarrow 10\,CO_2 + 10\,H_2O$

c. $CH_3CH_2CH_3 + Br_2 \longrightarrow CH_3CH_2CH_2Br$ or $CH_3\underset{\underset{Br}{|}}{C}HCH_3 + HBr$

d. 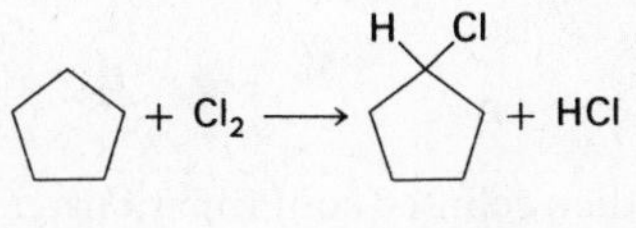 $+ Cl_2 \longrightarrow$ $+ HCl$

3.12. We can get 1,1- or 1,2- or 1,3-dichlorocyclopentanes. Of these, the last two types can exist as cis-trans isomers.

1,1-dichlorocyclopentane   *cis*-1,2-dichlorocyclopentane   *trans*-1,2-dichlorocyclopentane

cis-1,3-dichlorocyclopentane   *trans*-1,3-dichlorocyclopentane

3.13. The conformations are as shown for ethane in Fig. 3.5, except that one of the hydrogens is replaced by a methyl group.

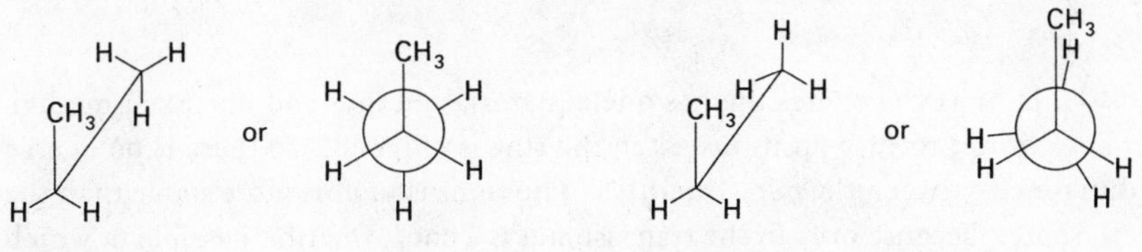

staggered   or      eclipsed   or

3.14.

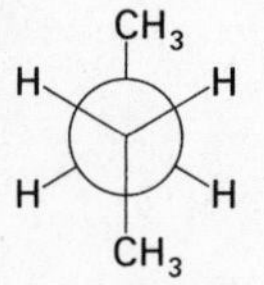

most stable staggered
conformation

A

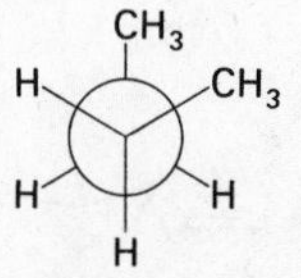

less stable staggered conformation
(large groups are closer together)

B

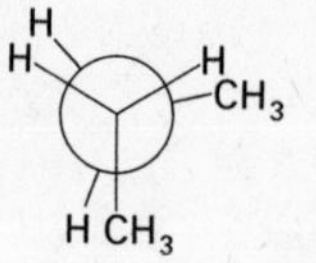

less stable than the staggered, but more stable than the eclipsed conformation with two methyls eclipsed

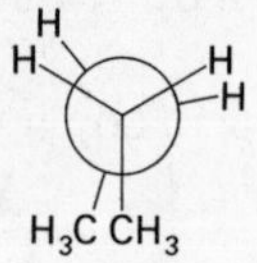

least stable of all four conformations

C

D

Staggered conformations are more stable than eclipsed conformations. Therefore **A** and **B** are more stable than **C** or **D**. Within each pair, CH_3—CH_3 interactions (for methyls on adjacent carbons) are to be avoided because of the large size of these groups.

3.15.

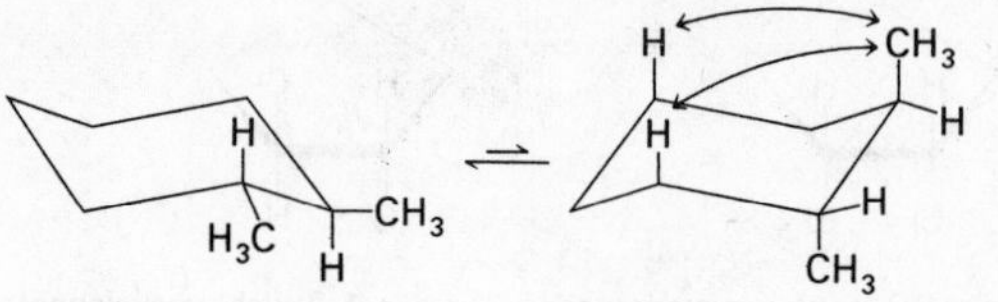

ee   aa

trans-1,2-Dimethylcyclohexane can exist in a conformation where both methyls are equatorial (ee) or in which both methyls are axial (aa). Of these, the ee form is by far the more stable, since it avoids serious 1,3-diaxial interactions.

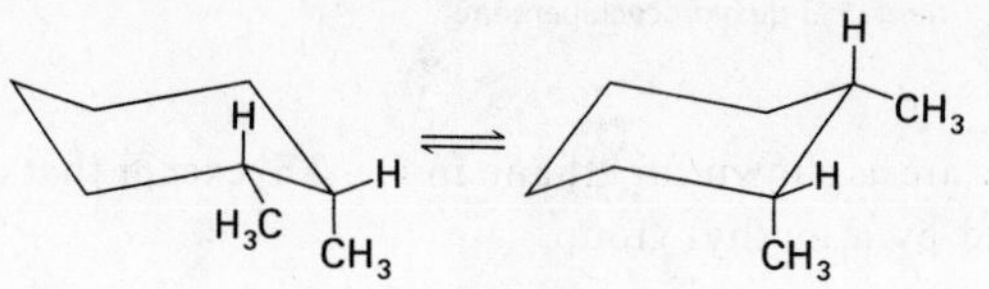

ea   ae

cis-1,2-Dimethylcyclohexane has one equatorial methyl and one axial methyl. These groups reverse positions when the ring is "flipped," so there is no energy difference between the two structures. The trans isomer is more stable than the cis isomer, because only in the trans isomer is a conformation possible in which both methyls are equatorial. There is no way that the trans and cis isomers can interconvert, since doing so would require bond-breaking processes.

3.16. cis-1,3

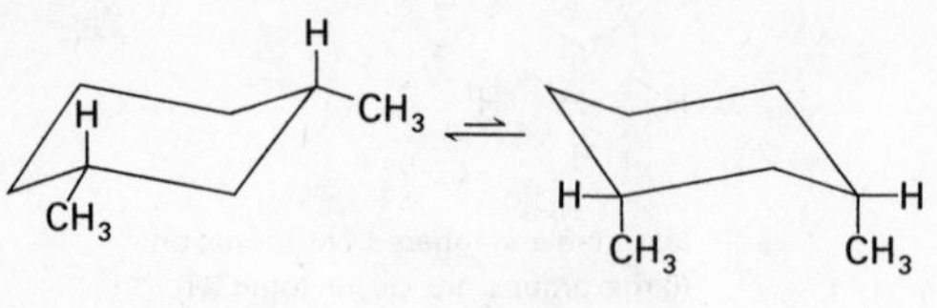

ee   aa

trans-1,3

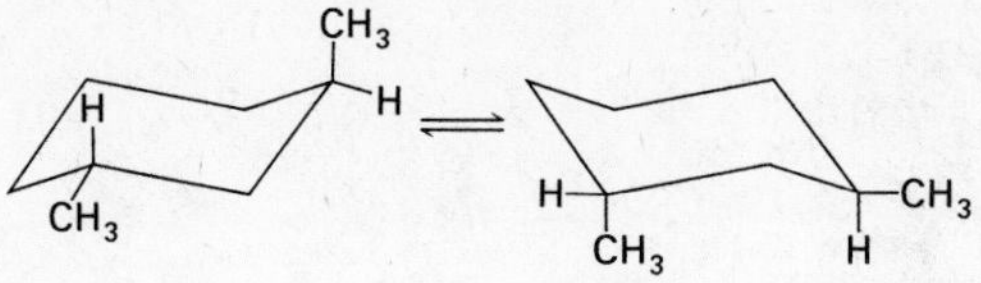

CH$_3$ ... H ⇌ ... H— ... —CH$_3$
H ... CH$_3$ ... CH$_3$ ... H

ea   ae

cis-1,4

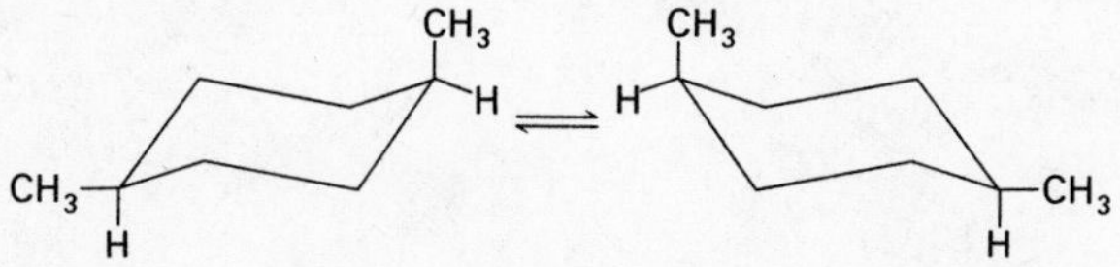

CH$_3$ ... CH$_3$
H ⇌ H
CH$_3$ ... —CH$_3$
H ... H

ea   ae

trans-1,4

H ... CH$_3$
CH$_3$ ⇌ H
CH$_3$ ... —H
H ... CH$_3$

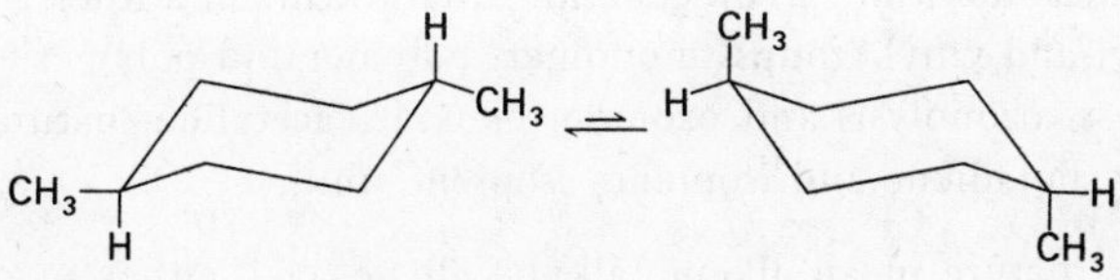

ee   aa

Only in the *cis*-1,3-, *trans*-1,2-, or *trans*-1,4-isomers can both methyls occupy equatorial positions. Therefore in the 1,2- or 1,4-isomers the trans compound is more stable than the cis, but in the 1,3-isomer the cis is more stable than the trans. Physical measurements have confirmed these predictions experimentally.

4. Unsaturated Hydrocarbons

OBJECTIVES

1. Know the meaning of: isolated, conjugated, and cumulated multiple bonds; π bond; sp^2 and sp hybridization; addition reaction; electrophilic addition; free-radical addition; hydrogenation; Markownikoff's rule; 1,2- and 1,4-addition; allyl and vinyl groups; monomer; polymer and polymerization; permanganate test; ozonolysis and ozonide; epoxide; acetylide; natural and synthetic rubber; butadiene and isoprene; isoprene unit.

2. Given the structure of an alkene, alkyne, diene, etc., either acyclic or cyclic, state its IUPAC name.

3. Given the IUPAC name, draw the structure.

4. Given the molecular formula of a hydrocarbon and given the number of double bonds, triple bonds, or rings, draw the possible structures.

5. Given the name or abbreviated structure of an unsaturated compound, tell whether it can exist in cis and trans isomeric forms, and if so, how many. Draw them.

6. Given an alkene, alkyne, or diene, and one of the following reagents, draw the structure of the product (reagents: acids such as HCl, HBr, HI, and H_2SO_4; water in the presence of an acid catalyst; halogens such as Br_2 and Cl_2; hydrogen).

7. Given the structure or name of a compound that can be prepared by an addition reaction, deduce what unsaturated compound and what reagent react to form it.

8. Write the steps in the mechanism of an electrophilic addition reaction.

9. Given an unsymmetrical alkene and an unsymmetrical electrophilic reagent, give the structure of the predominant product (i.e., apply Markownikoff's rule).

10. Given a conjugated diene and a reagent that adds to it, write the structures of the 1,2- and 1,4-addition products.

11. Given an alkyne, write the structures of products obtained by adding one or two moles of a particular reagent to it.

12. Given a vinyl compound, draw a structure for the corresponding polyvinyl compound. Also, given the structure of a polymer segment, deduce the structure of the monomer from which it can be prepared.

13. Write the steps in the mechanism of a free-radical-catalyzed vinyl polymerization reaction.

14. Given an alkene or cycloalkene (or diene, and so on), write the structures of the expected ozonolysis products.

15. Given the structures of ozonolysis products, deduce the structure of the unsaturated hydrocarbon that gave them.

16. Draw orbital pictures for a double bond, triple bond, an allyl radical, and an allyl cation.

17. Draw conventional structures for the contributors to the resonance hybrid of an allyl radical or allyl cation.

18. Draw the structure of the products expected from substitution in an allylic position, and write the steps in the reaction mechanism.

19. Describe simple chemical tests that can distinguish an alkane from an alkene, alkane from an alkyne; an alkene from a 1-alkyne.

ANSWERS TO THE EXERCISES AND PROBLEMS

4.1. In each case, start with the longest possible carbon chain and determine all possible positions for the double bond. Then shorten the chain by one carbon and repeat, and so on.

a. CH_2=$CHCH_2CH_3$ 1-butene

    CH_3CH=$CHCH_3$ 2-butene (cis and trans)

    CH_2=C—CH_3 2-methylpropene
         |
         CH_3

b. CH_2=$CHCH_2CH_2CH_3$ 1-pentene

    CH_3CH=$CHCH_2CH_3$ 2-pentene (cis and trans)

    CH_2=C—CH_2CH_3 2-methyl-1-butene
         |
         CH_3

CH₂=CHCHCH₃   3-methyl-1-butene
|
CH₃

CH₃C=CHCH₃   2-methyl-2-butene
|
CH₃

c. CH₂=C=CH—CH₂CH₃   1,2-pentadiene

CH₂=CH—CH=CH—CH₃   1,3-pentadiene

CH₂=CH—CH₂—CH=CH₂   1,4-pentadiene

CH₃—CH=C=CH—CH₃   2,3-pentadiene

CH₂=C=C—CH₃   3-methyl-1,2-butadiene
|
CH₃

CH₂=C—CH=CH₂   2-methyl-1,3-butadiene
|
CH₃

d. HC≡C—CH₂CH₂CH₃   1-pentyne

CH₃C≡CCH₂CH₃   2-pentyne

HC≡CCHCH₃   3-methyl-1-butyne
|
CH₃

4.2.   a. 2-Pentene   d. 2-Pentyne

b. 2-Methyl-2-butene (number the chain from the end with the methyl substituent)

e. 2-Chloro-1,3-butadiene (number from the end with the chlorine substituent)

c. 1,2-Dimethylcyclopentene (number the ring "through" the double bond)

f. *trans*-2-Hexene

g. *cis*-2-Hexene

4.3. In general, write the longest carbon chain or ring and number it, then locate the double bond, place the substituents, and finally, write the correct number of hydrogens on each carbon atom.

a. CH₃CH₂$\overset{3}{\text{CH}}$=CHCH₂CH₃

e. $\overset{1}{\text{CH}_2}$=CHCH₂$\overset{4}{\text{CH}}$=CHCH₃

b. CH=CH
   | |
  CH₂—CH₂

f. CH₂=CHBr (CH₂=CH— = vinyl)

c. $\overset{1}{\text{CH}_2}$—CH=$\overset{3}{\text{C}}$—CH₃
   | |
  Br   Br

g. CH₂=CHCH₂Cl (CH₂=CHCH₂— = allyl)

d. $\overset{1}{\text{HC}}$≡C—$\overset{3}{\text{CH}}$—CH₂CH₃
         |
        CH₃

h.

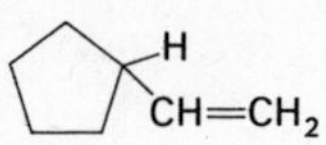

i. 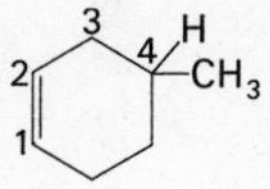 (structure) Number "through" the double bond.

j. 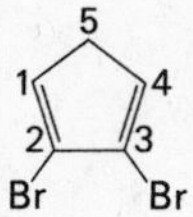 (structure) Number "through" both double bonds.

4.4. a. $\overset{1\quad2\quad\;3\;\;4}{CH_3CH=CHCH_3}$

2-butene; use the lower of the two numbers for the double bond.

b. $\overset{1\;\;2\;\;34\;\;5}{CH_3C\equiv CCH_2CH_3}$

2-pentyne; number the chain from the other end.

c. 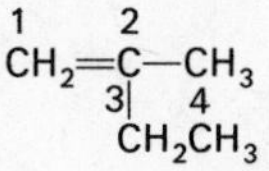 $\overset{1\qquad2}{CH_2=C-CH_3}$ with $\overset{3|\;\;4}{CH_2CH_3}$

2-methyl-1-butene; number the longest chain.

d. 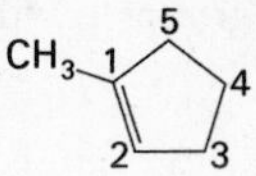 (structure) 1-methylcyclopentene *not* (structure)

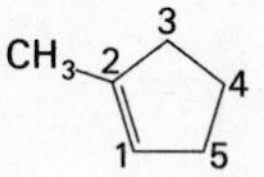

e. 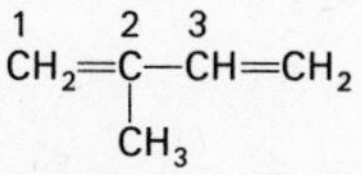 $\overset{1\quad\;2\quad3}{CH_2=C-CH=CH_2}$ with $\underset{CH_3}{|}$

2-methyl-1,3-butadiene; number to give the substituent the lowest possible number.

f. 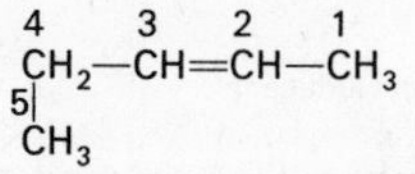 $\overset{4\qquad3\quad\;2\quad\;1}{CH_2-CH=CH-CH_3}$ with $\overset{5|}{CH_3}$

2-pentene; the "1-methyl" substituent lengthens the chain.

4.5. a. The average values are 1.54 Å, 1.34 Å, and 1.21 Å, respectively (Section 4.4).

b. These single bonds are shorter than the usual 1.54 Å because they are between sp^2–sp^2 (1.47 Å), sp^2–sp (1.43 Å), and sp–sp (1.37 Å) hybridized carbons. The more s character to the orbitals, the more closely the electrons are pulled in toward the nuclei and the shorter the bonds.

4.6. Review Section 4.3b if you have difficulty with this question.

a. Only one structure is possible, since one of the doubly bound carbons has two identical groups (hydrogens):

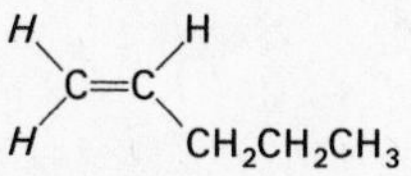

(structure)

b. 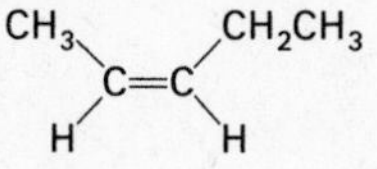 (structure)

cis-2-pentene 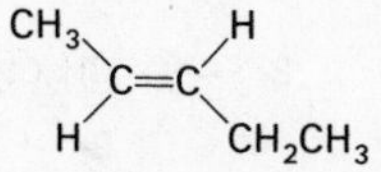   *trans*-2-pentene c.

Cl, CH₃
   C=C
H   H

cis-1-chloropropene

Cl,   H
   C=C
H   CH₃

trans-1-chloropropene

d. Only one structure:

H,   CH₂Cl
  C=C
H   H

e.

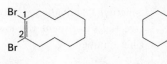

cis-1,3,5-hexatriene   *trans*-1,3,5-hexatriene

Only the central double bond has two different groups (a vinyl group and a hydrogen) attached to each carbon.

f. The ring is large enough to accommodate a trans double bond.

Br 1
  ‖
  2
Br

cis-1,2-dibromocyclodecene

Br

Br

trans-1,2-dibromocyclodecene

Normally, rings must be at least eight-membered to accomodate a trans double bond.

4.7. $\overset{13}{H}C\equiv\overset{12}{C}-\overset{11}{C}\equiv\overset{10}{C}-\overset{9}{C}H=\overset{8}{C}=\overset{7}{C}H-\overset{6}{C}H=\overset{5}{C}H-\overset{4}{C}H=\overset{3}{C}H-\overset{2}{C}H_2-\overset{1}{C}\overset{O}{\underset{OH}{\diagdown}}$

a. The 3–4, 5–6, and 7–8 double bonds are conjugated. Also, the 8–9, 10–11, and 12–13 multiple bonds are conjugated (alternate single and multiple bonds).

b. The 7–8 and 8–9 double bonds are cumulated.

c. Only the C=O bond is isolated (separated from the nearest multiple bond by two single bonds).

4.8. a. $CH_2=CHCH_2CH_3 + Br_2 \longrightarrow CH_2-CHCH_2CH_3$
                                                        $\underset{Br}{|}\;\underset{Br}{|}$

   1,2-dibromobutane

b. $CH_2=CHBr + Br_2 \longrightarrow CH_2CHBr_2$
                                       $\underset{Br}{|}$

   1,1,2-tribromoethane

c.

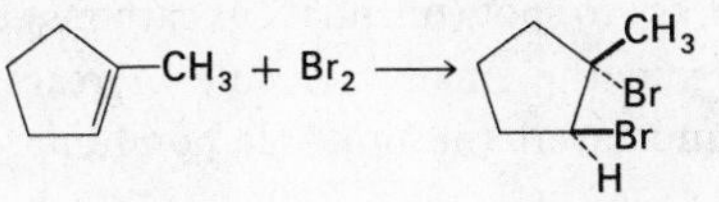

trans-1,2-dibromo-1-methylcyclopentane

The bromine adds in a trans manner; compare with Eq. 4.25.

d.

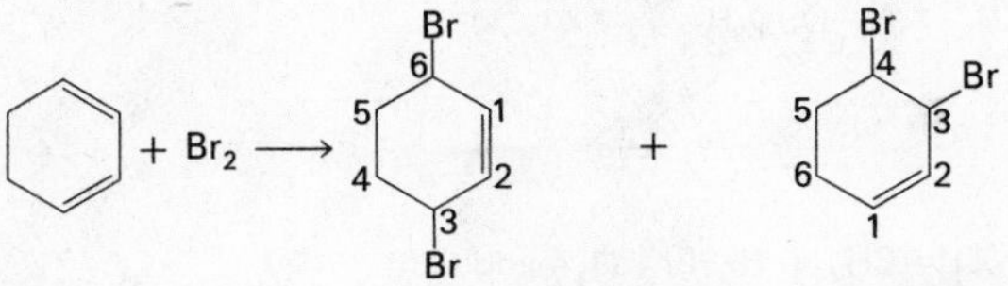

3,6-dibromocyclohexene   3,4-dibromocyclohexene
(1,4-addition)   (1,2-addition)

Compare with Eq. 4.27. The 1,4-addition product predominates. The geometry of the products (bromines cis or trans) is not shown, because a mixture is formed.

e.

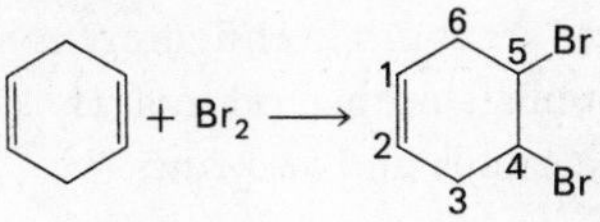

4,5-dibromocyclohexene

The double bonds are not conjugated, so only 1,2-addition is possible.

f. 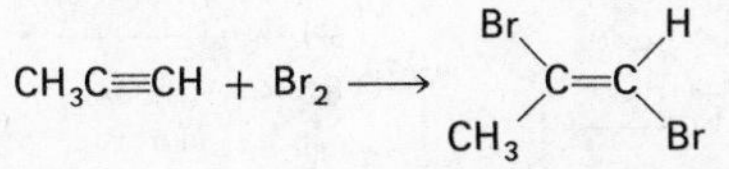 $CH_3C{\equiv}CH + Br_2 \longrightarrow$

trans-1,2-dibromopropene

Bromine usually adds to the triple bond in a trans manner, although some of the cis isomer may be formed.

4.9. a. $CH_2{=}CHCH_2CH_3 + Cl_2 \longrightarrow CH_2{-}CHCH_2CH_3$ with Cl, Cl   **(Eq. 4.3)**

b. In this reaction, and in parts c and f, Markownikoff's rule must be applied to give the correct product.

$CH_2{=}CHCH_2CH_3 + HCl \longrightarrow CH_3CHCH_2CH_3$ with Cl   **(Eq. 4.21)**

c. $CH_2{=}CHCH_2CH_3 + H_2 \xrightarrow{Pt} CH_3CH_2CH_2CH_3$ **(Eq. 4.15)**

d. See Eq. 4.44.

e. $CH_2{=}CHCH_2CH_3 + H_2O \xrightarrow{H^+} CH_3CHCH_2CH_3$ with OH   **(Eq. 4.20)**

4.10. To work this kind of problem, try to spot (on adjacent carbons) the atoms or groups that must have come from the small molecule or reagent. Then remove them from the structure and insert the multiple bond appropriately.

a. $CH_3CH{=}CHCH_3 + Br_2$

b. $CH_2{=}\underset{\underset{CH_3}{|}}{C}{-}CH_3 + HOH + H^+$

c. $CH_2{=}CHCH_3 + H{-}OSO_3H$

d. 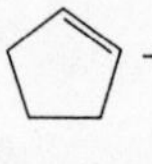 $+ H{-}Br$

e. $CH_2{=}CH{-}CH{=}CH_2 + H{-}Br$ (1,4-addition)

f. $CH_3C{\equiv}CCH_3 + 2\,Cl_2$

g. 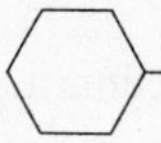 $-CH{=}CH_2 + HBr$

4.11. If the saturated hydrocarbon contained no rings, it would have a molecular formula $C_{40}H_{82}$ (C_nH_{2n+2}). Since there are four fewer hydrogens in $C_{40}H_{78}$, it must have two rings. Since β-carotene absorbed 11 mol H_2 ($C_{40}H_{56} + 11H_2 = C_{40}H_{78}$), it must have 11 double bonds and two rings.

4.12. a. Compare with Eq. 4.10. For the general mechanism, see Eqs. 4.22 and 4.23.

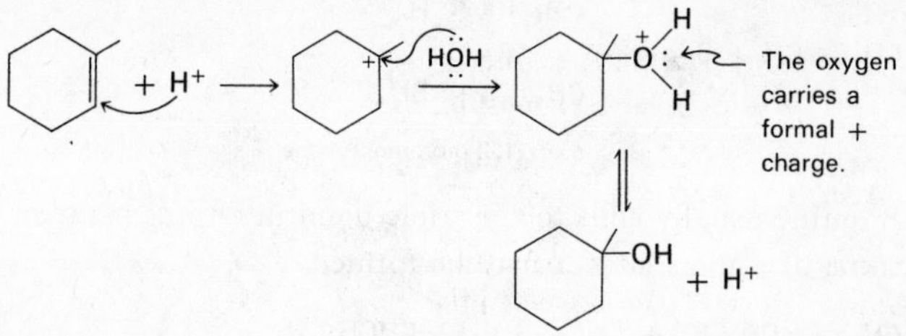

The oxygen carries a formal + charge.

Addition of H⁺ gives the tertiary carbonium ion (Markownikoff's rule).

b.

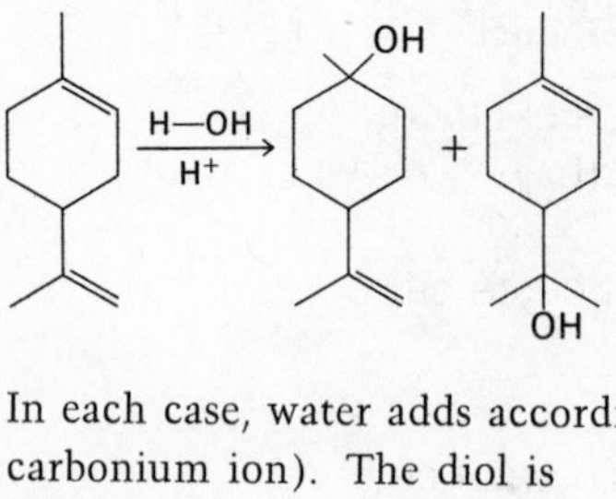

In each case, water adds according to Markownikoff's rule (via a 3° carbonium ion). The diol is

terpin

4.13. The reaction begins with formation of the cyclic bromonium ion (as in Eq. 4.26). But the nucleophile that attacks may then be either bromide ion or the solvent, methanol.

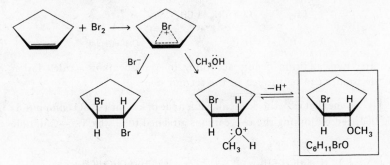

4.14. The mechanism is analogous to that for bromine addition (Eq. 4.28). See also Eq. 4.29.

$$CH_2=CH—CH=CH_2 + H^+ \longrightarrow [CH_3\overset{+}{C}H—CH=CH_2 \longleftrightarrow CH_3CH=CH—\overset{+}{C}H_2] \xrightarrow{HBr}$$

$$CH_3CH—CH=CH_2 + CH_3CH=CH—CH_2 + H^+$$
$$\quad\ \ |\qquad\qquad\qquad\qquad\qquad\qquad |$$
$$\quad\ \ Br\qquad\qquad\qquad\qquad\qquad\qquad Br$$

3-bromo-1-butene   1-bromo-2-butene

4.15. The two possible ions are:

$$CH_2=CH—CH=CH_2 \quad\begin{cases} \xrightarrow[\text{C1}]{\text{attack at}} \begin{bmatrix} CH_3\overset{+}{C}H—CH=CH_2 \\ \updownarrow \\ CH_3CH=CH—\overset{+}{C}H_2 \end{bmatrix} \\[2em] \xrightarrow[\text{C2}]{\text{attack at}} \overset{+}{C}H_2—CH_2—CH=CH_2 \end{cases}$$

Attack at C1 gives an allylic, resonance-stabilized carbocation, whereas attack at C2 gives a primary carbocation.

4.16.

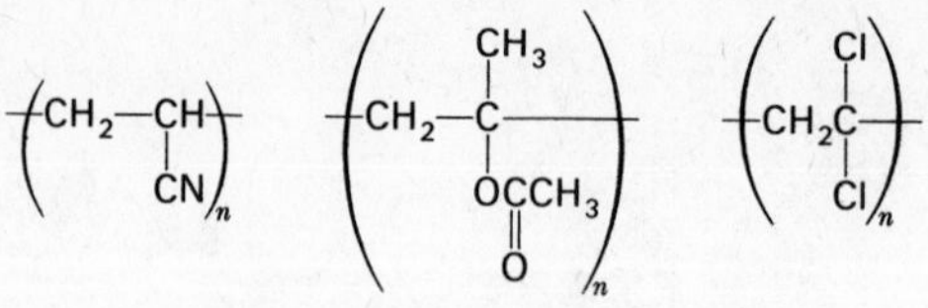

$$\left(CH_2-CH\right)_n \quad \left(CH_2-\underset{\underset{O}{\overset{\displaystyle CH_3}{\underset{|}{\overset{|}{C}}}}}{\overset{|}{\underset{|}{C}}}\right)_n \quad \left(CH_2C\right)_n$$

(orlon, CN)   (lucite, OCCH₃)   (saran, Cl/Cl)

orlon   lucite   saran

4.17. Review Section 4.9a.

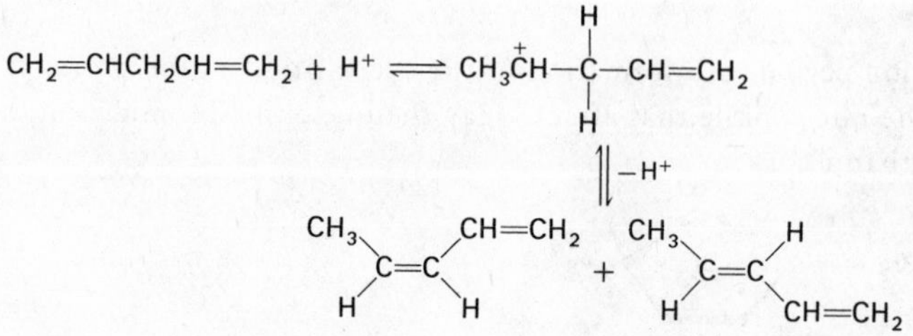

$$CH_2{=}CHCH_2CH{=}CH_2 + H^+ \rightleftharpoons CH_3\overset{+}{C}H-\underset{H}{\overset{H}{\underset{|}{\overset{|}{C}}}}-CH{=}CH_2$$

$$\Big\Updownarrow -H^+$$

$$\underset{H}{\overset{CH_3}{}}C{=}C\underset{H}{\overset{CH{=}CH_2}{}} \quad + \quad \underset{H}{\overset{CH_3}{}}C{=}C\underset{CH{=}CH_2}{\overset{H}{}}$$

In the first step, addition occurs according to Markownikoff's rule. Either geometric isomer can be formed in the second step.

4.18. The alkene that gave the particular aldehyde or ketone (C=O compound) can be deduced by joining the two carbons attached to O's by a C=C double bond:

a. $CH_3CH_2CH{=}CHCH_2CH_3$

b. $(CH_3)_2C{=}CHCH_3$

c. $CH_2{=}CHCH(CH_3)_2$

d. 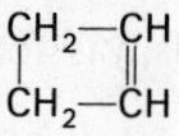 $\begin{array}{l} CH_2{-}CH \\ \,|\quad\;\; \| \\ CH_2{-}CH \end{array}$

In the case of part a, where cis and trans isomers are possible, either isomer gives the same ozonolysis products.

4.19. a. The mechanism involves a free-radical chain (review Section 3.6b).

$$Br_2 \xrightarrow[\text{light}]{\text{uv}} 2\,\ddot{B}r\cdot \quad \text{initiation step}$$

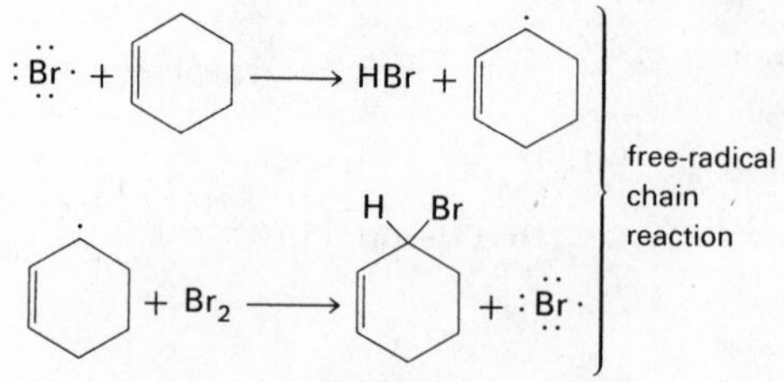

Notice that the cyclohexenyl radical is resonance-stabilized. However, because of its symmetry, reaction at either "end" gives the same product, 3-bromocyclohexene.

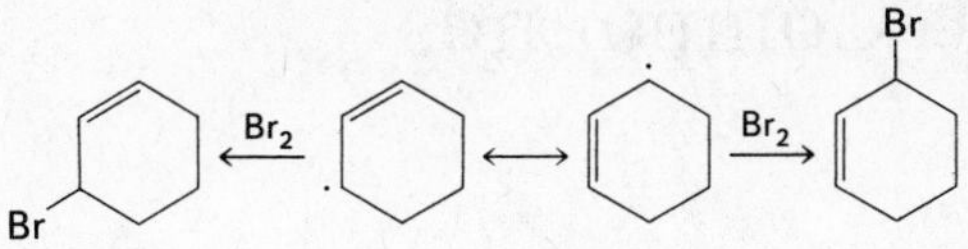

b. In this case, unlike the cyclohexene reaction in part a, the allylic radical intermediate is not symmetric. Therefore reaction at either end of the radical gives a different product. After initiation, the chain reaction is

$$:\ddot{Cl}\cdot + CH_2{=}CHCH_2CH_3 \longrightarrow HCl + CH_2{=}CH{-}\dot{C}HCH_3$$

4.20. The reaction may be initiated by addition of a free radical from the catalyst to either butadiene or styrene.

$$R\cdot + CH_2{=}CHCH{=}CH_2 \longrightarrow RCH_2\dot{C}H{-}CH{=}CH_2$$

$$RCH_2CH{=}CH\dot{C}H_2$$

$$R\cdot + CH_2{=}CHC_6H_5 \longrightarrow RCH_2\dot{C}HC_6H_5$$

These radicals may then add either to butadiene or to styrene; the allylic radical from butadiene may add in either a 1,2- or a 1,4-manner (we show below only one of several alternative sequences of addition):

$$RCH_2CH{=}CH\dot{C}H_2 + CH_2{=}CHCH{=}CH_2 \longrightarrow RCH_2CH{=}CHCH_2CH_2\dot{C}HCH{=}CH_2$$

$$RCH_2CH{=}CHCH_2CH_2CH{=}CH\dot{C}H_2$$

$$RCH_2CH{=}CHCH_2CH_2CH{=}CH\dot{C}H_2 + CH_2{=}CHC_6H_5 \longrightarrow$$

$$RCH_2CH{=}CHCH_2CH_2CH{=}CHCH_2CH_2\dot{C}HC_6H_5 \xrightarrow{\ CH_2{=}CHCH{=}CH_2\ }$$

$$RCH_2CH{=}CHCH_2CH_2CH{=}CHCH_2CH_2\underset{\underset{C_6H_5}{|}}{CH}CH_2CH{=}CH\dot{C}H_2, \text{ and so on.}$$

5. Aromatic Compounds

OBJECTIVES

1. Know the meaning of: aromatic; resonance and resonance energy; ortho, meta, and para; phenyl and benzyl groups; electrophilic aromatic substitution; halogenation, nitration, sulfonation, and alkylation; benzenonium ion; ring-activating or deactivating group; ortho-para or meta-directing group; benzyl free radical; naphthalene, anthracene, and phenanthrene; pyridine and pyrrole.

2. Name and write the structures for aromatic compounds, especially mono- and disubstituted benzenes and toluenes.

3. Write the structure of the main organic product, when the reactants are given, for the common electrophilic aromatic substitution reactions (halogenation, nitration, sulfonation, and alkylation).

4. Write the steps in the mechanism for an electrophilic aromatic substitution reaction.

5. Draw the structures of the main contributors to the benzenonium ion resonance hybrid.

6. Draw the structures of the main contributors to substituted benzenonium ions and tell whether the substituent stabilizes or destabilizes the ion.

7. Know which groups are ortho-para directing, which are meta-directing, and explain why each group directs the way it does.

8. Make use of the orienting effect of substituents to introduce them by electrophilic substitution in the proper order to obtain a desired orientation.

9. Given an alkyl-substituted aromatic compound, write the structure of the acid that is obtained by side-chain oxidation.

10. Given an alkylbenzene, tell what conditions are required to obtain halogenation selectively in the ring or on the alkyl side chain.

11. Draw the resonance contributors to the intermediate cations in electrophilic substitution at a particular position of pyridine, pyrrole, or other given aromatic structures. From these, predict the favored substitution position.

ANSWERS TO THE EXERCISES AND PROBLEMS

5.1. a.

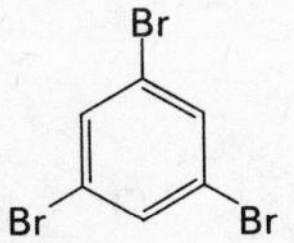

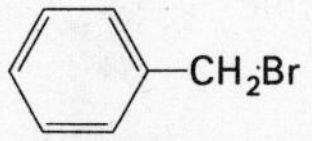

f. CH_3CH——$CHCH_3$

b.

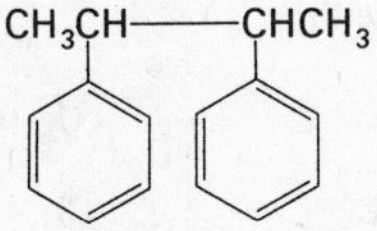

g. Br—⟨⟩—$CH=CH_2$

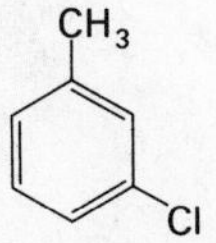

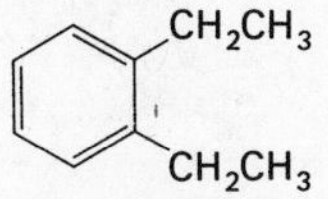

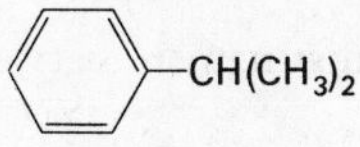

c.

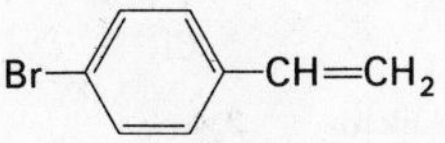

h.

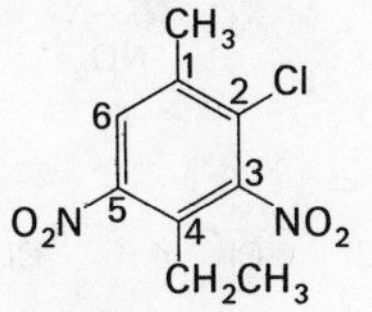

d. ⟨⟩—$CH(CH_3)_2$

i.

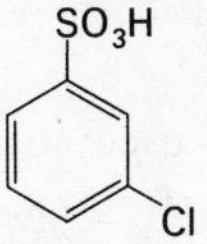

e. ⟨⟩—CH_2Br

j. Br—⟨⟩—CO_2H

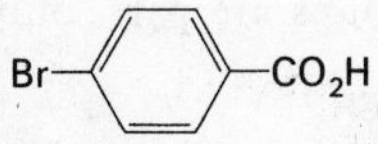

5.2. a. n-propylbenzene (or 1-phenylpropane)

b. o-chlorotoluene

c. m-bromochlorobenzene (alphabetic order)

d. 3,5-dibromostyrene

e. naphthalene

f. hexamethylbenzene (No numbers are necessary, since all possible positions on the benzene ring are substituted.)

g. 2,5-dichlorotoluene; number as shown in the following structure.

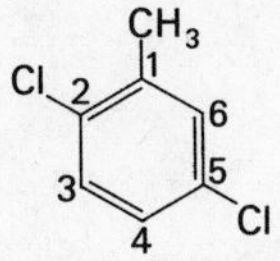

h. 1-methyl-1-phenylcyclopropane (substituents in alphabetic order)

5.3. a.

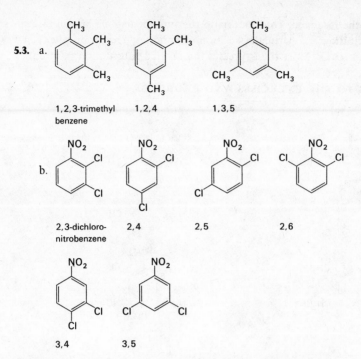

1,2,3-trimethyl benzene   1,2,4   1,3,5

b.

2,3-dichloro-nitrobenzene   2,4   2,5   2,6

3,4   3,5

5.4. This method was used many years ago to distinguish between and determine the structure of *o*-, *m*-, and *p*-isomers.

If the methyl groups are para, only one isomer is possible.

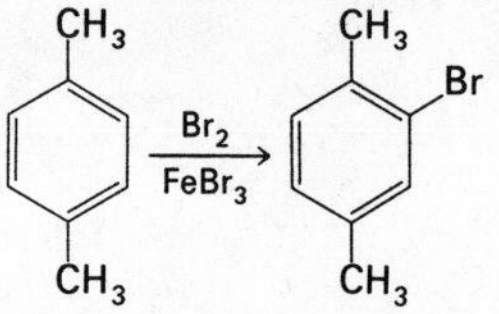

If the methyl groups are ortho, two isomers are possible.

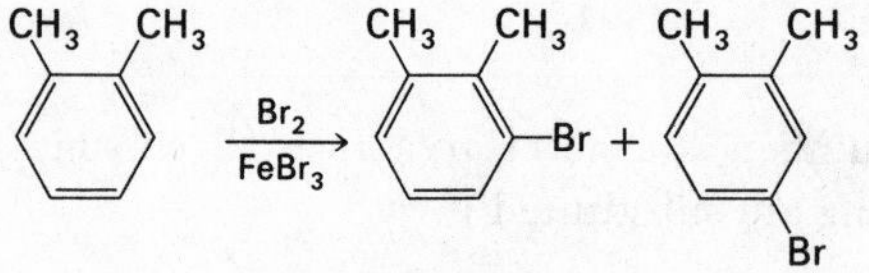

If the methyl groups are meta, three isomers are possible.

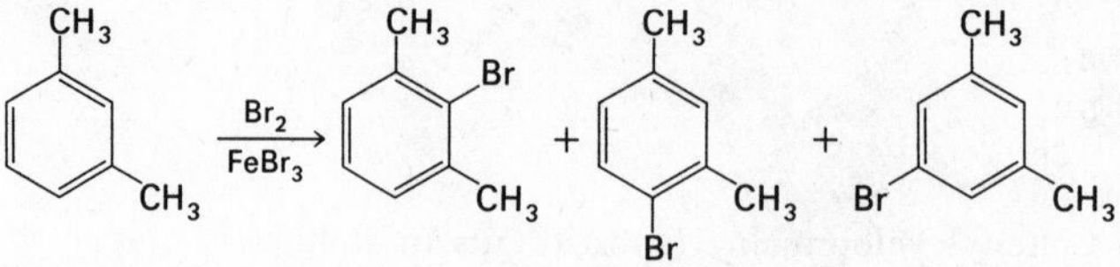

Aromatic Compounds

5.5. The energy released on hydrogenating a carbon–carbon double bond is 26.5–30 kcal/mol (Eq. 5.3). With four double bonds, we can calculate that 106–120 kcal/mol should be liberated when cyclooctatetraene is hydrogenated. The observed value (110 kcal/mol) falls within this range and suggests that cyclooctatetraene has no appreciable resonance energy. The reason is that cyclooctatetraene is not planar, and its tublike shape prevents appreciable overlap of the p orbitals around the ring.

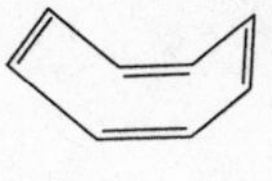

5.6. In each case six carbons are required for the benzene ring; the remaining carbons must be present as alkyl substituents.

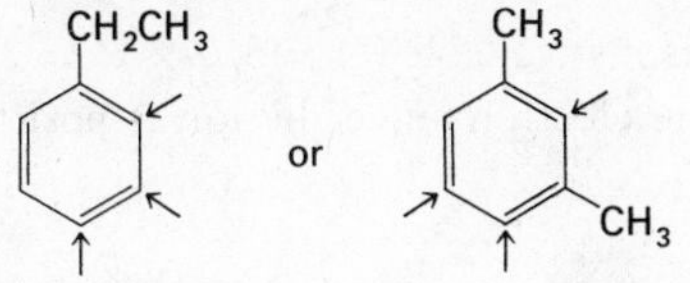

Each compound gives three monobromo derivatives, as shown by the arrows.

b.

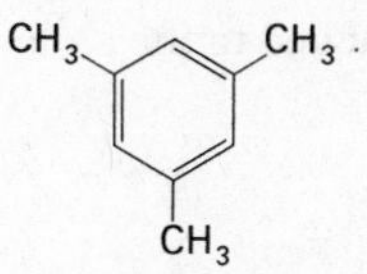

The structure is symmetric, and all three positions for aromatic substitution are equivalent.

c.

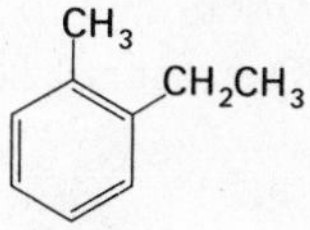

Substitution at each unoccupied ring position gives a different product.

5.7. The general mechanism is described in Section 5.5b.

a. $CH_3CH_2Br + AlBr_3 \rightleftharpoons CH_3CH_2^+ \cdots AlBr_4^-$

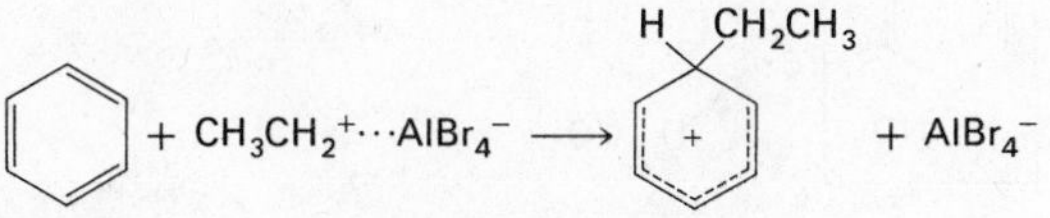

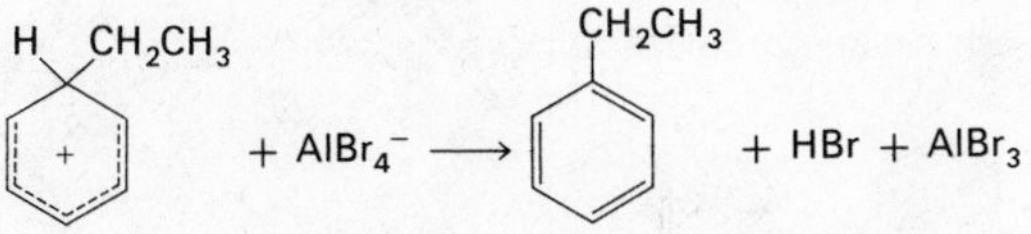

b. The first step is the formation of NO_2^+:

$HONO_2 + 2H^+ \rightleftharpoons H_3O^+ + NO_2^+$

Then:

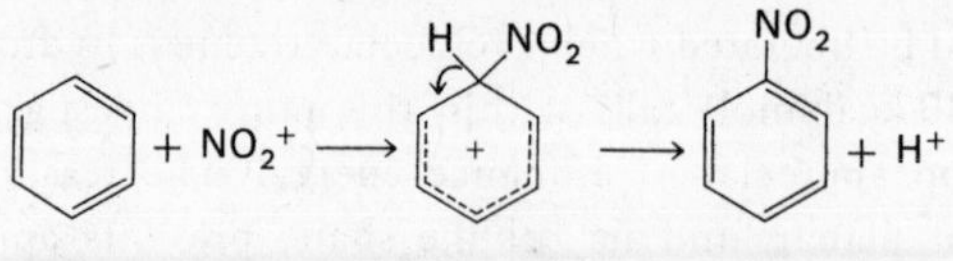

5.8. The nitro group has two main contributing structures:

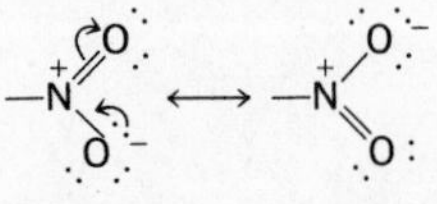

Since they are identical and contribute equally, there is only one type of N—O bond, intermediate between double and single in length.

5.9. NO_2^+: There are 16 valence electrons available (N = 5, 2 × O = 2 × 6 = 12; total 17, but we must subtract one electron since the ion is positive).

The structure with the + charge on the nitrogen is preferred because each atom has an octet of electrons. In the structure with the + charge on the oxygen, it has only six electrons around it. Notice that in aromatic nitrations, it is the nitrogen atom of NO_2^+ that attacks and becomes attached to the aromatic ring.

5.10. Ortho

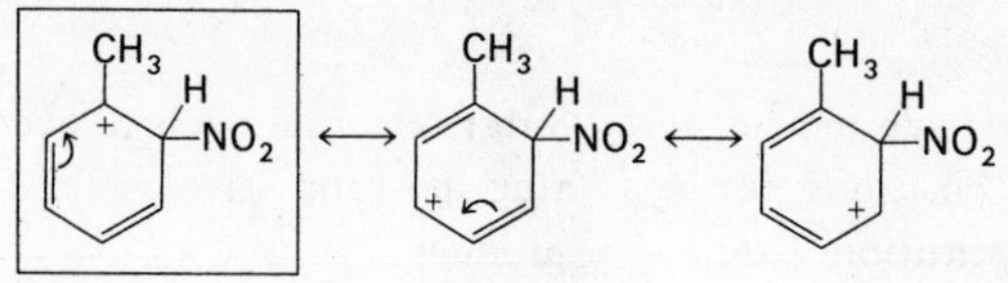

Para

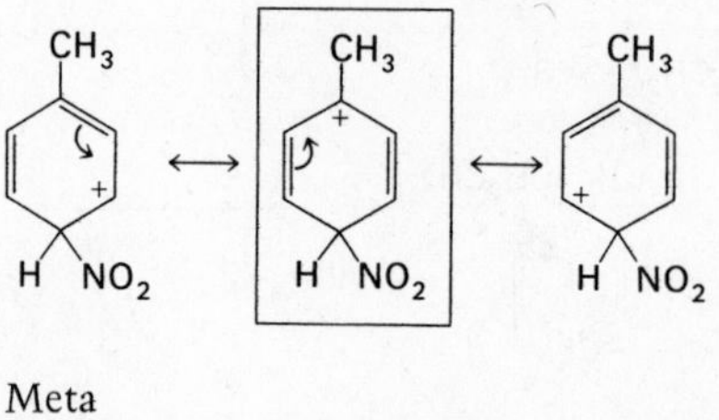

Meta

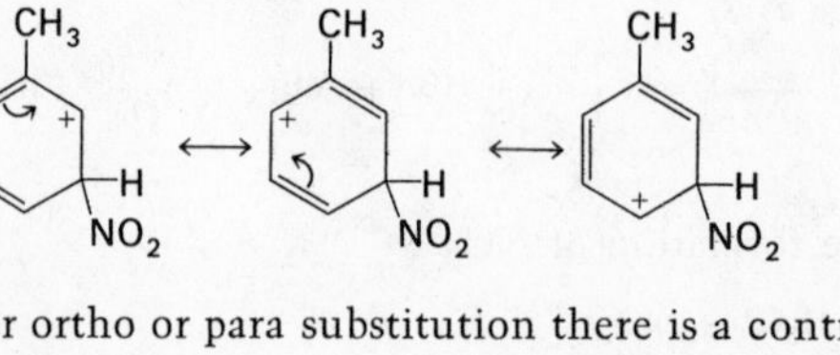

In either ortho or para substitution there is a contributor (shown in a box) to the resonance hybrid in which the positive charge is adjacent to and therefore stabilized by the methyl group—a tertiary carbocation structure. No such stabilized contributor is possible for meta substitution. Consequently, ortho-para substitution predominates.

5.11. The structures are identical with those written for the answer to Question 5.10, except that the methyl group in each structure is replaced by a nitro group. The nitro group *destabilizes* carbocations. Therefore the structures in the boxes (but with NO_2 in place of CH_3) are particularly *unfavorable*. No such destabilized structures are present for meta substitution.

5.12. Nitration, then chlorination:

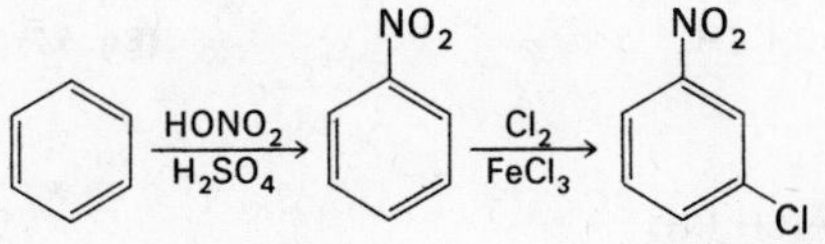

mainly meta

Chlorination, then nitration:

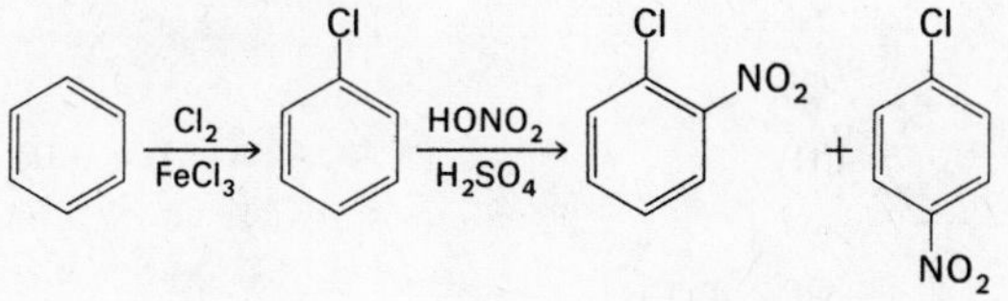

mainly ortho and para

The first substituent directs the second substitution reaction. The nitro group is meta directing, whereas the chloro substituent is ortho-para directing.

5.13. See Section 5.5c for a discussion of the orienting influence of substituents.

a. 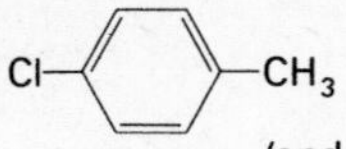 Cl—〈 〉—CH$_3$

(and ortho)

e. Same as c.

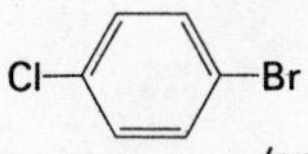

b.

f. Br—〈 〉—CH$_2$CH$_3$

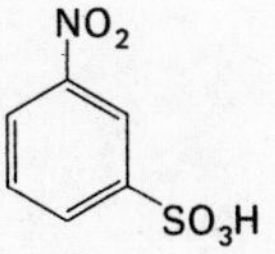

(and ortho)

c. Cl—〈 〉—Br

(and ortho)

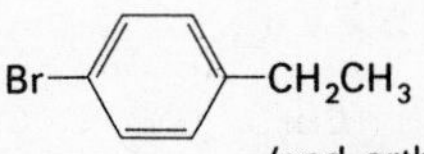

g. 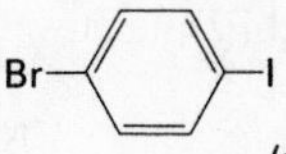 Br—〈 〉—I

(and ortho)

d. Same as b.

5.14. a. Since the two substituents must end up in a meta relationship, the first one introduced into the benzene ring must be meta directing. Therefore nitrate first, then brominate.

benzene $\xrightarrow[\text{H}^+]{\text{HONO}_2}$ nitrobenzene (NO_2) $\xrightarrow[\text{FeBr}_3]{\text{Br}_2}$ m-bromonitrobenzene (NO_2, Br)

b. (benzene)–CH_3 $\xrightarrow{\text{H}_2\text{SO}_4}$ HO_3S–(benzene)–CH_3

Alkyl groups are o,p-directing, but the —SO_3H group is meta directing.

c. First make the ethylbenzene, then nitrate it.

(benzene) + $CH_2{=}CH_2$ $\xrightarrow{\text{H}^+}$ (benzene)–CH_2CH_3 **(Eq. 5.7)**

or

(benzene) + CH_3CH_2Cl $\xrightarrow{\text{AlCl}_3}$ (benzene)–CH_2CH_3

(benzene)–CH_2CH_3 $\xrightarrow[\text{H}^+]{\text{HONO}_2}$ O_2N–(benzene)–CH_2CH_3 + some ortho isomer

d. (benzene)–CH_3 $\xrightarrow[\text{Ni}]{3\text{H}_2}$ (cyclohexane)–CH_3 **(Eq. 5.16)**

e. (toluene, CH_3) $\xrightarrow[\text{FeBr}_3]{\text{Br}_2}$ (p-bromotoluene, CH_3 / Br) $\xrightarrow[\substack{\Delta \\ \text{(Eq. 5.18)}}]{\text{KMnO}_4}$ (p-bromobenzoic acid, CO_2H / Br)

f. Compare with part a. The bromination must be performed first.

(benzene) $\xrightarrow[\text{FeBr}_3]{\text{Br}_2}$ (bromobenzene, Br) $\xrightarrow[\text{H}^+]{\text{HONO}_2}$ (p-bromonitrobenzene, Br / NO_2)

g. (toluene, CH_3) $\xrightarrow[\text{H}^+]{\text{HONO}_2}$ (p-nitrotoluene, CH_3 / NO_2) $\xrightarrow[\text{FeCl}_3]{\text{Cl}_2}$ (CH_3 / Cl / NO_2)

If the chlorination were done first, one would get a considerable amount of product with the chlorine para to the methyl group. Also note that in the second step, above, both substituents "direct" the chlorine to the desired position (CH_3 is o,p directing, NO_2 is m directing).

h.

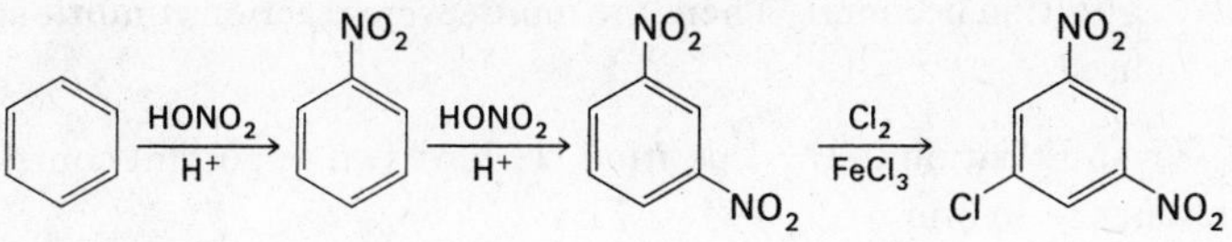

5.15. $Cl_2 \xrightarrow[\text{light}]{\text{uv}} 2\ Cl\cdot$ initiation step

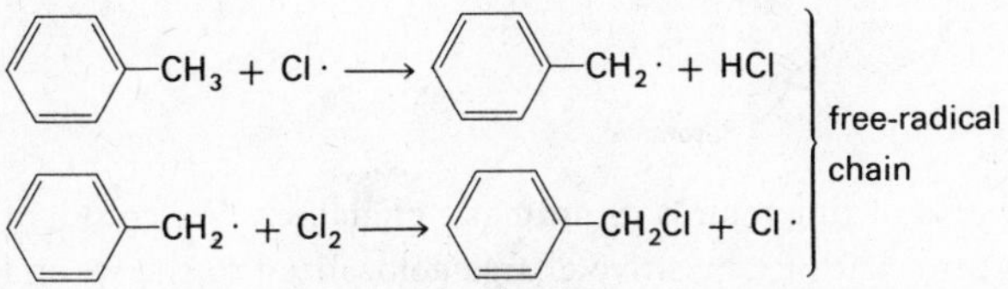

free-radical chain

The chain may be terminated by any radical combination reaction.

5.16. Review Section 5.7.

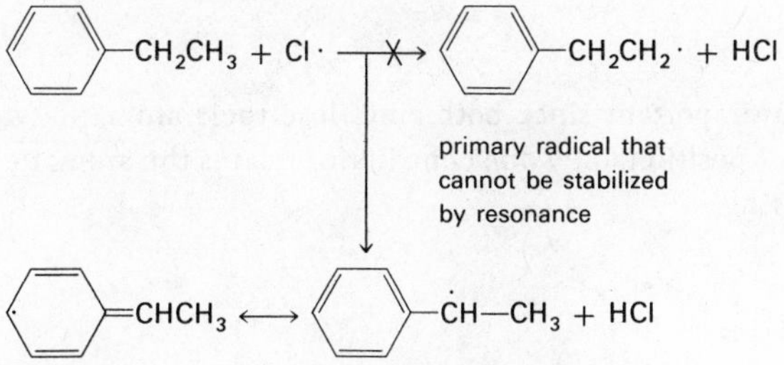

primary radical that cannot be stabilized by resonance

and other structures in which the odd electron is in the ortho positions

secondary, benzyl-type radical that can be stabilized by resonance.

5.17. a. The methyl group is ortho-para directing and the nitro group is meta directing. Since we start with the methyl group already present, the nitro group takes positions ortho and para to it (and consequently, meta to one another).

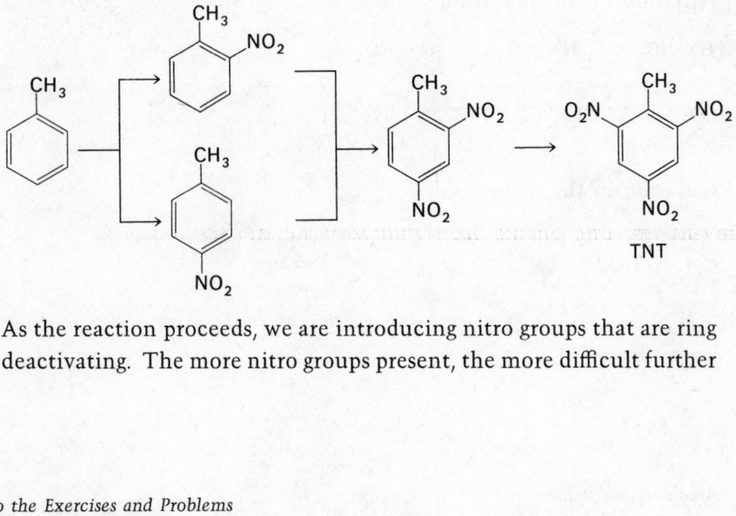

b. As the reaction proceeds, we are introducing nitro groups that are ring deactivating. The more nitro groups present, the more difficult further nitration becomes. Therefore more severe reaction conditions must be used.

5.18. For substitution in the 1-position, we have two important contributors to the resonance hybrid:

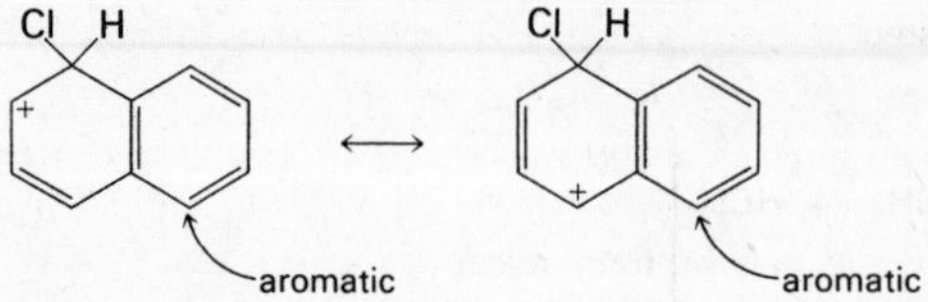

In both structures the second ring retains its aromatic character. We could, of course, also have structures with the positive charge delocalized to the second ring, such as

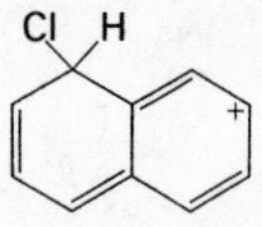

but these are relatively unimportant since both rings lose their aromaticity.

For substitution at the 2-position, only *one* contributor retains the aromatic structure of at least one ring.

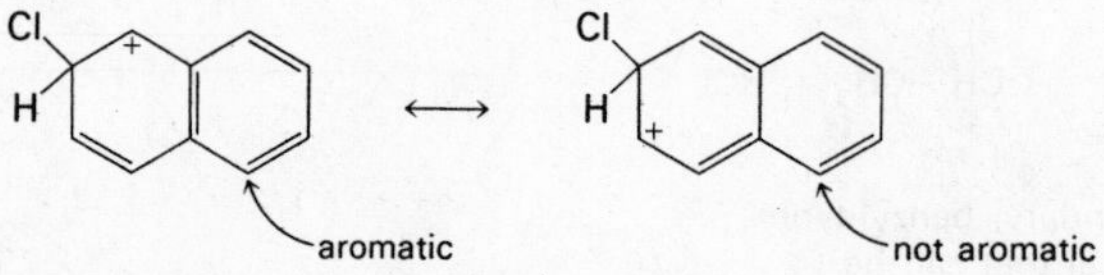

Consequently substitution at C1 is favored.

5.19. Nitration in the 2-position:

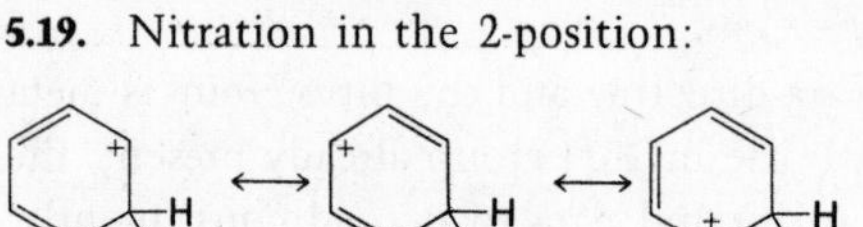

Nitration in the 4-position:

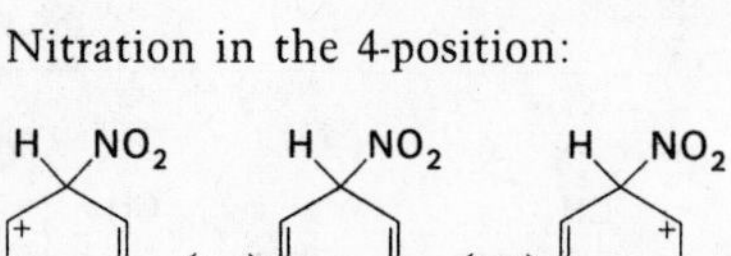

Nitration in the 3-position:

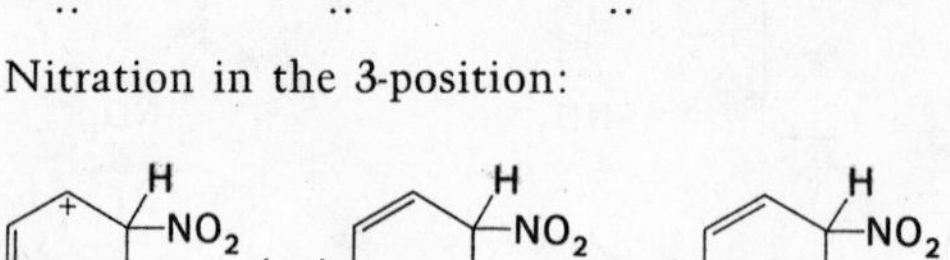

The nitrogen atom tends to avoid a structure with only six electrons (and a positive charge). This is possible only for substitution in the 3-position. Notice also that if the pyridine nitrogen were protonated, as it most certainly is in the acidic medium required for nitration, it would have to carry a 2+ formal charge in some of the resonance contributors for 2- or 4-substitution (those contributors in which it already carries a +1 charge when not protonated). The double charge would be especially avoided.

5.20. 2-position:

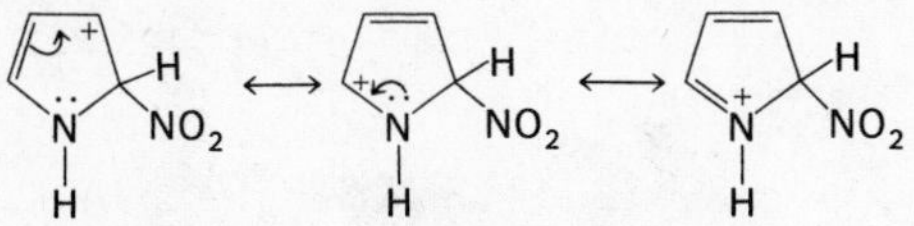

3-position:

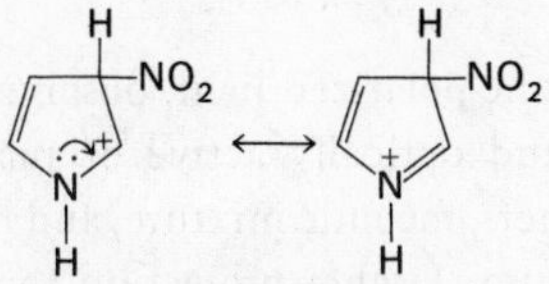

The positive charge can be more favorably delocalized in the intermediate for substitution at the 2-position; consequently, this position is favored for electrophilic substitution in pyrroles.

6. Stereoisomerism and Optical Activity

OBJECTIVES

1. Know the meaning of: stereoisomers; plane-polarized light, observed and specific rotation, dextro- and levorotatory, and optically active or inactive; chiral or achiral; plane of symmetry; enantiomers, racemic mixture, and resolution; chiral center and asymmetric carbon atom; Fischer projection formula; R-S convention and priority order; absolute and relative configuration; diastereomers and meso form: van't Hoff rule.

2. Given the concentration of an optically active compound, length of the polarimeter tube, and observed rotation, calculate the specific rotation. Given any three of the four quantities mentioned, calculate the fourth.

3. Given a structural formula, draw it in three dimensions and locate any plane of symmetry.

4. Given the structure of a compound, determine if any asymmetric carbon atoms are present.

5. Given the structure or name of a compound, tell whether or not it is capable of optical activity.

6. Given the three-dimensional drawing of an acyclic compound with a chiral center, draw its Fischer projection formula.

7. Given two Fischer projection formulas for the same compound, tell whether they represent the same or opposite configurations of the compound.

8. Know the rules for establishing priority orders of groups in the R-S convention.

9. Given a compound with a chiral center, assign the priority order of groups attached to it.

10. Given a chiral center in a molecule, assign the R or S configuration to it.

11. Draw a three-dimensional or Fischer projection formula of a molecule with a particular configuration, R or S.

12. Given a structure with more than one chiral center, tell how many stereoisomers are possible and draw the structure of each. Tell what relationship the stereoisomers have to each other (e.g., enantiomeric, diastereomeric).

ANSWERS TO THE EXERCISES AND PROBLEMS

6.1. Each of these definitions can be found explicitly or implicitly in the text. The sections where they appear are indicated below:

a. 6.2	f. 6.3b
b. 6.2c	g. 6.8
c. 6.1	h. 6.6
d. 6.1	i. 6.3a
e. 6.3b	j. 6.2a

6.2. Most commonly, examine the structure for a plane of symmetry—if none is present, enantiomers are usually possible. But the decisive test is to compare the molecule with its mirror image and determine whether they are superimposable.

6.3. a. CH_3 Ⓒ $H(Br)CH_2CH_3$

b. CH_3 Ⓒ $H(Cl)$ Ⓒ $H(Cl)CH_3$

c. C_6H_5 Ⓒ $H(OH)CO_2H$

d. $CH_2(OH)$ Ⓒ $H(OH)$ Ⓒ $H(OH)CH_2OH$

e.

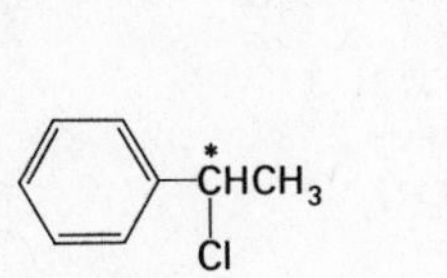

6.4. a.

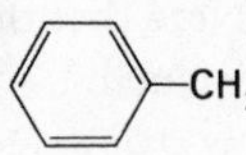

Optically inactive; the molecule has several planes of symmetry, for example, the one that passes through the three carbon atoms.

b.

Can be optically active; the asterisked carbon is asymmetric.

c.

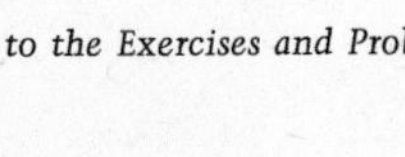

Optically inactive; there are no chiral centers.

d. $CH_3CH_2\overset{*}{C}HCH_2CH_2CH_3$
$\underset{\textstyle CH_3}{|}$

Can be optically active; the asterisked carbon is asymmetric.

e. $CH_3CH_2CHCH_2CH_2CH_3$
$\underset{\textstyle CH_2CH_3}{|}$

Optically inactive; the carbon that was chiral is part d is now achiral because it has two identical groups (ethyl) attached to it.

f.

Optically inactive; although the two asterisked carbons are asymmetric, the molecule has a plane of symmetry perpendicular to the plane of the four-membered ring and bisecting the C_1—C_2 and C_3—C_4 bonds. Therefore it has a mirror image identical to itself.

g.

Can be optically active; no plane of symmetry in the molecule.

h.

Optically inactive; the molecule has several planes of symmetry and is identical to its mirror image.

i.

Optically inactive; the plane that passes through carbons 1 and 3, perpendicular to the plane of the ring, is a plane of symmetry.

j.

The substance is optically inactive; it has a plane of symmetry perpendicular to the five-membered ring, through carbon 1 and bisecting the C_3—C_4 bond.

6.5. One interchange (H for OH) converts one Fischer formula to the other. Or, if we begin by interchanging the OH and CH_3 as suggested, we get

The symbol $\multimap$ represents an inversion of configuration. Note that three steps are necessary to get from the (−) structure to the particular (+) Fischer projection shown in the problem. An odd number of steps is always required to convert one chiral center to its enantiomer in a Fischer projection formula, whereas an even number of steps gives a molecule with the identical configuration at the chiral center.

One can, of course, also see the enantiomeric relationship between the two structures by examining their three-dimensional equivalent (horizontal groups project out of the paper, and vertical groups project behind the plane of the paper):

$$CO_2H \quad\quad CO_2H$$

H—OH   HO—H

$$CH_3 \quad\quad\quad CH_3$$

$$(-) \quad\quad\quad (+)$$

6.6. Start with the Fischer projection of the ($-$) enantiomer as it is usually written:

$$CO_2H \qquad CO_2H \qquad OH \qquad\qquad H$$

H—OH $\longrightarrow$ CH$_3$—OH $\longrightarrow$ CH$_3$—CO$_2$H $\longrightarrow$ CH$_3$—CO$_2$H

$$CH_3 \qquad\quad H \qquad\qquad H \qquad\qquad OH$$

$$(-) \qquad\quad (+) \qquad\quad (-) \qquad\quad (+)$$

An odd number of interchanges (at least three) is necessary.

6.7. The rules are given in Section 6.4b.

    a. $OH > CH_3CH_2 > CH_3 > H$

    b. $Cl > C_6H_5 > CH_3 > H$

C_6H_5 takes precedence over CH_3 because the carbon marked with an asterisk in C_6H_5—

has three bonds to other carbons, whereas in CH_3— those bonds are to hydrogen (which has a lower atomic number than carbon).

    c. $-OH > -CH_2Cl > -CH_2OH > -CH_3$

    d. $-C(CH_3)_3 > -CH(CH_3)_2 > -CH_2CH_3 > -CH_3$

6.8. Draw a representation of the tetrahedron and locate the lowest priority group; then look at the model from the opposite side of that group and locate the remaining three groups in a clockwise order according to their priority.

    a.

Other equivalent structures are

All have the R configuration.

b.
$$\text{H---}\overset{\text{Cl}}{\underset{\text{CH}_3}{\text{C}}}\text{---C}_6\text{H}_5$$

c.
$$\text{CH}_3\text{---}\overset{\text{OH}}{\underset{\text{HOCH}_2}{\text{C}}}\text{---CH}_2\text{Cl}$$

d.
$$\text{CH}_3\text{---}\overset{\text{C(CH}_3)_3}{\underset{\text{CH}_3\text{CH}_2}{\text{C}}}\text{---CH(CH}_3)_2$$

6.9. a. $\text{CH}_3\text{CH}_2\text{---}\overset{\text{CH}_3}{\underset{\text{H}}{|}}\text{---OH}$ c. $\text{ClCH}_2\text{---}\overset{\text{CH}_2\text{OH}}{\underset{\text{CH}_3}{|}}\text{---OH}$

b. $\text{C}_6\text{H}_5\text{---}\overset{\text{CH}_3}{\underset{\text{H}}{|}}\text{---Cl}$ d. $(\text{CH}_3)_2\text{CH---}\overset{\text{CH}_2\text{CH}_3}{\underset{\text{CH}_3}{|}}\text{---C(CH}_3)_3$

In each case, notice that the remaining three groups, in priority order, are arranged in a clockwise manner.

6.10. The following are examples; there may be other possibilities.

a. $\text{CH}_3\overset{*}{\text{C}}\text{HCH}_2\text{CH}_3$
     c. $\text{HOCH}_2\overset{*}{\text{C}}\text{HCH}_2\text{CH}_3$
      OH   OH

b. $\text{CH}_3\overset{*}{\text{C}}\text{HCH}_2\text{CH}_2\text{CH}_3$
     d. $\text{CH}_3\overset{*}{\text{C}}\text{HCH}=\text{CH}_2$
      Br CH_2CH_3

In each case the asymmetric carbon atom is marked with an asterisk.

6.11. All structures must contain only one double bond and no rings. We can tell this because if the monovalent Cl were replaced by H we would have C_5H_{10}, corresponding to the general formula C_nH_{2n} (a molecule with one double bond or with one ring). Since the chloride is described in the question as unsaturated, there can be no rings present.

a. $\text{CH}_2=\text{CHCH}_2\text{CH}_2\text{CH}_2\text{Cl}$ c. $\text{CH}_2=\text{CH}\overset{*}{\text{C}}\text{HClCH}_2\text{CH}_3$ or $\text{CH}_2=\text{CHCH}_2\overset{*}{\text{C}}\text{HClCH}_3$

b. $\text{CH}_3\text{CH}=\text{C(CH}_3)\text{CH}_2\text{Cl}$ d. $\text{CH}_3\text{CH}=\text{CH}\overset{*}{\text{C}}\text{HClCH}_3$

6.12. For three different asymmetric carbons, $2^3 = 8$. The possibilities are

R—R—R	S—R—R
R—R—S	S—R—S
R—S—R	S—S—R
R—S—S	S—S—S

For four different asymmetric carbons, $2^4 = 16$. The possibilities are

R—R—R—R	*R—S—R—R*	*S—R—R—R*	*S—S—R—R*
R—R—R—S	*R—S—R—S*	*S—R—R—S*	*S—S—R—S*
R—R—S—R	*R—S—S—R*	*S—R—S—R*	*S—S—S—R*
R—R—S—S	*R—S—S—S*	*S—R—S—S*	*S—S—S—S*

6.13. When the bromine adds in a trans manner to the cyclopentene double bond, it can do so in two ways:

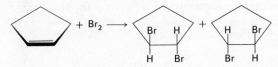

The products are enantiomers and are formed in exactly equal quantities. The product is therefore a racemic mixture of *trans*-1,2-dibromocyclopentane.

6.14. The compound has two identical chiral centers, and can therefore exist in three forms, two of which are optically active (*RR* and *SS*) and one of which is meso (*RS*); see Section 6.8.

The *RR* and *SS* forms are enantiomers; *RS* is an optically inactive diastereomer of the *RR* and *SS* forms.

6.15. Suppose we consider the "sawhorse" formula for one of the two enantiomers.

No matter which conformer we choose, the two hydrogens H_a and H_b (one of which is replaced by chlorine when the compound is chlorinated to give 2,3-dichlorobutane) are in different environments. For example, in the left conformer, H_a is flanked by H and CH_3 on C2, whereas H_b is flanked by H and Cl. If we rotate to get the "right" conformer, H_b now has the position occupied formerly by H_a (flanked by H and CH_3) *but H_a does not have the position occupied formerly by H_b* (it is flanked by CH_3 and Cl not H and Cl). The positions of H_a and H_b cannot be interchanged; these hydrogens are said to be *diastereotopic*, since if one or the other were replaced by some group that would make C3 asymmetric, the products would be diastereomers.

Since H_a and H_b are diastereotopic (and not enantiotopic), there is no reason why they should react identically. Thus the ratio of meso to racemic product need not be $1:1$. The argument applies regardless of which isomer of 2-chlorobutane we consider, and is therefore true of the racemic mixture as well.

6.16. Review Section 6.9. The groups in the ortho positions are surely sufficient to restrict rotation. However, since two of the groups attached to one ring are identical, the molecule possesses a plane of symmetry and is incapable of optical activity. For example, in the conformation shown below, the plane of the paper passes through the right ring and its substituents and is a symmetry plane for the molecule.

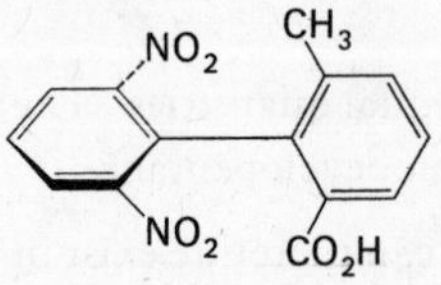

6.17. The compound has three different chiral centers, indicated by arrows in the formula below. There are, applying the van't Hoff rule, eight possible stereoisomers.

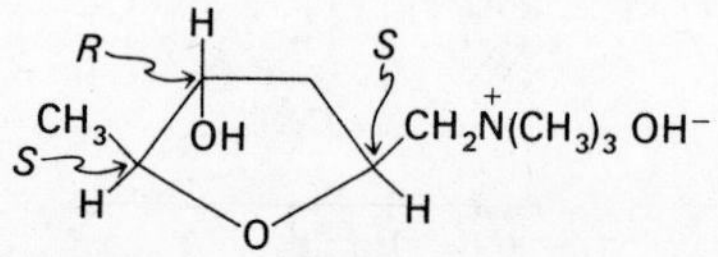

The configurational designation (R or S) at each center in the naturally occurring poison is shown.

7. Alcohols and Phenols

OBJECTIVES

1. Know the meaning of: alcohol and phenol; primary, secondary, and tertiary alcohol; carbinol; hydrogen bond; alkoxide and phenoxide; elimination reaction, ester, aldehyde, and ketone; oxidative coupling; polyhydric alcohol; glycol and glycerol; wood and grain alcohol; geraniol; farnesol, vitamin A, and cholesterol; thiol, mercaptan, and sulfhydryl group.

2. Given the structure of an alcohol, tell whether it is a primary, secondary, or tertiary alcohol.

3. Given the IUPAC name of an alcohol or phenol, draw its structure.

4. Given the structure of an alcohol or phenol, assign it a correct name.

5. Explain the significance of hydrogen bonding of an alcohol or phenol with regard to solubility in water and boiling point.

6. Given a small group of compounds, including alcohols, phenols, and hydrocarbons, arrange them in order of water solubility.

7. Given a group of compounds with similar molecular weights but differing potential for hydrogen bonding, arrange them in order of boiling point.

8. Draw the resonance contributors to phenoxide or substituted phenoxide ions, and discuss the acidity of the corresponding phenols.

9. Account for the acidity difference between alcohols and phenols.

10. Write equations for the reaction of a specific alcohol or phenol with sodium or with a strong base (NaOH, KOH).

11. Write the structures for all possible dehydration products of a given alcohol.

12. Write the steps in the mechanism for the dehydration of an alcohol.

13. Write equations for the reaction of a given alcohol with HCl, HBr, or HI,

with cold, concentrated H_2SO_4 or HNO_3, with PCl_3 or PBr_3, with thionyl chloride ($SOCl_2$), with acetic acid, or with an oxidant such as chromic oxide.

14. Write the steps in the mechanism for conversion of an alcohol to an alkyl halide.

15. Given the structure of a phenol, write structures for the likely products of its oxidative coupling.

16. Write equations for the reaction of phenol with dilute aqueous nitric acid and with bromine water.

17. Contrast the acidity of alcohols and thiols; also contrast their reactivity toward oxidizing agents.

ANSWERS TO THE EXERCISES AND PROBLEMS

7.1. a. 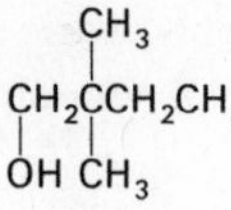 $CH_2\overset{\underset{\displaystyle CH_3}{|}}{\underset{\underset{\displaystyle CH_3}{|}}{C}}CH_2CH_3$
 OH

f.

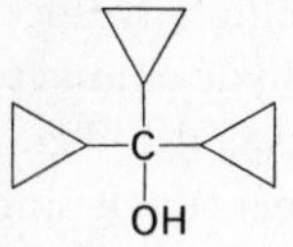

b. 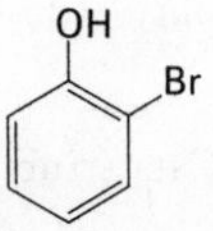 (phenol with Br, OH)

g. Na^+ $^-OCH_3$

c. 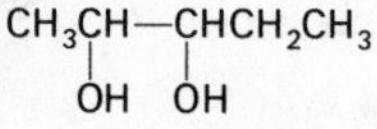 $CH_3\overset{\underset{\displaystyle OH}{|}}{CH}-\overset{\underset{\displaystyle OH}{|}}{CH}CH_2CH_3$

h. 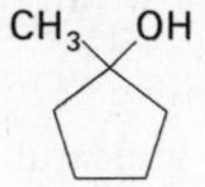 (CH_3, OH on cyclopentane)

d. 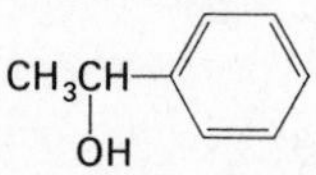 $CH_3\overset{\underset{\displaystyle OH}{|}}{CH}-$⟨phenyl⟩

i. 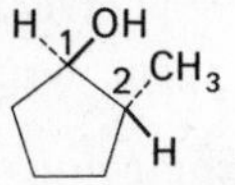 (cyclopentane with H, OH, CH₃, H)

e. $CH_3CH_2CH_2OSO_3H$

j. 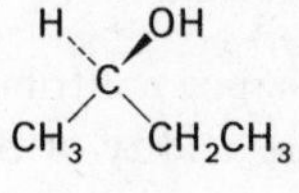
 $\underset{CH_3}{}\overset{HOH}{C}\underset{CH_2CH_3}{}$

7.2. Proceed in a systematic way, from straight-chain to branched-chain structures.

$CH_3CH_2CH_2CH_2OH$ 1-butanol (1°)

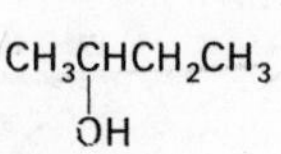

$CH_3\overset{\underset{\displaystyle OH}{|}}{CH}CH_2CH_3$ 2-butanol (2°)

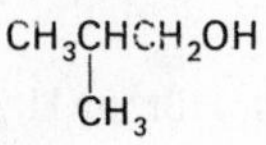

$CH_3\overset{\underset{\displaystyle CH_3}{|}}{CH}CH_2OH$ 2-methyl-1-propanol (1°)

$$
\begin{array}{c}
\quad \text{OH} \\
\quad | \\
\text{CH}_3\text{CCH}_3 \\
\quad | \\
\quad \text{CH}_3
\end{array}
\qquad \text{2-methyl-2-propanol (3°)}
$$

7.3.
a. 3,3-dimethyl-2-butanol

b. 2,4-dichlorophenol

c. 3-bromo-2-methyl-2-butanol

d. cyclopropanol

e. *m*-bromophenol

f. diphenylcarbinol

g. 2-buten-1-ol

h. 2-propanethiol (or isopropyl mer-captan)

i. 1,2,3,4-butanetetraol

j. *cis*-3-methylcyclobutanol

7.4.
a. The hydroxyl should get the lower number; 3,3-dimethyl-2-butanol.

b. 2-Methyl-1-butanol; the longest chain was not selected.

c. 2-Propen-1-ol (or allyl alcohol); the hydroxyl group should get the lower number.

d. 3-Chlorocyclohexanol; number the ring from the hydroxyl-bearing carbon, in a direction that gives substituents the lowest possible numbers.

e. Phenol; the term alcohol is not used when the hydroxyl group is attached to an aromatic ring.

f. 2-Bromo-*p*-cresol or 2-bromo-4-methylphenol; give substituents the lowest possible numbers.

g. 1,2-Propanediol; the chain was numbered in the wrong direction.

7.5.
a. Ethyl chloride $<$ 1-hexanol $<$ ethanol. Both alcohols can hydrogen-bond to water and will be more soluble than the alkyl chloride. The lower molecular weight alcohol will be more soluble (it has a shorter hydrophobic carbon chain).

b. 1-Pentanol $<$ 2,3-pentanediol $<$ $\text{CH}_2\text{OH(CHOH)}_3\text{CH}_2\text{OH}$; the more hydroxyl groups, the more possibilities for hydrogen bonding and the greater the water solubility.

c. Benzene $<$ phenol $<$ hydroquinone $<$ sodium phenoxide. The hydrocarbon is nonpolar; hydroquinone has two hydroxyl groups and is expected to be more soluble than phenol, which has only one; the phenoxide is an ionic compound and would be expected to be most soluble of all.

7.6. Boiling point: dimethyl ether $<$ methanol $<$ water
Molecular weight: $\text{H}_2\text{O} < \text{CH}_3\text{OH} < \text{CH}_3\text{OCH}_3$

In the absence of other factors, boiling point and molecular weight usually parallel one another; the greater the molecular weight, the greater the number of atoms and electrons per molecule, the greater the intermolecular attractive forces and the greater the energy needed to separate molecules from each other—hence, the greater the boiling point.

The other factor, which reverses the order in the example being discussed, is hydrogen bonding. This is greatest for water, less significant for methanol, and unimportant with dimethyl ether. Review Section 7.3.

7.7. Cyclohexanol < p-cresol < phenol < p-chlorophenol. Phenols are much more acidic than alcohols for reasons discussed in Section 7.4. Therefore cyclohexanol, which is the only alcohol in the group, would be the least acidic of the four. Amongst the three phenols, acidity is enhanced by electron-withdrawing substituents and diminished by electron-donating substituents. Since Cl is electron withdrawing and CH_3 is electron donating, relative to hydrogen, the expected order is as shown.

7.8

The negative charge is spread over the three oxygens (as well as other positions). Since this is not possible for phenoxide ion itself, p-nitrophenol is expected to be a stronger acid than phenol. In fact, the K_a's are 1.1×10^{-10} for phenol and 6.9×10^{-8} for p-nitrophenol (the nitrophenol is the stronger acid by a factor of more than 600).

7.9. The p-cresol reacts with the base, whereas the cyclohexanol is not acidic enough to react (compare Eq. 7.3, 7.4).

sodium p-cresoxide

The sodium p-cresoxide, being ionic, dissolves in the aqueous base, whereas cyclohexanol remains in the organic solvent. After the layers are separated, the cyclohexanol can be recovered from the organic layer by evaporating the solvent. If the aqueous layer is acidified, the sodium p-cresoxide is converted back to p-cresol (compare with Eq. 7.5).

p-Cresol is much less soluble in water than its sodium salt; it can be extracted from the water layer by an organic solvent and thus can be recovered.

The overall process described in this question constitutes a fairly general method for separating alcohols from phenols (see also Problem 7.10).

7.10. In the laboratory separations of this type are usually performed by dissolving the mixture in a low-boiling, inert organic solvent such as ether or methylene chloride. The solution is then extracted with an aqueous (neutral, acidic, or alkaline) solution that extracts one of the two components. The layers are then separated, and the organic layer is evaporated to recover the compound that was *not* extracted into the aqueous phase. The aqueous layer is then treated in some way to recover the extracted compound.

a.

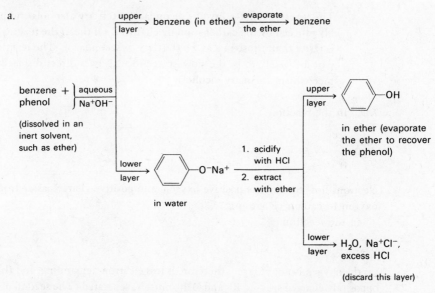

b. The same procedure used in part a works here, since phenol is extracted by base, whereas 1-hexanol, a much weaker acid, is not.

c. An ether solution of the two alcohols can be extracted with water. 1-Propanol is soluble, whereas 1-heptanol, with a much longer carbon chain, is not.

7.11. If this problem causes any difficulty, review Section 7.5a.

a.

$$ \underset{\text{heat}}{\overset{\text{H}^+}{\longrightarrow}} \quad + \; H_2O $$

b. $CH_3CHCH_2CH_3 \xrightarrow[\text{heat}]{\text{H}^+} CH_2=CHCH_2CH_3$ and $CH_3CH=CHCH_3 + H_2O$
  $\quad\quad\; |$
  $\quad\quad OH$

Of the two alkenes, 2-butene is the more stable (most substituted double bond) and it predominates.

c.

$$\xrightarrow{H^+}$$

and

$+ H_2O$

The predominant product is 1-methylcyclopentene, for the same reason as in part b.

d.

$-CH_2CH_2OH \xrightarrow[\text{heat}]{H^+}$ $-CH{=}CH_2 + H_2O$

The reactions in a–c involve secondary or tertiary alcohols and probably proceed by the carbocation mechanism. Of these, the reaction in c is faster than those in a and b (tertiary > secondary). The reaction in part d is likely to be the slowest; it proceeds by a direct displacement mechanism (primary alcohol).

7.12. In the reaction

$$R\overset{+}{\longrightarrow}\overset{H}{\underset{H}{O}} \longrightarrow R^+ + H{-}\overset{..}{O}{-}H$$

electrons flow toward the positive oxygen, and positive charge passes from the oxygen to carbon (R group).

In the reaction

$$R\overset{..}{O}{-}H \longrightarrow R^+ + {}^-{:}\overset{..}{O}H$$

(a) the oxygen is not charged, therefore is less electron-demanding, and (b) two oppositely charged species, R^+ and OH^-, must be separated. The second process therefore requires much more energy than the first.

7.13 a. $(CH_3)_3COH + HCl \longrightarrow (CH_3)_3CCl + H_2O$ **(Eq. 7.14)**

b. $2\ CH_3CH_2CH_2CH_2CH_2OH + 2\ Na \longrightarrow$

$2\ CH_3CH_2CH_2CH_2CH_2O^-Na^+ + H_2$ **(Eq. 7.2)**

sodium 1-pentoxide

c.

3 $+ PBr_3 \longrightarrow 3$ $+ H_3PO_3$ **(Eq. 7.20)**

d. $CH_3CH\underset{OH}{\overset{|}{}}$— $+ SOCl_2 \longrightarrow CH_3CH\underset{Cl}{\overset{|}{}}$— $+ SO_2 + HCl$ **(Eq. 7.19)**

e. $CH_3CH_2CH_2CH_2OH + HOSO_3H \xrightarrow{cold}$

$$CH_3CH_2CH_2CH_2OSO_3H + H_2O \quad \textbf{(Eq. 7.22)}$$

f. $CH_2CH_2 + 2\,HONO_2 \longrightarrow CH_2-CH_2 + 2\,H_2O \qquad \textbf{(Eqs. 7.21 and 7.40)}$
   $\ \ \ |\ \ \ |$ $|\ \ \ \ \ |$
   $\ \ OH\ OH$ $ONO_2\ ONO_2$

g. $CH_3CH_2CH_2CH_2CH_2OH + NaOH \longrightarrow$ no reaction   **(Section 7.4)**

h. $CH_3(CH_2)_6CH_2OH + HBr \xrightarrow{ZnBr_2} CH_3(CH_2)_6CH_2Br + H_2O$ **(Eq. 7.15)**

i. $CH_3CH_2CHCH_2CH_3 \xrightarrow[H^+]{CrO_3} CH_3CH_2CCH_2CH_3$ **(Eq. 7.30)**
          $|$ $\|$
         OH O

j. $\langle\!\!\!\bigcirc\!\!\!\rangle - CH_2OH + CH_3\overset{O}{\overset{\|}{C}}-OH \xrightarrow{H^+} \langle\!\!\!\bigcirc\!\!\!\rangle - CH_2O\overset{O}{\overset{\|}{C}}CH_3 + H_2O$ **(Eq. 7.24)**

7.14. The mechanism involves protonation of the hydroxyl group and loss of water to form a carbocation:

$$CH_2{=}CH-CH-CH_3 \xrightarrow[-H_2O]{H^+} CH_2{=}CH-\overset{+}{C}H-CH_3 \qquad \textbf{(Eqs. 7.10 and 7.11)}$$
$$\ \ \ \ \ \ \ \ \ \ \ \ \ \ \ \ \ \ |$$
$$\ \ \ \ \ \ \ \ \ \ \ \ \ \ \ OH$$

The carbocation is allylic and stabilized by resonance. It can react with the nucleophile Cl⁻ at either end of the allylic ion, giving the observed products.

$$CH_2{=}CH-\overset{+}{C}HCH_3$$

$$\overset{..}{C}H_2{=}CH-CHCH_3$$
$$\ \ \ \ \ \ \ \ \ \ \ \ \ \ |$$
$$\ \ \ \ \ \ \ \ \ \ \ \ \ Cl$$

3-chloro-1-butene

$\overset{\uparrow}{\downarrow}$ $\xrightarrow{Cl^-}$ or

$$CH_2-CH{=}CHCH_3$$
$$\ |$$
$$Cl$$

$\overset{+}{C}H_2-CH{=}CHCH_3$

1-chloro-2-butene

7.15 a.

$$
\begin{array}{c}
\text{H}\ \ \text{H}\ \ \ \ \overset{..}{\underset{..}{\text{O}}} \\
|\ \ \ |\ \ \ \ \ \ \| \\
\text{H}-\text{C}-\text{C}-\overset{..}{\underset{..}{\text{O}}}-\text{S}-\overset{..}{\underset{..}{\text{O}}}-\text{H} \\
|\ \ \ |\ \ \ \ \ \ | \\
\text{H}\ \ \text{H}\ \ \ \ \ \ \overset{..}{\underset{..}{\text{O}}}
\end{array}
$$

The two doubly bound oxygens have a 0 formal charge, and the sulfur has a 0 formal charge (exactly as in sulfuric acid)

b. $CH_3CH_2CH_2CH_2-\overset{..}{\underset{..}{O}}-\overset{\overset{\displaystyle :\overset{..}{O}:}{\|}}{P}-\overset{..}{\underset{..}{O}}-CH_2CH_2CH_2CH_3$
$$\ :\overset{..}{\underset{..}{O}}CH_2CH_2CH_2CH_3$$

Written this way, with 10 electrons around the phosphorus, there are no formal charges. We can write the structure with a single bond in place of the double bond (move an electron pair out on to the oxygen). In this structure, that oxygen would have a -1 formal charge, and the phosphorus would have a $+1$ formal charge.

c. 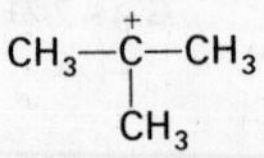 $CH_3-\overset{+}{C}-CH_3$
      $|$
      CH_3

The central carbon shares three single bonds with its neighbors and has no additional electrons. It therefore has a $+1$ formal charge.

d. 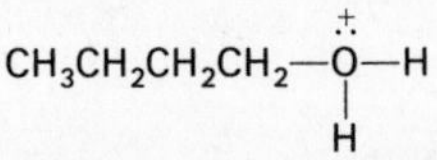 $CH_3CH_2CH_2CH_2-\overset{\cdot\cdot}{\overset{+}{O}}-H$
                        $|$
                        H

The oxygen has one unshared pair and owns one more electron from the shared pairs, for a total of five electrons. It has a $+1$ formal charge.

e. $K^+ {}^-: \overset{\cdot\cdot}{\underset{\cdot\cdot}{O}}-CH_2CH_3$

The oxygen has three unshared pairs and owns one more electron from the shared pair for a total of seven electrons. It has a -1 formal charge.

f.

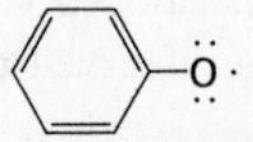

The oxygen has five unshared electrons and one more from the shared pair, for a total of six. It is therefore neutral. The same is true for the other contributors to the resonance hybrid.

7.16. Oxidation gives the corresponding phenoxy radical, whose various resonance structures are shown (see Section 7.6b).

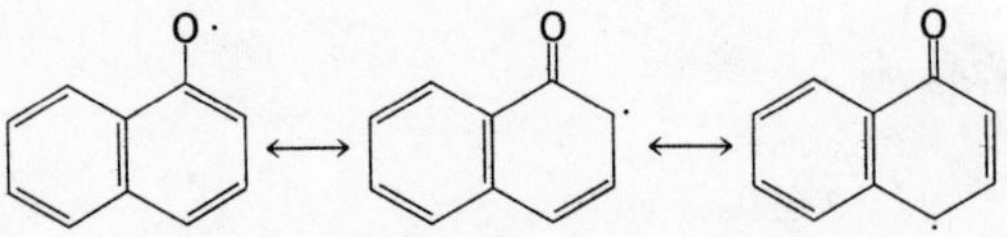

The three products are formed by para-para, ortho-ortho, and ortho-para coupling, respectively. We illustrate only the para-para coupling here:

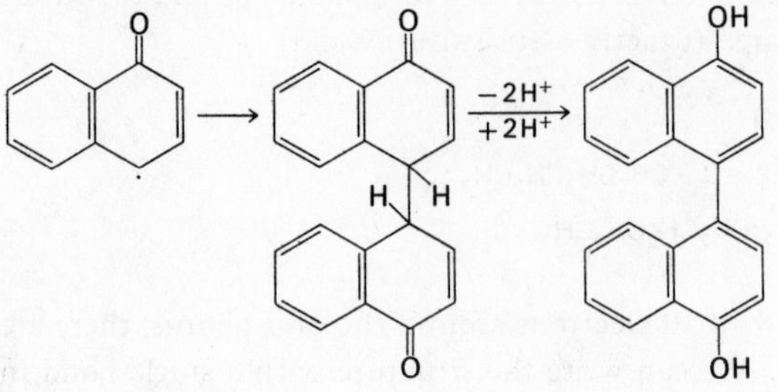

The last step involves ionization of a proton and recombination of the proton with the oxygen. The driving force for the last step is that it produces an aromatic ring.

7.17. The symmetric structure of iridoskyrin suggests that it was formed by para-para oxidative coupling of the phenol whose structure is shown below.

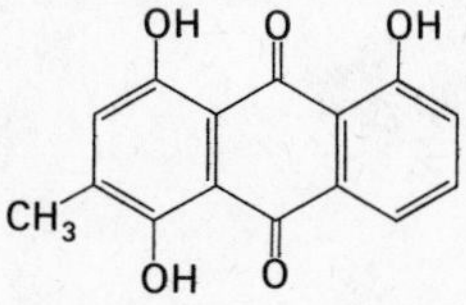

7.18. a. For the structure of pentaerythritol, see Section 7.7. The tetranitrate is formed in a manner similar to nitroglycerine, Eq. 7.40.

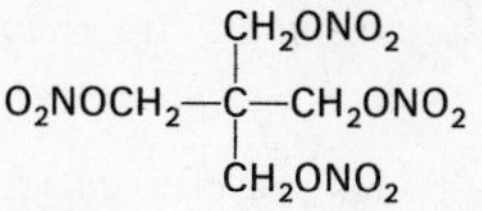

PETN

b. For the structure of resorcinol, see Section 7.7. If you ever use Sucrets for an irritated throat, look on the label for the active ingredient. It is hexylresorcinol.

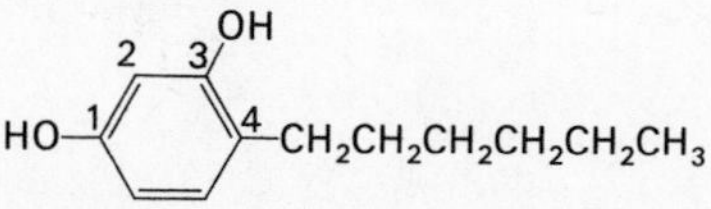

4-hexylresorcinol

c. For the structure of geraniol, see Section 7.9, and for the structure of pyrophosphates, see Section 7.5d.

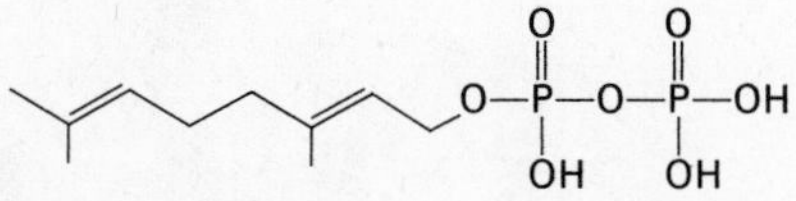

geranyl pyrophosphate

Geranyl pyrophosphate is an intermediate in many biosyntheses (e.g., see Eq. 9.24).

d. For the structure of cholesterol, see Section 7.9. Oxidation with chromic acid (Eq. 7.30) might be expected to give the corresponding ketone.

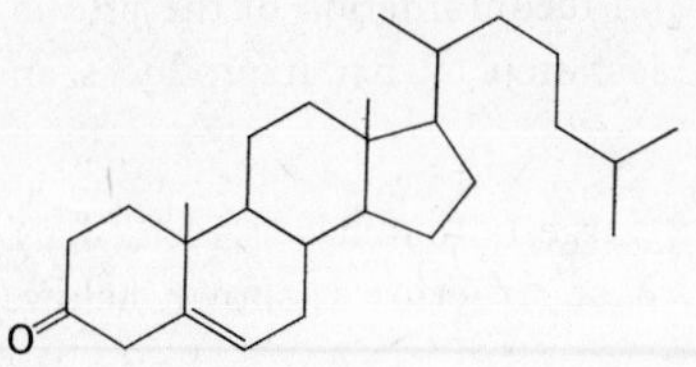

7.19

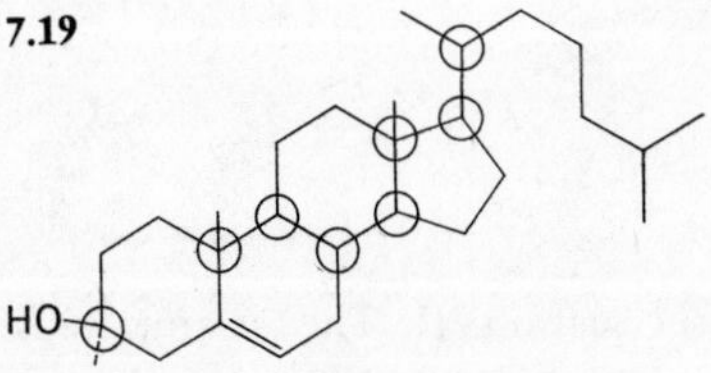

There are eight chiral centers (four different groups attached to the carbon), which are all different. Therefore $2^8 = 256$ stereoisomers are theoretically possible.

7.20. When the hair is reduced, the —S—S— bonds are cleaved (reverse of Eq. 7.47). After the hair is curled in the desired manner, the —S—S— bonds are reformed (Eq. 7.47 in the forward direction) but in a different pattern. The S—S bonds serve as cross-links between protein chains and hold them in the desired shape. The wave is not truly permanent, however, since hair grows.

8. Ethers

OBJECTIVES

1. Know the meaning of: ether and alkoxy group; furan and pyran; epoxide and oxirane; organic peracid; "crown" ether; thioether, sulfide, sulfoxide, and sulfone.

2. Given the name of an ether, thioether, or epoxide, write its structure, and the converse of this.

3. Given the molecular formula, draw the structures of isomeric ethers and alcohols.

4. Compare the boiling points and solubilities in water of isomeric alcohols and ethers.

5. Write the equation for the cleavage of an ether by strong acid (HBr, HI, H_2SO_4).

6. Write the steps in the mechanism for cleavage of an ether by acid.

7. Write equations for the reaction of ethylene oxide or other epoxides with nucleophiles such as H^+ and H_2O, H^+ and alcohols, ammonia and amines.

8. Write the steps in the mechanism for ring-opening reactions of ethylene oxide and other epoxides.

ANSWERS TO THE EXERCISES AND PROBLEMS

8.1 a. $CH_3CH_2CH_2OCH_2CH_2CH_3$

b. $CH_3OC(CH_3)_3$

c. $CH_3CH_2CHCH_2CH_2CH_3$
      $\quad\quad\quad |$
      $\quad\quad OCH_3$

d. $CH_2{=}CHCH_2OCH_2CH{=}CH_2$

e. Br—⟨⟩—OCH_2CH_3

f. $HOCH_2CH_2OCH_2CH_2OH$

g. $CH_3OCH_2CH_2OCH_3$

h. $CH_3CH_2SCH_2CH_3$

i. $ClCH_2OCH_2Cl$

j. 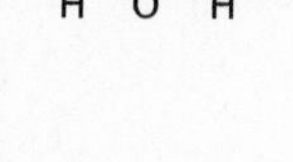 $\begin{array}{ccc} CH_3 & & CH_3 \\ \diagdown & & \diagup \\ & C{-}C & \\ \diagup\;\diagdown & \diagup\;\diagdown \\ H & O & H \end{array}$

8.2.
  a. isopropyl ether

  b. methyl isobutyl ether

  c. propylene oxide

  d. *p*-bromoanisole (or *p*-bromo-
    phenyl methyl ether)

  e. 2-methoxyethanol

  f. phenyl *t*-butyl ether

  g. 2-ethoxypentane

  h. 1,2-epoxybutane

  i. methyl *n*-propyl sulfide

  j. methoxycyclopentane (or
    methyl cyclopentyl ether)

8.3. Be systematic.

$CH_3CH_2CH_2CH_2OH$ 1-butanol

$CH_3CH_2\underset{\underset{OH}{|}}{C}HCH_3$ 2-butanol

$CH_3\underset{\underset{CH_3}{|}}{C}HCH_2OH$ 2-methyl-1-propanol

$(CH_3)_3COH$ 2-methyl-2-propanol

$CH_3OCH_2CH_2CH_3$ methyl *n*-propyl ether

$CH_3OCH(CH_3)_2$ methyl isopropyl ether

$CH_3CH_2OCH_2CH_3$ diethyl ether

8.4. The only compound capable of forming hydrogen bonds *with itself* is 1-pentanol; it has the highest boiling point. The actual boiling points are: 1-pentanol, 137°; 1,2-dimethoxyethane, 83°; hexane, 69°; ethyl *n*-propyl ether, 64°.

The 1,2-dimethoxyethane has two oxygens that can hydrogen bond with water; the pentanol and other ether have only one oxygen, and the hexane has none. We expect the 1,2-dimethoxyethane to be most soluble in water, and it is. In fact, the dimethoxyethane is completely soluble in water, the 1-pentanol and ethyl *n*-propyl ether are only slightly soluble in water, and the hexane is essentially insoluble in water.

8.5.
  a. No reaction; ethers (except for epoxides) are inert toward base.

  b. $CH_3OCH_2CH_2CH_3 + 2\ HBr \longrightarrow CH_3Br + CH_3CH_2CH_2Br + H_2O$ **(Eq. 8.2)**

  c. No reaction; ethers can be distinguished from alcohols by the inertness
    of ethers toward sodium metal.

  d. $CH_3CH_2\overset{..}{\underset{..}{O}}CH_2CH_3 + H_2SO_4 \xrightarrow{\text{cold}} CH_3CH_2\underset{\underset{H}{|}}{\overset{+}{\overset{..}{O}}}CH_2CH_3 + HSO_4^-$

The ether acts as a base (Eq. 8.1) and dissolves in the strong acid.

  e. ⟨◯⟩—$OCH(CH_3)_2$ + HI $\longrightarrow$ ⟨◯⟩—OH + $(CH_3)_2CHI$ **(Eq. 8.4)**

The mechanism involves protonation of the oxygen followed by a displacement reaction with iodide ion.

Such displacements cannot readily occur at an sp^2 carbon. Consequently, the products are as shown (and *not* isopropyl alcohol and iodobenzene).

8.6. Reaction begins by protonation of the ether oxygen (Eq. 8.1).

$$(CH_3)_3C\overset{..}{\underset{..}{O}}CH_3 + H^+ \rightleftharpoons (CH_3)_3C-\overset{\overset{H}{|}}{\underset{..}{O}}{}^{\oplus}-CH_3$$

Cleavage now occurs, giving the tertiary carbocation (*t*-butyl cation) in preference to the primary methyl cation (Eq. 8.3, right half).

$$(CH_3)_3C\overset{\overset{H}{|}}{\curvearrowleft\underset{..}{O}}{}^{\oplus}-CH_3 \longrightarrow (CH_3)_3C^+ + CH_3OH$$

The tertiary cation can lose a proton from one of the methyl groups to give the observed product (see Eq. 7.12).

$$\overset{H}{\underset{|}{CH_2}}\overset{\oplus}{\underset{\underset{CH_3}{|}}{-C}}-CH_3 \longrightarrow H^+ + CH_2{=}\overset{}{\underset{\underset{CH_3}{|}}{C}}-CH_3$$

8.7. This question is based on Eq. 8.2. Since the product is a dibromide, the original ether must have been cyclic (i.e., the two groups attached to the ether oxygen in the starting material must have been joined to one another).

$$\begin{array}{c} CH_2{-}CH_2 \\ |\qquad\quad| \\ CH_2\quad CH_2 \\ \searrow O \nearrow \end{array} \xrightarrow{\text{2 HBr}} BrCH_2CH_2CH_2CH_2Br + H_2O$$

tetrahydrofuran

8.8. $CH_3\overset{*}{C}HCH_2CH_3 + H^+ \rightleftharpoons CH_3\overset{*}{C}HCH_2CH_3$
$\qquad\quad :\underset{..}{O}CH_3 \qquad\qquad\qquad H-\underset{..}{O}{}^+-CH_3$

$$Br^- + CH_3\overset{\frown}{\underset{\overset{|}{H}}{\overset{+}{\underset{..}{O}}}}-\overset{\overset{CH_3}{|}}{\underset{*}{C}}HCH_2CH_3 \longrightarrow CH_3Br + HO-\overset{\overset{CH_3}{|}}{\underset{*}{C}}HCH_2CH_3$$

The chiral carbon is marked with an asterisk. After protonation of the ether oxygen (as in Eq. 8.1), the second step involves a direct displacement at the methyl carbon atom (Eq. 8.3, left half). No bonds to the chiral carbon are broken during the reaction; that is, the C—O bond in the starting ether remains intact and becomes the C—O bond in the alcohol product. Since no bond to the chiral carbon is broken during the reaction, it retains its absolute configuration.

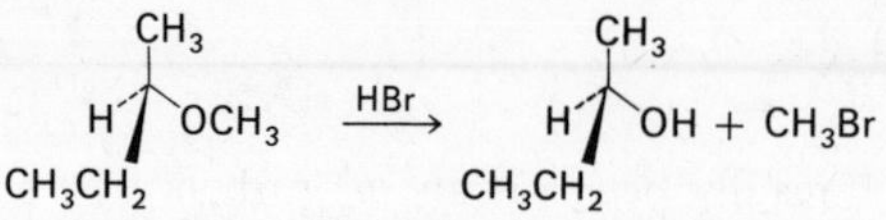

R-2-methoxybutane → R-2-butanol

8.9. The oxygen has one unshared electron pair; it also owns three electrons from the bonds it shares with the adjacent carbon atoms. It therefore has a total of five electrons, for a net formal charge of $+1$.

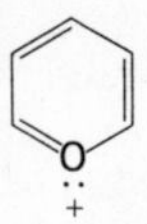

8.10. Use Eq. 8.10 as a guide to the mechanisms.

a. The overall equation is

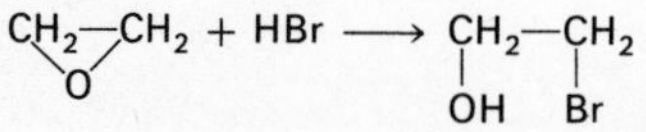

The steps in the mechanism are:

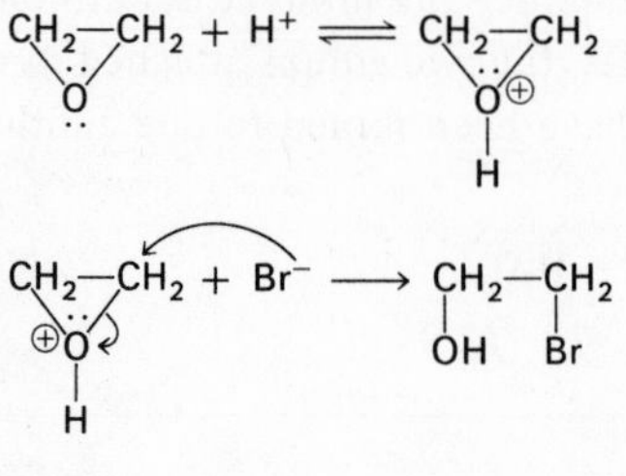

b. The overall equation is

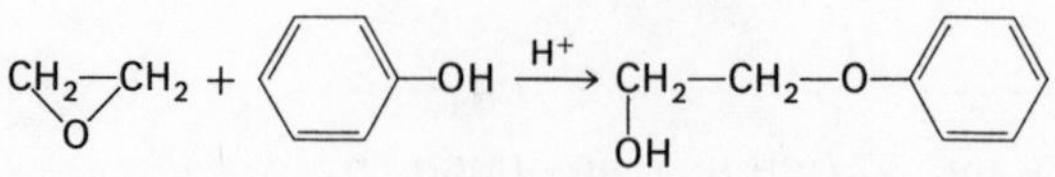

The first step in the mechanism is identical with that in part a. (i.e., protonation of the ether oxygen—Eq. 8.1). This is followed by a direct displacement.

8.11. The reactions are analogous to those shown in Eq. 8.11.

$$CH_2\underset{O}{-\!\!\!\!\triangle\!\!\!\!-}CH_2 + CH_3CH_2OH \xrightarrow{H^+} HOCH_2CH_2OCH_2CH_3$$

ethyl cellosolve

$$CH_2\underset{O}{-\!\!\!\!\triangle\!\!\!\!-}CH_2 + HOCH_2CH_2OCH_2CH_3 \xrightarrow{H^+} HOCH_2CH_2OCH_2CH_2OCH_2CH_3$$

ethyl carbitol

8.12. a. Add a little of each compound, in separate test tubes, to concentrated sulfuric acid. The ether dissolves (Eq. 8.1), whereas the hydrocarbon, being inert and less dense than sulfuric acid, simply floats on top.

b. Add a little bromine in carbon tetrachloride to each ether. The allyl phenyl ether, being unsaturated, quickly decolorizes the bromine, whereas the ethyl phenyl ether does not.

$$CH_2{=}CHCH_2OC_6H_5 + Br_2 \longrightarrow \underset{Br}{\overset{|}{C}H_2}{-}\underset{Br}{\overset{|}{C}HCH_2OC_6H_5} \qquad \textbf{(Eq. 4.3)}$$

$$CH_3CH_2OC_6H_5 + Br_2 \longrightarrow \text{ no reaction}$$

c. Add a small piece of sodium to each compound; the alcohol liberates a gas (hydrogen), whereas no gas bubbles are apparent in the ether.

$$2\ CH_3\underset{OH}{\overset{|}{C}HCH_2CH_3} + 2\ Na \longrightarrow 2\ CH_3\underset{O^-Na^+}{\overset{|}{C}HCH_2CH_3} + H_2 \qquad \textbf{(Eq. 7.2)}$$

$$CH_3OCH_2CH_2CH_3 + Na \longrightarrow \text{ no reaction}$$

Note: The alcohol and ether are isomers.)

d. Add each compound to a little 10% aqueous sodium hydroxide. The phenol dissolves, whereas the ether is inert toward base.

$$\text{C}_6\text{H}_5{-}OH + Na^+OH^- \longrightarrow \text{C}_6\text{H}_5{-}O^-Na^+ + H_2O \qquad \textbf{(Eq. 7.4)}$$

$$\text{C}_6\text{H}_5{-}OCH_3 + Na^+OH^- \longrightarrow \text{ no reaction}$$

8.13. Since the stereochemistry of the starting alkene (cis or trans) determines the stereochemistry of the product (meso or racemic), the reactions must be stereospecific. The reaction involves electrophilic addition to the C=C bond (review Section 4.6c).

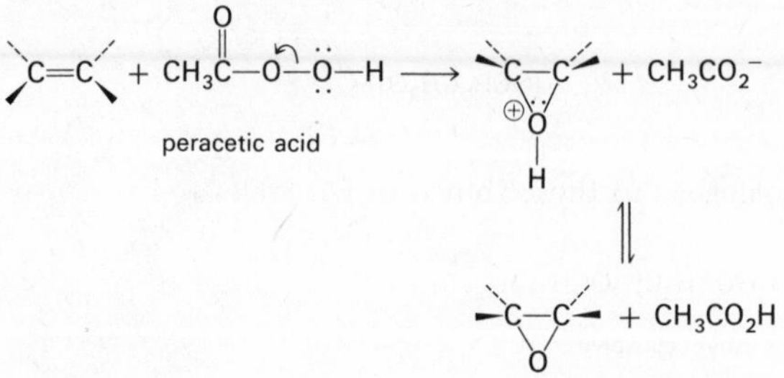

$$\ce{>C=C< + CH_3\overset{O}{\overset{\|}{C}}-O-O-H \longrightarrow} \quad \ce{>C-C< + CH_3CO_2^-}$$

peracetic acid

$$\ce{-C-C- + CH_3CO_2H}$$

Applying this mechanism to *cis*- and *trans*-2-butenes gives

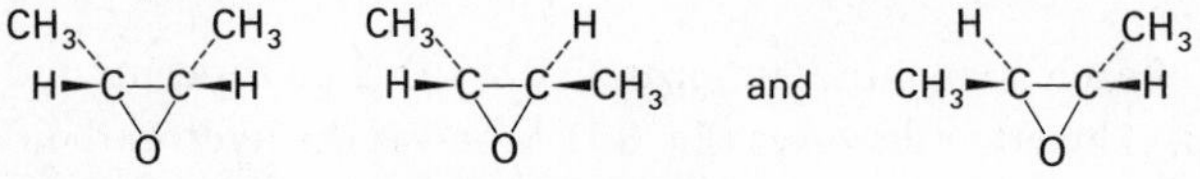

meso-2,3-epoxy-
butane (has two
identical chiral
carbons and a
plane of symmetry)

racemic 2,3-epoxybutane
(has two identical chiral
carbons, but two possible
enantiomers; no symmetry
except for a simple axis)

8.14. For structures of crown ethers, see Section 8.6. The two possible structures are:

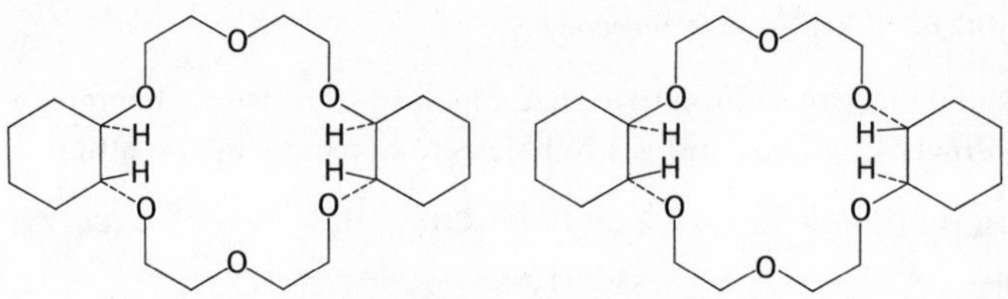

Both have trans geometry at each cyclohexane ring. The structure at the left corresponds to a meso compound, whereas the structure at the right is one of two possible enantiomers in a racemic mixture.

8.15. Since the product has only two carbons, and the starting material has four carbons, two groups of two carbons must be separated by an ether oxygen.

—C—C—O—C—C—

The remaining two oxygens ($C_4H_{10}O_3$) must be at the ends of the chain. The desired structure is

$$\ce{HO-CH_2-CH_2-O-CH_2-CH_2-OH}$$

and the equation for the reaction with HBr is

$$HOCH_2CH_2OCH_2CH_2OH + 4 HBr \longrightarrow 2 BrCH_2CH_2Br + 3 H_2O$$

In this step the ether is cleaved, and the alcohol functions are also converted to alkyl halides.

8.16. a. $CH_3—\overset{..}{\underset{..}{S}}—CH_3$ No formal charges.

b. $CH_3—\overset{\overset{\overset{..}{O}:^{\ominus}}{|}}{\underset{\oplus}{S}}—CH_3$ The oxygen has a -1 formal charge, and the sulfur has a $+1$ formal charge.

c. $CH_3—\overset{\overset{..}{O}:^{\ominus}}{\underset{\underset{..\ominus}{:O:}}{S}}\overset{\oplus}{\longleftarrow}CH_3$ Each oxygen has a -1 formal charge, and the sulfur now has a $+2$ formal charge.

Because of the formal charges, there is a strong dipole from the sulfur to the oxygen $\overset{+\longrightarrow}{S—O}$ in the sulfoxide and sulfone. These compounds are highly polar, in contrast with the sulfide, which is essentially nonpolar. Polarity causes association of the molecules, and it requires additional energy (heat) to break up the molecular association.

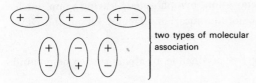

two types of molecular association

Consequently, the sulfoxide and sulfone boil much higher than the sulfide. The boiling point rise is spectacular in going from the nonpolar sulfide to the polar sulfoxide. The rise is much less in going from the polar sulfoxide to the somewhat more polar (and higher-molecular-weight) sulfone.

9. Organic Halogen Compounds

OBJECTIVES

1. Know the meaning of: nucleophile and leaving group; Williamson ether synthesis; primary, secondary, and tertiary amine; quaternary ammonium salt; alkyl cyanide, nitrile, S_N1, and S_N2 mechanisms; $E1$ and $E2$ mechanisms; inversion of configuration; racemization; pyrophosphate leaving group; nucleophilic aromatic substitution; chlorofluorocarbons, Freons, Teflon, and DDT; organometallic compound and Grignard reagent.

2. Given the name of an alkyl or aryl halide, or a polyhalogen compound, write its structural formula.

3. Given the structural formula of an alkyl or aryl halide, write a correct name for it.

4. Write the equation for the reaction of an alkyl halide with any of the nucleophiles listed in Table 9.1. Recognize the class of organic compound to which the product belongs.

5. Given the name or structure of an ether, write an equation for its synthesis by way of a nucleophilic substitution reaction (Williamson synthesis).

6. Given the structure of an alkyl halide, predict whether it is most likely to react with nucleophiles by an S_N1 or S_N2 mechanism.

7. Given the structure of an alkyl halide and a nucleophile, write the equations that illustrate the formation of both the substitution and elimination products, and be able to predict which path is likely to be favored.

8. Know the stereochemical outcome of S_N1 and S_N2 substitutions, $E1$ and $E2$ eliminations.

9. Given an alkyl halide with a particular stereochemistry, a nucleophile, and the reaction conditions, predict the stereochemistry of the product of nucleophilic substitution.

10. Write the steps in the mechanism for a nucleophilic aromatic substitution.

11. Write the structures of the resonance contributors to the intermediate in nucleophilic aromatic substitution.

12. Write the equation for the preparation of a Grignard reagent.

13. Write equations for the reaction of a particular Grignard reagent with water, D_2O, or ethylene oxide.

ANSWERS TO THE EXERCISES AND PROBLEMS

9.1. a.

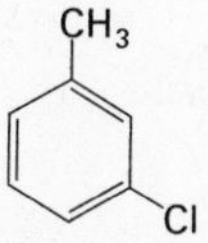

b. $CH_3CH-CHCH_3$
  $\quad\quad\ |\quad\ \ |$
  $\quad\quad Br\quad Br$

c. $CHBr_3$

d.

e.

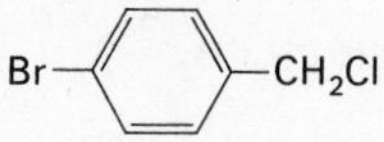

f. $CH_2{=}CHCH_2I$

g. $CFCl_3$

h.

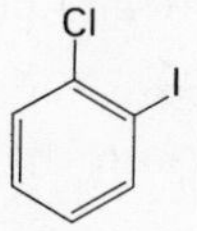

i. $CH_2{=}CHBr$

j. $CH_3CH_2CH_2CH_2F$

9.2. a. 2,2-dimethyl-1-bromopropane (also called neopentyl bromide)

b. *p*-bromochlorobenzene (alphabetic order of substituents)

c. 4-bromo-3-methyl-1-chloropentane (if the bromine is given preference, the numbers will be higher).

d. 3-phenyl-1-chloropropane

e. 2,2-difluorobutane

f. 1,4-dichloronaphthalene

g. 1,4-dibromo-2-butyne

h. *n*-propylmagnesium chloride

i. *p*-chloroanisole

j. 2-bromopropene

9.3. Each of these reactions involves displacement of a halogen by a nucleophile; review Section 9.1a and Table 9.1.

a. $CH_3CH_2CH_2CH_2Br + NaI \xrightarrow{\text{acetone}} CH_3CH_2CH_2CH_2I + NaBr$

b. $CH_3\underset{\underset{Cl}{|}}{C}HCH_2CH_3 + Na^{+-}OC_2H_5 \longrightarrow CH_3\underset{\underset{OC_2H_5}{|}}{C}HCH_2CH_3 + Na^+Cl^-$

(the Williamson ether synthesis)

c. $(CH_3)_3CBr + H_2O \longrightarrow (CH_3)_3COH + H_2O$

The mechanism here is S_N1 (most of the other reactions in this section occur by an S_N2 mechanism).

d. 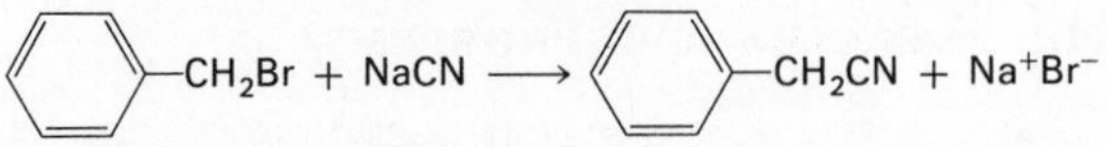 —$CH_2Br + NaCN \longrightarrow$ —$CH_2CN + Na^+Br^-$

e. $CH_3CH_2CH_2I + Na^{+-}C{\equiv}CH \longrightarrow CH_3CH_2CH_2C{\equiv}CH + Na^+I^-$

f. $CH_3\underset{\underset{Cl}{|}}{C}HCH_3 + NaSH \longrightarrow CH_3\underset{\underset{SH}{|}}{C}HCH_3 + Na^+Cl^-$

g. $CH_2{=}CHCH_2Cl + 2\ NH_3 \longrightarrow CH_2{=}CHCH_2NH_2 + NH_4^+Cl^-$

h. $\underset{\underset{Br}{|}}{C}H_2CH_2CH_2\underset{\underset{Br}{|}}{C}H_2 + 2\ NaCN \longrightarrow \underset{\underset{CN}{|}}{C}H_2CH_2CH_2\underset{\underset{CN}{|}}{C}H_2 + 2\ Na^+Br^-$

Displacement occurs at both possible positions.

i. 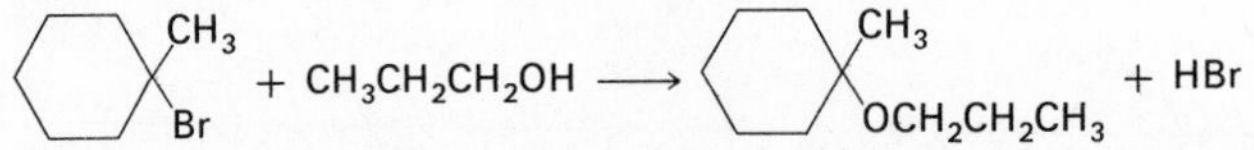 $+ CH_3CH_2CH_2OH \longrightarrow$ $+ HBr$

The starting halide is tertiary, and the mechanism is S_N1.

9.4. In the Williamson synthesis (Eq. 9.5), one R group of the ether comes from an alkyl halide, the other from an alkoxide. If the R groups differ, two combinations of reagents are possible:

$CH_3O^-Na^+ + CH_3\underset{\underset{Br}{|}}{C}HCH_2CH_3 \longrightarrow CH_3\underset{\underset{OCH_3}{|}}{C}HCH_2CH_3 + Na^+Br^-$

$CH_3\underset{\underset{O^-Na^+}{|}}{C}HCH_2CH_3 + CH_3Br \longrightarrow CH_3\underset{\underset{OCH_3}{|}}{C}HCH_2CH_3 + Na^+Br^-$

Since the mechanism involves an S_N2 displacement, it generally occurs better with primary than with secondary halides. Consequently, the second pair of reactants is best. Notice also that an elimination reaction cannot occur with the second pair of reactants but can with the first (to give a butene and methanol).

$CH_3O^- + CH_3\underset{\underset{Br}{|}}{C}HCH_2CH_3 \longrightarrow CH_3CH{=}CHCH_3 \text{ (and } CH_2{=}CHCH_2CH_3) + Br^- + CH_3OH$

9.5. $CH_3CH_2Br + NH_3 \longrightarrow CH_3CH_2\overset{+}{N}H_3 + Br^-$ ⎫ The sum of these two equations

$CH_3CH_2\overset{+}{N}H_3 + NH_3 \rightleftharpoons CH_3CH_2NH_2 + NH_4^+$ ⎬ gives the overall reaction to ⎭ form ethylamine.

The first two equations are now repeated, using ethylamine in place of ammonia, and so on.

$CH_3CH_2Br + CH_3CH_2NH_2 \rightleftharpoons (CH_3CH_2)_2\overset{+}{N}H_2 + Br^-$

$(CH_3CH_2)_2\overset{+}{N}H_2 + NH_3 \text{ (or } CH_3CH_2NH_2) \longrightarrow (CH_3CH_2)_2NH + NH_4^+ \text{ (or } CH_3CH_2\overset{+}{N}H_3)$

$CH_3CH_2Br + (CH_3CH_2)_2NH \longrightarrow (CH_3CH_2)_3\overset{+}{N}H + Br^-$

$(CH_3CH_2)_3\overset{+}{N}H + NH_3 \rightleftharpoons (CH_3CH_2)_3N + NH_4^+$

$CH_3CH_2Br + (CH_3CH_2)_3N \longrightarrow (CH_3CH_2)_4N^+ + Br^-$

9.6. The first step in the hydrolysis of any one of these halides is the ionization to a t-butyl cation:

$(CH_3)_3C—X \xrightarrow{H_2O} (CH_3)_3C^+ + X^-$

$(X = Cl, Br, \text{ or } I)$

The product-determining step involves the partition of this intermediate between two paths—reaction with water, or loss of a proton:

$(CH_3)_3COH \xleftarrow{H_2O} (CH_3)_3C^+ \xrightarrow{-H^+} CH_2{=}C(CH_3)_2$

Since the halide ion is, to a first approximation, not involved in these steps, this partition occurs in the same ratio regardless of which alkyl halide is being hydrolyzed. This result provides experimental support for the S_N1 mechanism.

9.7. If this problem causes you difficulty, review the generalizations in Section 9.1b regarding S_N1 and S_N2 displacements.

If only water is present as the nucleophile, the reaction follows an S_N1 path:

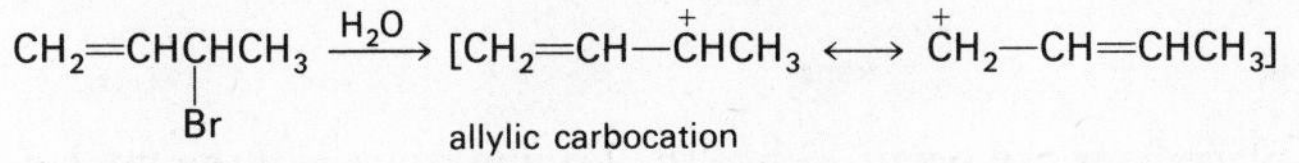

$CH_2{=}CHCHCH_3 \xrightarrow{H_2O} [CH_2{=}CH—\overset{+}{C}HCH_3 \longleftrightarrow \overset{+}{C}H_2—CH{=}CHCH_3]$
       |
       Br   allylic carbocation

The allylic carbocation can react with water at either of two sites, giving two different alcohols:

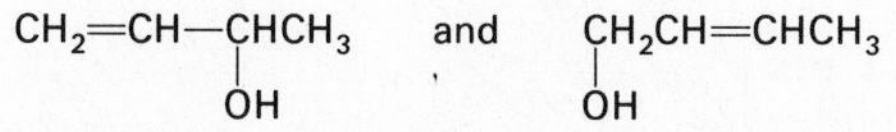

$CH_2{=}CH—CHCH_3$ and $CH_2CH{=}CHCH_3$
          | |
          OH   OH

When the nucleophile is hydroxide ion (20% NaOH), the mechanism changes to S_N2; only the alcohol corresponding to the original halide is produced.

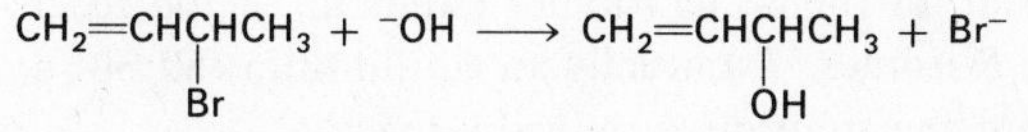

$CH_2{=}CHCHCH_3 + {^-}OH \longrightarrow CH_2{=}CHCHCH_3 + Br^-$
       | |
       Br   OH

9.8. The configuration inverts if the reaction occurs by an S_N2 mechanism, but if the S_N1 mechanism prevails considerable racemization occurs.

a. The nucleophile is methoxide ion, CH_3O^-; the alkyl halide is secondary, and the mechanism is S_N2.

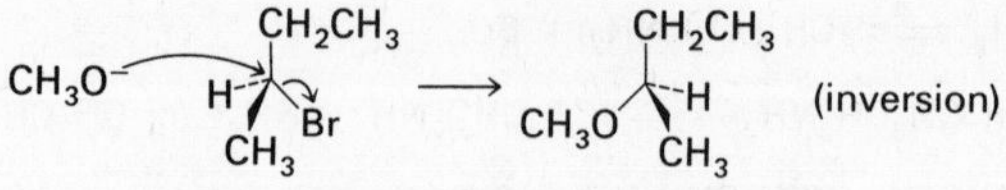

S-2-bromobutane   R-2-methoxybutane

b. The alkyl halide is tertiary and the nucleophile is methanol (a weaker nucleophile than methoxide ion). The mechanism is S_N1 and the product is a mixture of R and S isomers.

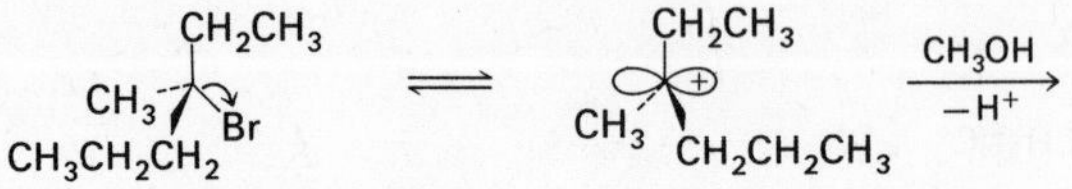

R-3-bromo-3-methylhexane

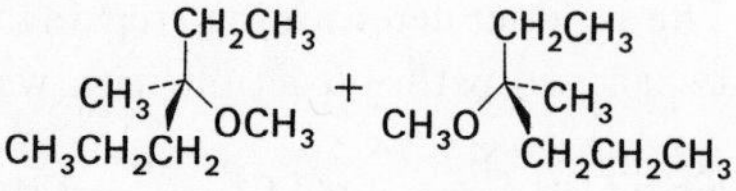

R S

c. The alkyl halide is secondary, and the HS^- ion is a strong nucleophile; the mechanism is S_N2.

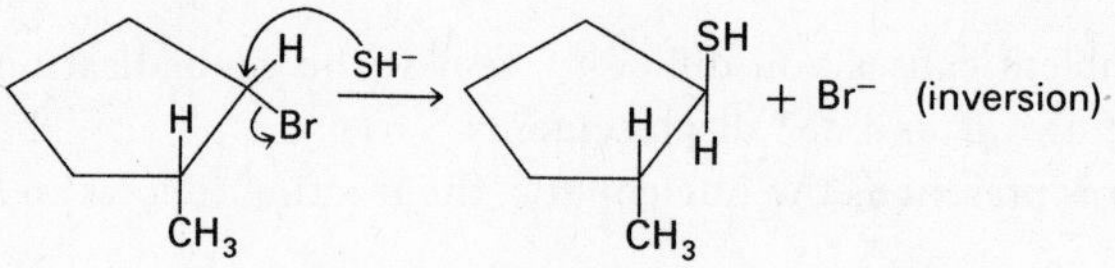

cis   trans

9.9. An S_N2 displacement can occur. Since the leaving group and the nucleophile are identical (iodide ion), there is no change in the gross structure of the product. However, the configuration inverts every time a displacement occurs.

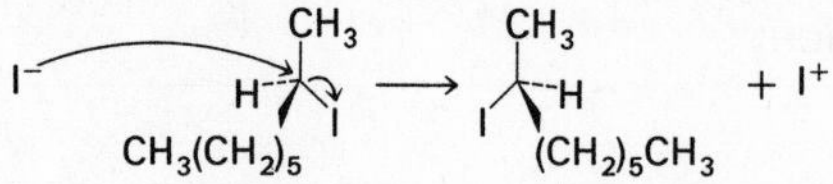

R-2-iodooctane   S-2-iodooctane

Since the enantiomer is produced, the optical rotation of the solution decreases. Eventually, as the concentration of the S enantiomer builds up, it too reacts with iodide ion to form some R isomer. Eventually an equilibrium (50:50) or racemic mixture is formed and the solution is optically inactive.

9.10. If we write the formula for geranyl pyrophosphate in the way shown below, its structural relationship to α-pinene can be seen. In the first step, the pyrophosphate group leaves, thus forming an allylic (and therefore stabilized) carbocation.

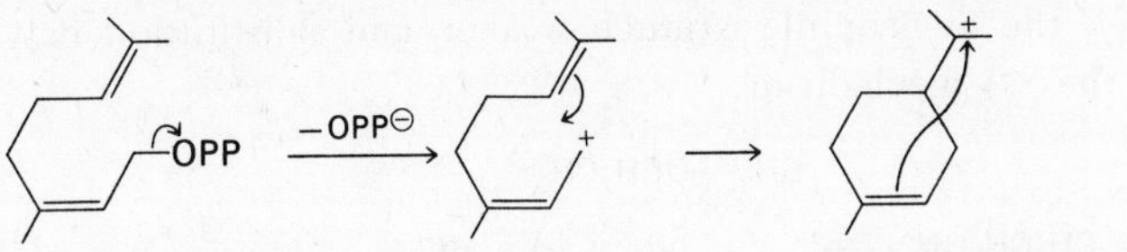

geranyl pyrophosphate   allylic carbocation   tertiary carbocation

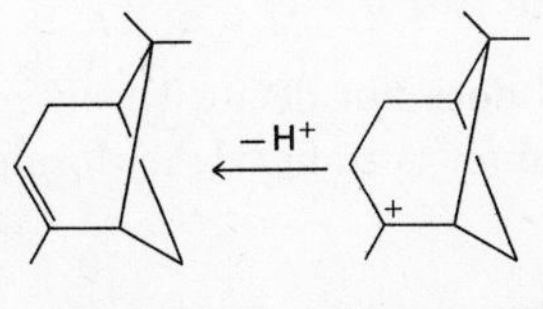

α-pinene   tertiary carbocation

The allylic ion adds to the nearby double bond in accordance with Markowni-koff's rule to close the ring and form a tertiary carbocation. This in turn can add to the remaining double bond, again in Markownikoff fashion, to produce another tertiary carbocation. The reaction is completed by loss of a proton from the adjacent carbon.

9.11. a. The alkyl halide is tertiary; therefore S_N2 displacement is unlikely. Instead, elimination can occur by an $E2$ mechanism. The favored product is the most-substituted alkene, 2-methyl-2-butene.

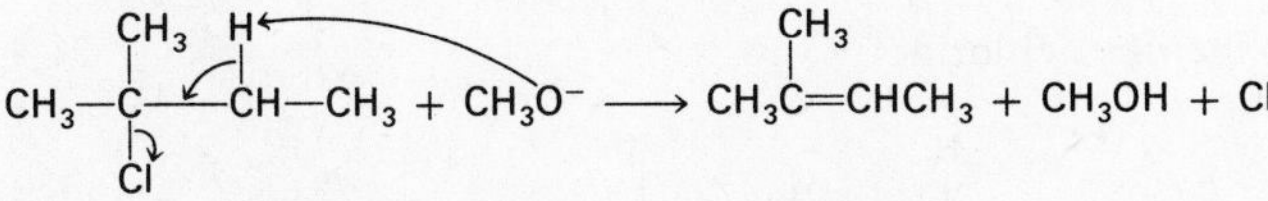

Some 2-methyl-1-butene may also be formed.

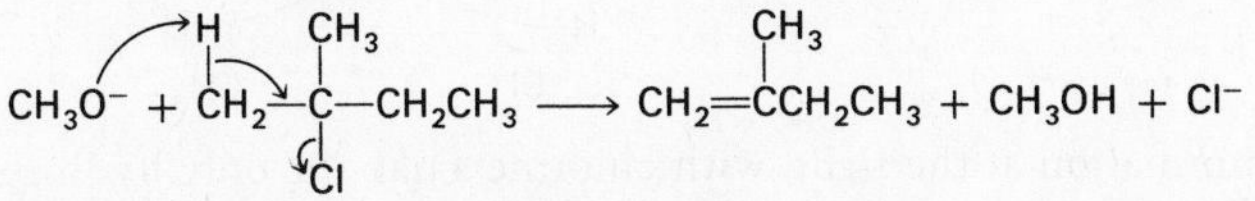

b. The mechanism is exactly as in part a.

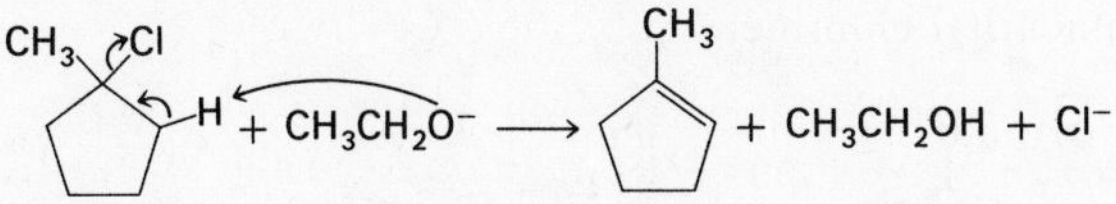

or

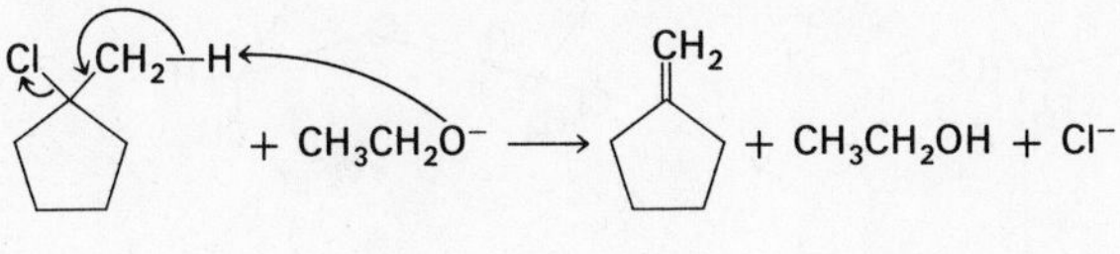

The predominant product is 1-methylcyclopentene, the more stable of the two possible alkenes.

c. In this case the nucleophile is much weaker, and substitution may occur by the S_N1 mechanism.

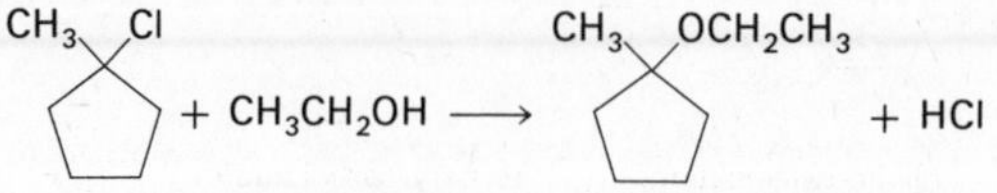

$$+ CH_3CH_2OH \longrightarrow \qquad + HCl$$

Undoubtedly some elimination occurs by an $E1$ mechanism to give the alkenes shown in part b.

d. An S_N2 reaction does *not* occur, because the alkyl halide is tertiary. Instead, the product is isobutylene, formed by an $E2$ reaction.

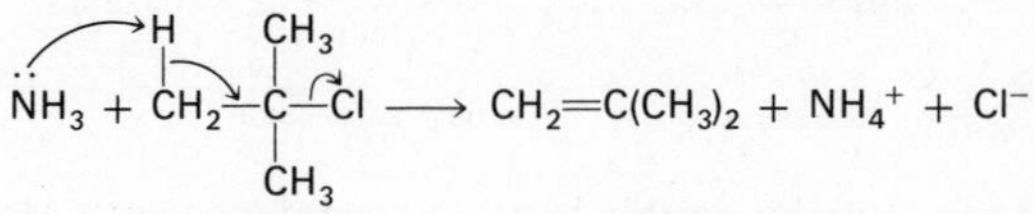

$$\ddot{N}H_3 + CH_2-C-Cl \longrightarrow CH_2=C(CH_3)_2 + NH_4^+ + Cl^-$$

9.12. Cyclohexyl chlorides have the transoid coplanar geometry of the $E2$ transition state only when the chlorine is in an axial position:

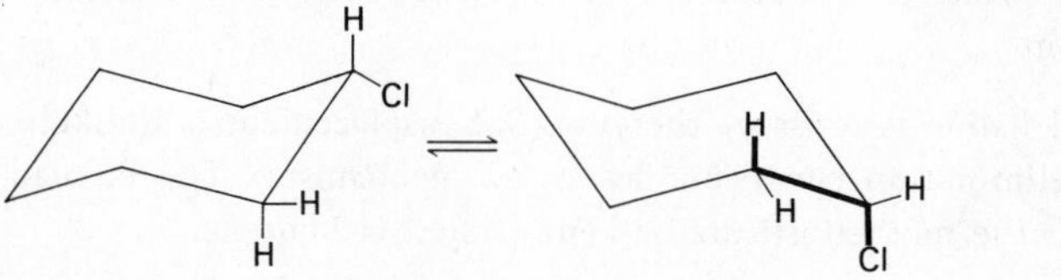

Consider menthyl chloride:

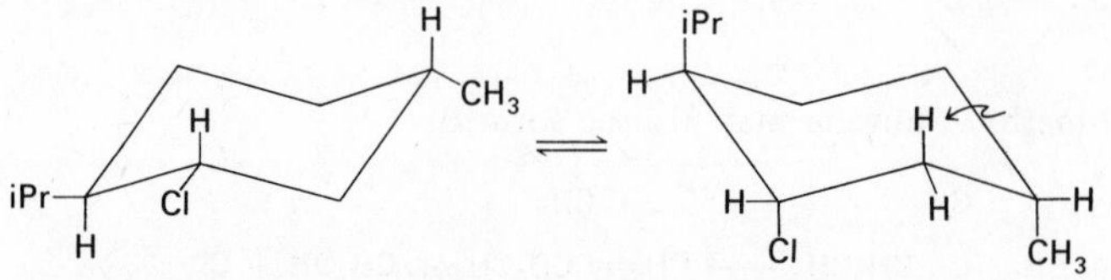

In the conformation at the right, with chlorine axial, the only hydrogen on an adjacent carbon suitably located for $E2$ elimination is shown by the arrow. Therefore the product is 2-menthene.

Consider neomenthyl chloride:

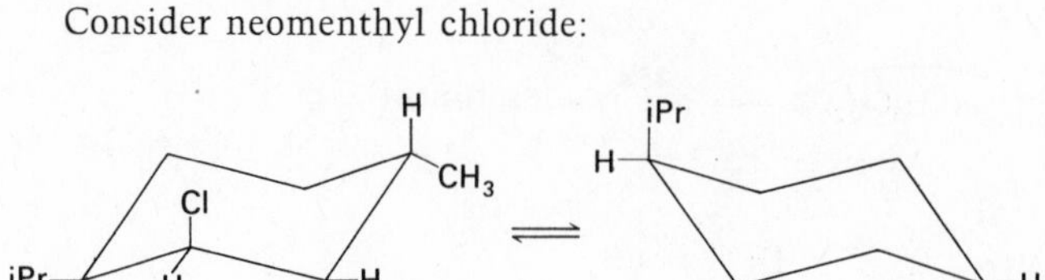

In this case the conformation with chlorine axial is on the left. Two hydrogens (marked with arrows) have the suitable geometry for E2 elimination, and both are eliminated (75% 3-menthene, 25% 2-menthene).

9.13.

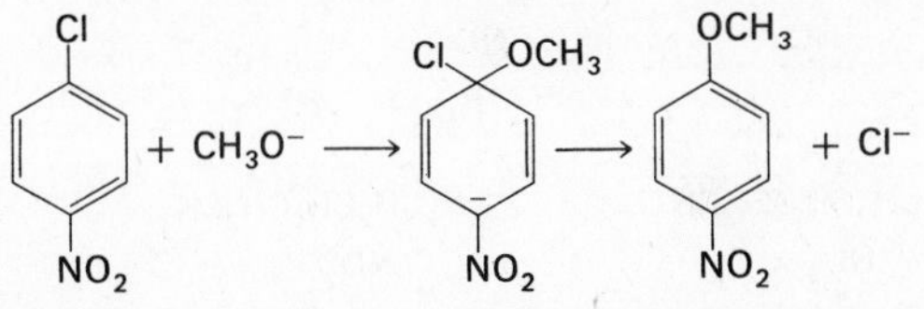

The important contributors to the anion intermediate are:

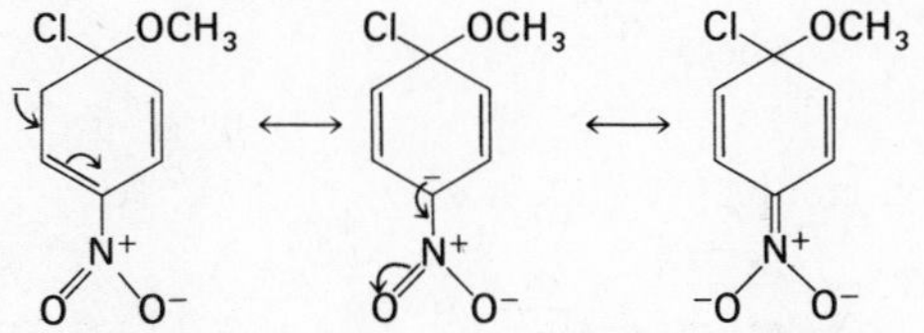

The negative charge can be delocalized to the ring positions ortho and para to the chlorine, and also to the oxygens of the nitro group.

9.14. The second step is a nucleophilic aromatic substitution, facilitated by the electron-withdrawing chlorine substituents. Its mechanism is:

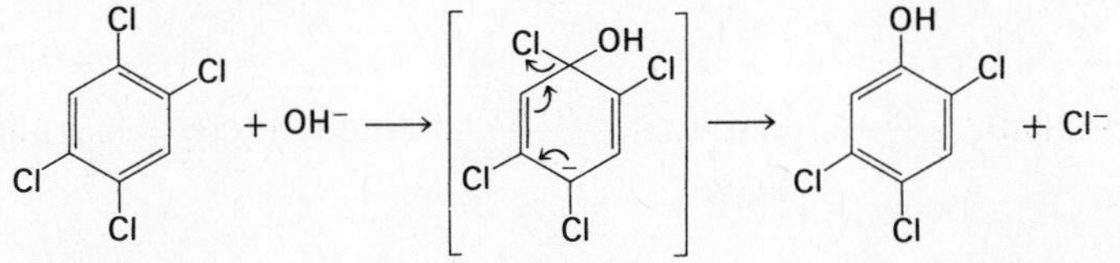

The last step is an example of the Williamson ether synthesis, and the mechanism is an S_N2 displacement.

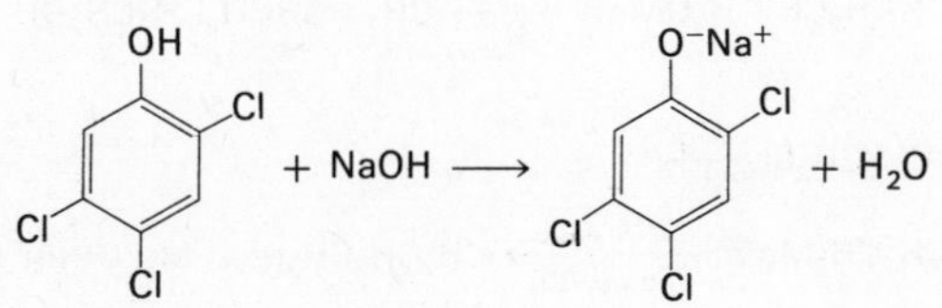

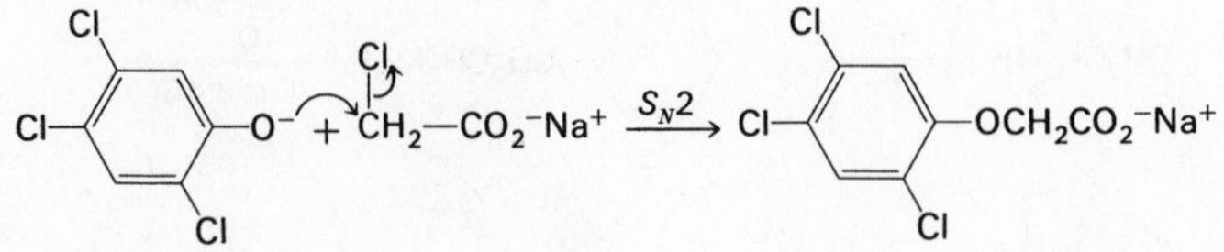

2,4,5-T

9.15. $CH_3CH_2CH_2CH_2NH_2$ +

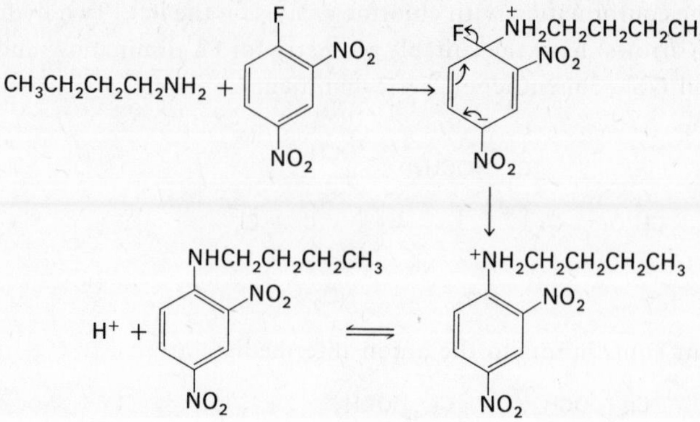

9.16. Let R in Eq. 9.46 be a phenyl group.

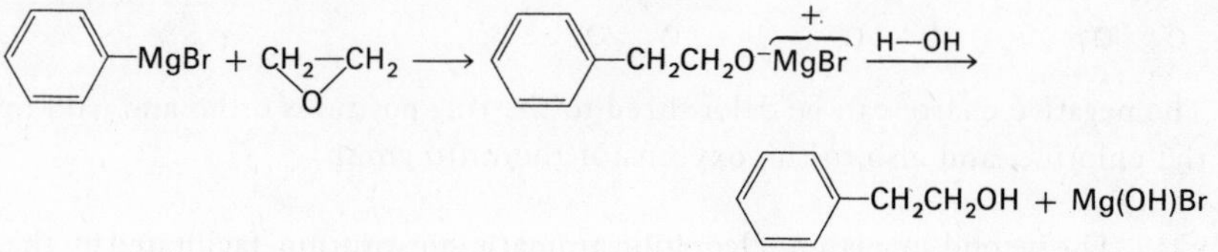

2-phenylethanol
(oil of roses)

9.17. a. $CH_3CHCH_2CH_3 \xrightarrow[\text{ether}]{Mg} CH_3CHCH_2CH_3 \xrightarrow[\text{(Eq. 9.44)}]{H_2O, H^+} CH_3CH_2CH_2CH_3 + Mg(OH)Br$
   |Br |MgBr

b. $CH_2{=}CHCH_2Br \xrightarrow[\text{ether}]{Mg} CH_2{=}CHCH_2MgBr \xrightarrow[\text{(Eq. 9.46)}]{\underset{O}{CH_2{-}CH_2}}$

$CH_2{=}CHCH_2CH_2CH_2OMgBr \xrightarrow[H^+]{H_2O} CH_2{=}CHCH_2CH_2CH_2OH$

c. $CH_3CH_2CH_2OH \xrightarrow{HBr} CH_3CH_2CH_2Br \xrightarrow{Mg}$

$CH_3CH_2CH_2MgBr \xrightarrow[\text{(Eq. 9.45)}]{D_2O} CH_3CH_2CH_2D + Mg(OD)Br$

d.

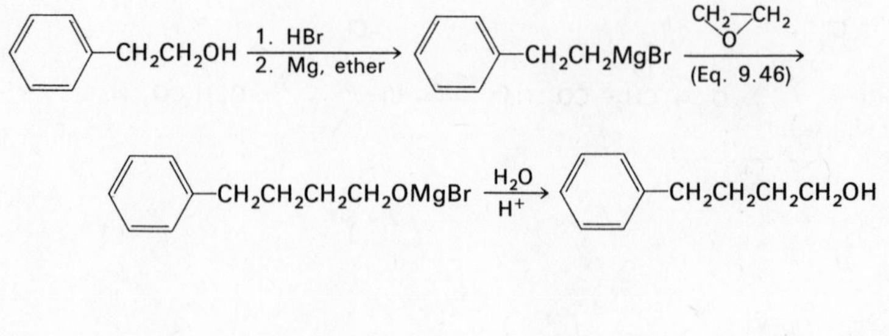

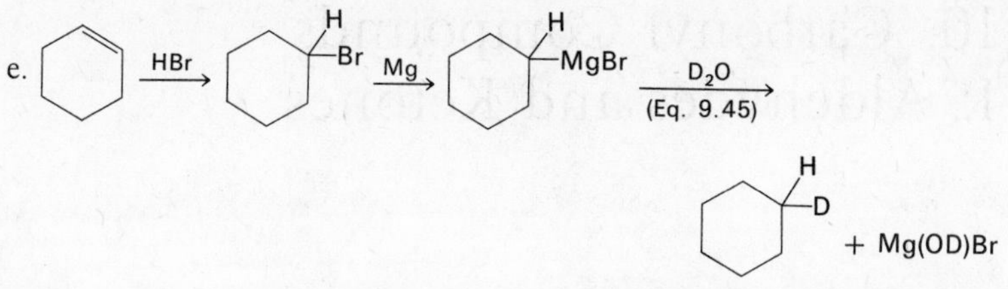

e.

9.18. The sodium hydroxide converts the catechol (a phenol) to the corresponding phenoxide, which then reacts with the primary alkyl halide, S_N2 fashion, to produce the crown ether. This is an example of the Williamson ether synthesis. It can occur in a stepwise fashion.

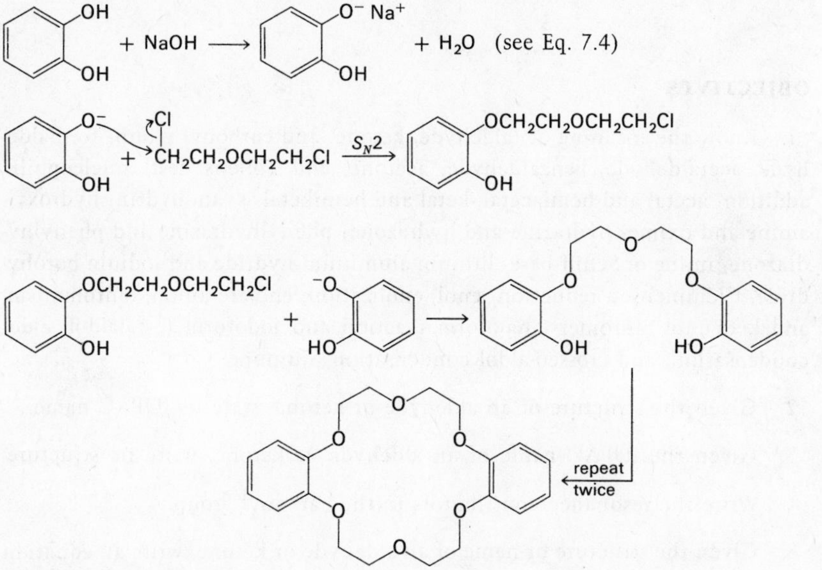

10. Carbonyl Compounds
I: Aldehydes and Ketones

OBJECTIVES

1. Know the meaning of: aldehyde, ketone, and carbonyl group; formaldehyde, acetaldehyde, benzaldehyde, acetone, and Tollens' test; nucleophilic addition; acetal and hemiacetal, ketal and hemiketal; cyanohydrin; hydroxylamine and oxime; hydrazine and hydrazone; phenylhydrazine and phenylhydrazone; imine or Schiff base; lithium aluminum hydride and sodium borohydride; Clemmensen reduction; enol, enolization, enolate anion, tautomerism, and keto-enol tautomers; haloform reaction and iodoform test; aldol, aldol condensation, and crossed-aldol condensation; quinone.

2. Given the structure of an aldehyde or ketone, state its IUPAC name.

3. Given the IUPAC name of an aldehyde or ketone, write its structure.

4. Write the resonance contributors to the carbonyl group.

5. Given the structure or name of an aldehyde or ketone, write an equation for its reaction with the following nucleophiles: alcohol or thiol, cyanide ion, Grignard reagent or acetylide, hydroxylamine, hydrazine, phenylhydrazine, 2,4-dinitrophenylhydrazine, primary amine, lithium aluminum hydride, and sodium borohydride.

6. Explain mechanistically acid and base catalysis of nucleophilic additions to the carbonyl group.

7. Write the steps in the mechanism of acetal formation and hydrolysis; draw the structures of resonance contributors to intermediates in the mechanism.

8. Given a group of organic compounds, place them in order according to their oxidation states.

9. Given the structure of an aldehyde, write the structure of the acid that is formed from it by oxidation.

10. Given a group of aldehydes and ketones, apply simple chemical tests that distinguish them from one another.

11. Given a carbonyl compound and a Grignard reagent, write the structure of the alcohol that is formed when they react.

12. Given the structure of a primary, secondary, or tertiary alcohol, deduce what combination of aldehyde or ketone and Grignard reagent can be used for its synthesis.

13. Given the structure of an aldehyde or ketone, write the formula of the alcohol that is obtained from it by reduction.

14. Given the structure of an aldehyde or ketone, write the structure of the corresponding enol and enolate anion.

15. Identify the α-hydrogens in an aldehyde or ketone, and be able to recognize that it is these hydrogens that can be exchanged readily for deuterium, or can be replaced by halogens.

16. Tell whether a particular aldehyde, ketone, or alcohol gives a positive or negative iodoform test.

17. Write the structure of the aldol formed by the self-condensation of an aldehyde of given structure.

18. Given two reacting carbonyl compounds, write the structure of the crossed-aldol product obtained from them.

19. Write the steps in the mechanism of the aldol condensation.

20. Be able to account for the acidity of hydrogens that are α to two or three carbonyl groups.

ANSWERS TO THE EXERCISES AND PROBLEMS

10.1. a. 3-pentanone

    b. hexanal

    c. benzophenone

      (also, diphenyl ketone)

    d. p-bromobenzaldehyde

    e. cyclopentanone

    f. 2,2-dimethylpropanal

    g. crotonaldehyde

      (or 2-butenal)

    h. 3-penten-2-one

    i. bromoacetone

      (or bromopropanone)

    j. 2,3-pentanedione

10.2. a. $CH_3\overset{\displaystyle O}{\overset{\|}{C}}CH_2CH_2CH_2CH_2CH_3$ b. $(CH_3)_2CHCH_2CH_2CHO$

c. 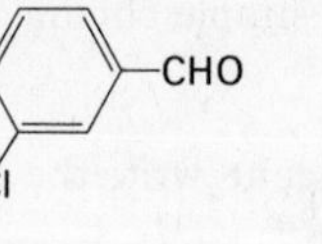 [benzene ring]—CHO with Cl substituent

g. 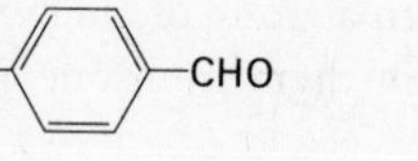 CH_3—[benzene ring]—CHO

d. 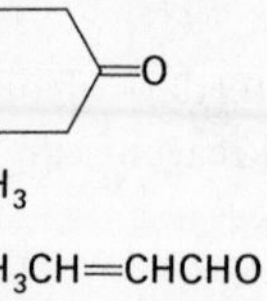 [cyclohexanone ring]=O with CH_3

h. 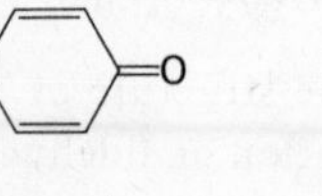 O=[benzene ring]=O

e. $CH_3CH=CHCHO$

i. $CH_3(CH_2)_3CBr_2CHO$

f. 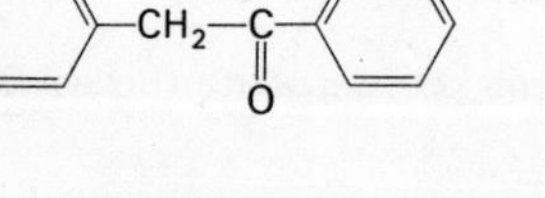 [benzene ring]—CH_2—C(=O)—[benzene ring]

j. 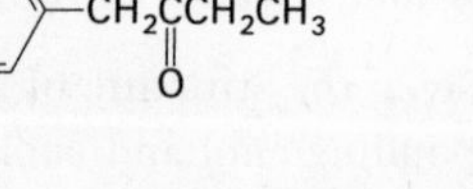 [benzene ring]—$CH_2CCH_2CH_3$ with O below C

10.3. a.–d. See Section 10.7   g.–i. Section 10.9 and Table 10.3

e. Section 10.8a   j. Section 10.11a

f. Section 10.13

10.4. a. 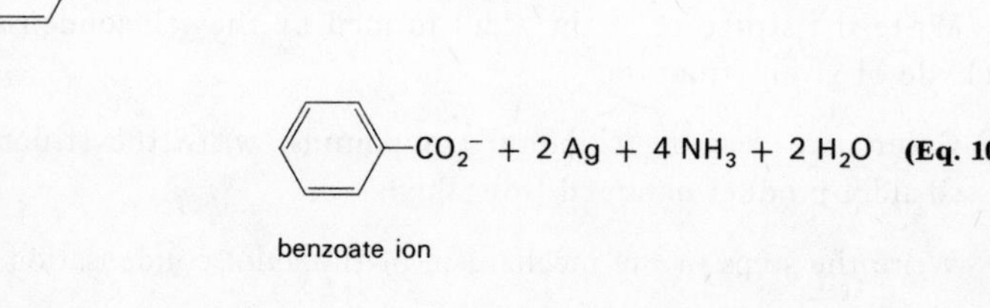 [benzene ring]—CHO + 2 Ag(NH$_3$)$_2^+$ + 3 OH$^-$ $\longrightarrow$

[benzene ring]—CO_2^- + 2 Ag + 4 NH$_3$ + 2 H$_2$O   **(Eq. 10.4)**

benzoate ion

b. 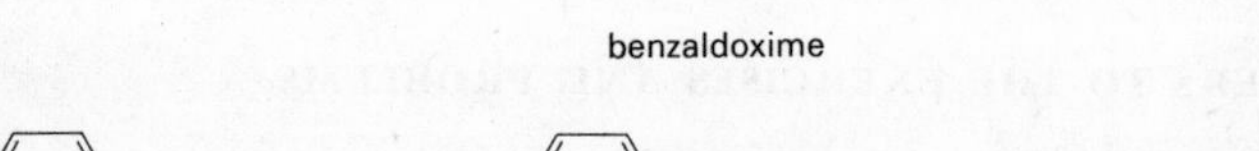 [benzene ring]—CH=O + NH$_2$OH $\longrightarrow$ [benzene ring]—CH=NOH + H$_2$O   **(Eq. 10.34)**

benzaldoxime

c. [benzene ring]—CH=O + H$_2$ $\xrightarrow{Ni}$ [benzene ring]—CH$_2$OH   **(Eq. 10.37)**

benzyl alcohol

d. 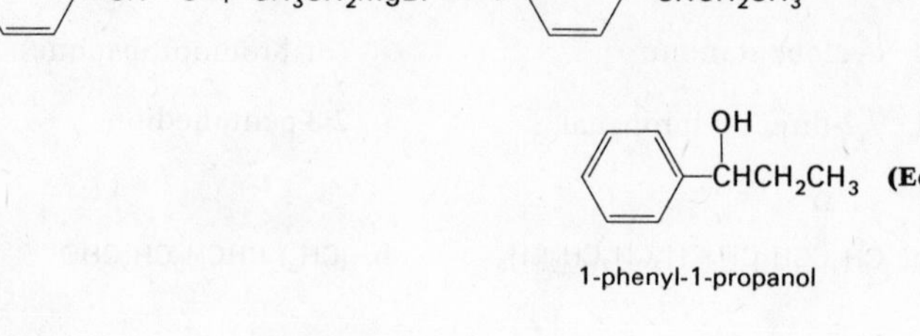 [benzene ring]—CH=O + CH$_3$CH$_2$MgBr $\longrightarrow$ [benzene ring]—$\overset{O^-\overset{+}{M}gBr}{\underset{}{CH}}CH_2CH_3$ $\xrightarrow{H_3O^+}$

[benzene ring]—$\overset{OH}{\underset{}{CH}}CH_2CH_3$ **(Eq. 10.26)**

1-phenyl-1-propanol

e.

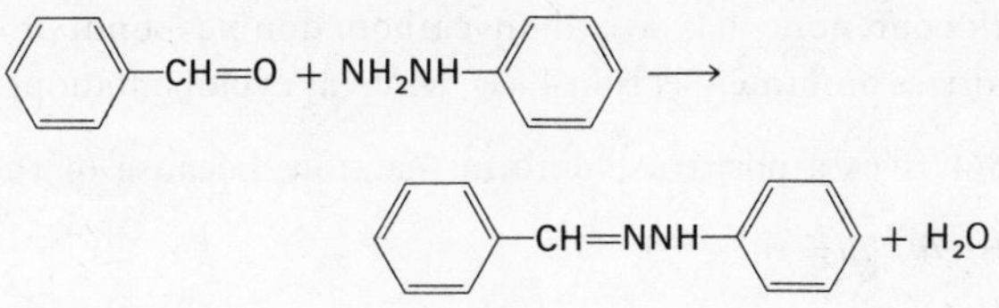

benzaldehyde phenylhydrazone

f. No reactions; there are no α-hydrogens in benzaldehyde, so it cannot form an enolate anion. See Section 10.11c.

g.

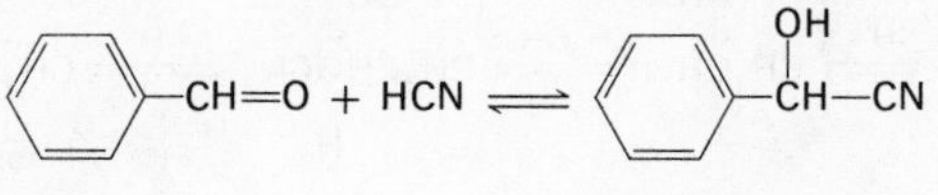

(Eq. 10.19)

benzaldehyde cyanohydrin

h.

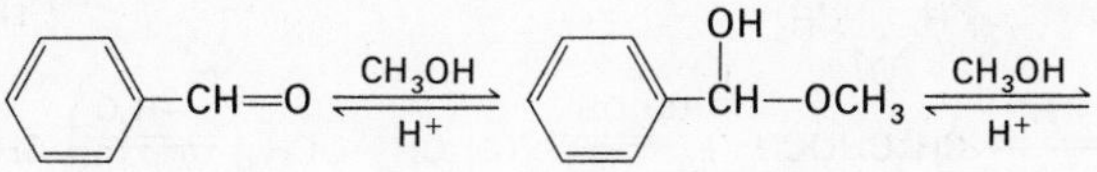

benzaldehyde
methyl hemiacetal

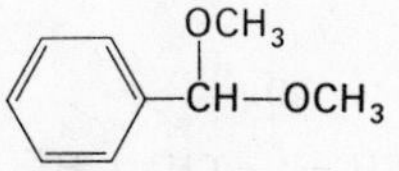

(Eq. 10.11)

benzaldehyde
methyl acetal

i.

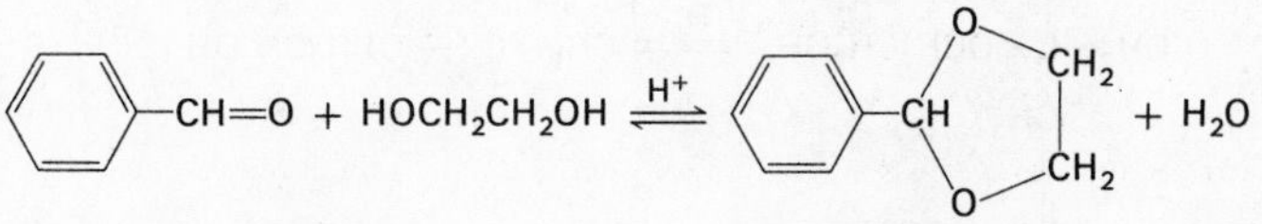

2-phenyl-1,3-dioxolane
(benzaldehyde ethylene
glycol acetal)   **(Eq. 10.12)**

j.

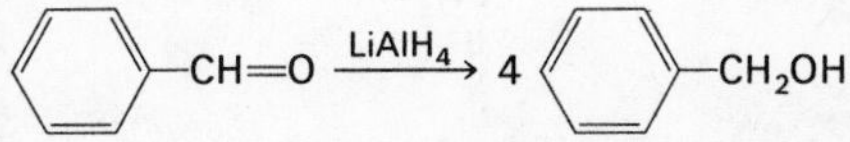

(Eq. 10.39)

benzyl alcohol

10.5 a. 2-Pentanone has the $CH_3\underset{\underset{O}{\|}}{C}-$ structural feature that gives a positive

haloform reaction, whereas 3-pentanone does not (Section 10.11c).

b. Any test that distinguishes aldehydes from ketones will work; the Tollens' silver mirror test is one (Section 10.5).

c. The Tollens' test is positive for benzaldehyde, but is negative for alcohols.

d. 2-Cyclopentenone has a carbon–carbon double bond; it therefore decolorizes bromine (Section 4.6a), whereas cyclopentanone does not.

e. Ethanol gives a positive haloform reaction, because of the group

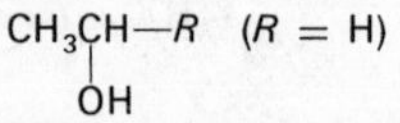

$$CH_3CH-R \quad (R = H)$$
$$\quad\ \ |$$
$$\quad\ \ OH$$

Methanol does not (Section 10.11c).

10.6. a. In Eqs. 10.13 and 10.14, we allow $R = R' = CH_3$.

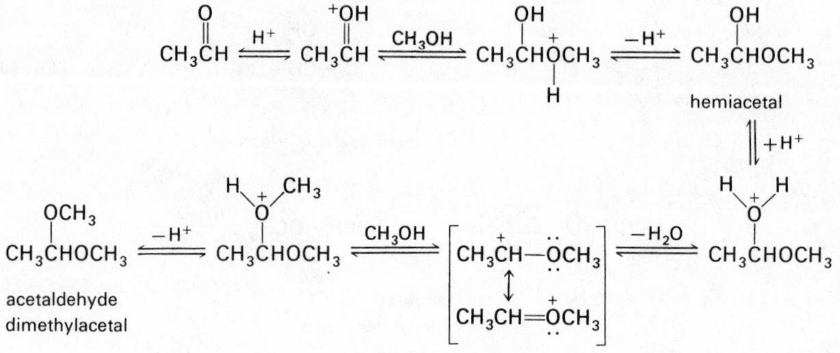

b.

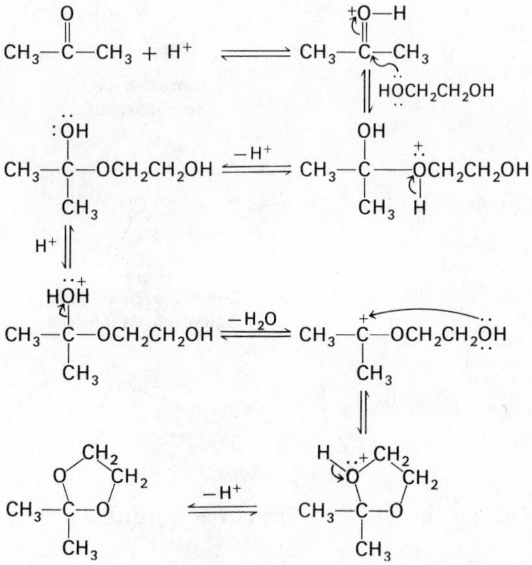

10.7. a. $CH_3CH_2CH_2CH{=}O + 2\ CH_3CH_2OH \xrightarrow{H^+} CH_3CH_2CH_2(OCH_2CH_3)_2 + H_2O$

(Sum of Eqs. 10.9 and 10.10; $R = CH_3CH_2{-}$, $R' = CH_3CH_2CH_2{-}$)

b. In this reaction, we convert a hemiacetal to an acetal (Eq. 10.10).

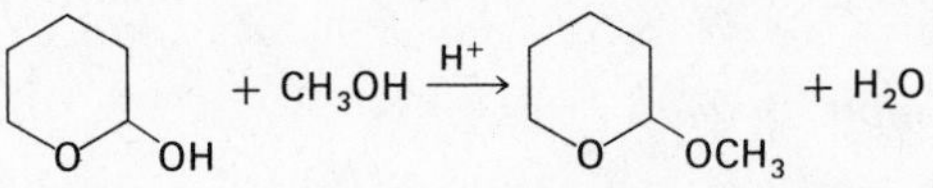

c. The starting material is an acetal twice over; it is completely hydrolyzed to the alcohol and carbonyl compound.

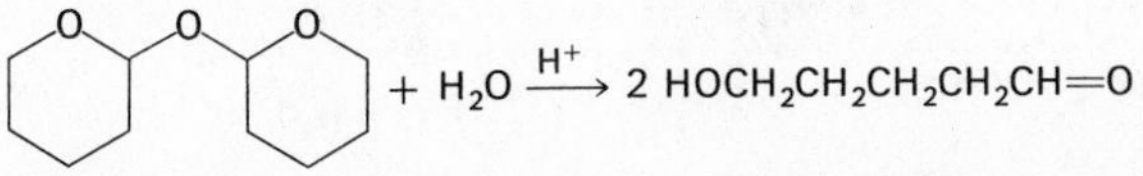

The reaction is analogous to the hydrolysis of certain carbohydrates
(e.g., disaccharides to monosaccharides; see Chapter 14). For practice,
write the steps in the mechanism for this reaction.

d. 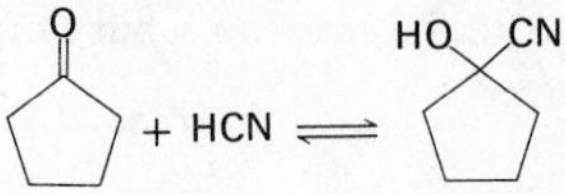 **(Eq. 10.19)**

cyclopentanone
cyanohydrin

e. $CH_3CCH_2CH_3 + NH_2OH \rightleftharpoons CH_3CCH_2CH_3 + H_2O$ (Eq. 10.34; $R = CH_3CH_2-$)
    $\overset{||}{O}$ $\overset{||}{NOH}$

10.8. The general equations for these reactions are given in Section 10.8b
(Eqs. 10.25, 10.26, and 10.27).

a. $CH_3CH{=}O + CH_3MgBr \longrightarrow CH_3\overset{O^- \overset{+}{MgBr}}{\underset{|}{C}}H{-}CH_3 \xrightarrow{H^+, H_2O} CH_3\overset{OH}{\underset{|}{C}}HCH_3$

b.

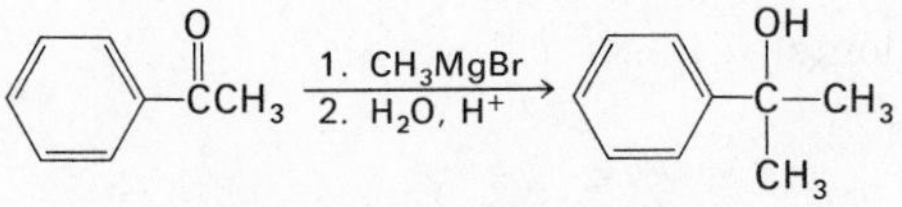

c. $CH_2{=}O \xrightarrow[\text{2. H}_2\text{O, H}^+]{\text{1. CH}_3\text{MgBr}} CH_3CH_2OH$

d.

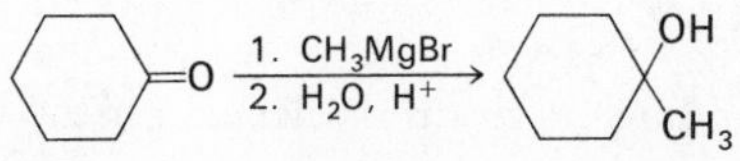

10.9. In each case write the structure of the alcohol:

$$R_1-\overset{R_2}{\underset{R_3}{\overset{|}{\underset{|}{C}}}}-O-H$$

One of the R groups comes from the Grignard reagent; the rest of the molecule
comes from the carbonyl compound. For example, if we select R_1 as the alkyl
group to be derived from the Grignard reagent, then the carbonyl compound is

$$R_2-\overset{O}{\overset{||}{C}}-R_3.$$

a. 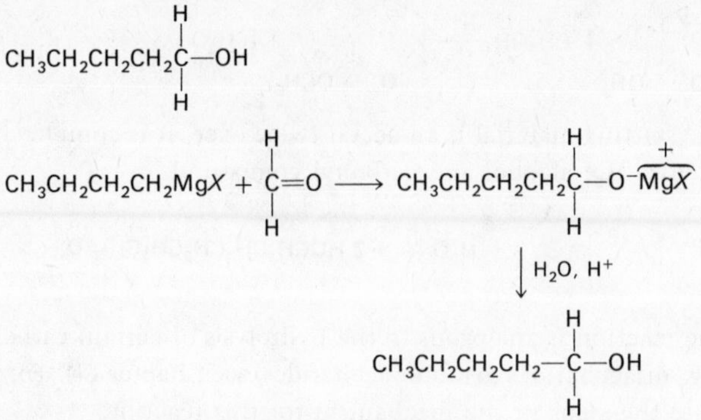 $CH_3CH_2CH_2CH_2\overset{\displaystyle H}{\underset{\displaystyle H}{C}}{-}OH$

$$CH_3CH_2CH_2CH_2MgX + \overset{\displaystyle H}{\underset{\displaystyle H}{C}}{=}O \longrightarrow CH_3CH_2CH_2CH_2\overset{\displaystyle H}{\underset{\displaystyle H}{C}}{-}O^-\overset{+}{MgX}$$

$$\downarrow H_2O,\ H^+$$

$$CH_3CH_2CH_2CH_2{-}\overset{\displaystyle H}{\underset{\displaystyle H}{C}}{-}OH$$

In the remaining cases we do not write the equations, but simply show how the initial reactants are derived.

b. 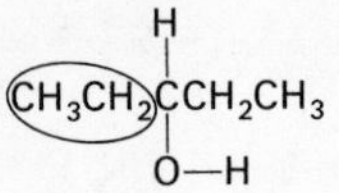 $\underset{\displaystyle O{-}H}{CH_3CH_2\overset{\displaystyle H}{C}CH_2CH_3}$ from $CH_3CH_2MgX + CH_3CH_2CH{=}O$

c. 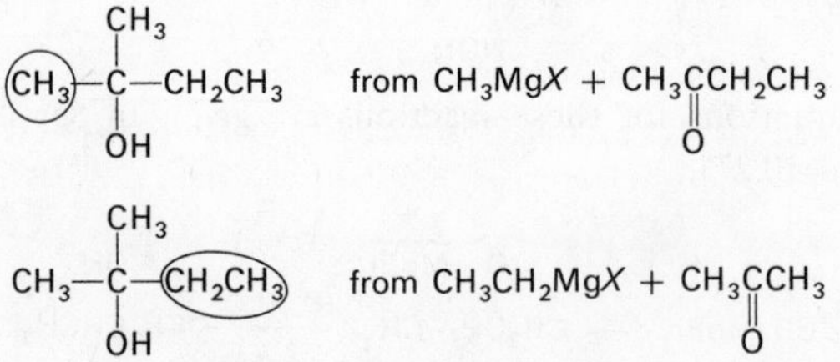 $\underset{\displaystyle OH}{\overset{\displaystyle CH_3}{(CH_3){-}C{-}CH_2CH_3}}$ from $CH_3MgX + \underset{\displaystyle O}{CH_3\overset{\|}{C}CH_2CH_3}$

$\underset{\displaystyle OH}{\overset{\displaystyle CH_3}{CH_3{-}C{-}(CH_2CH_3)}}$ from $CH_3CH_2MgX + \underset{\displaystyle O}{CH_3\overset{\|}{C}CH_3}$

Either combination of reagents will work.

d.

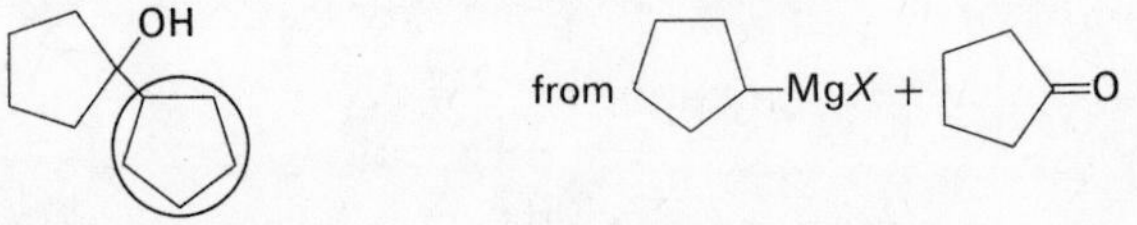

from

In this case the "free-standing" R group is selected for the Grignard reagent.

e.

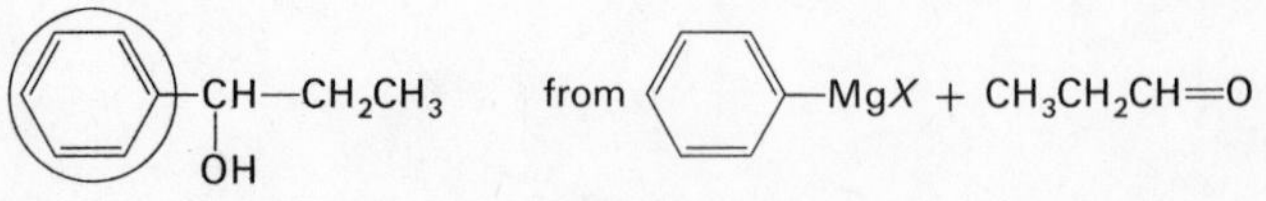

from

or

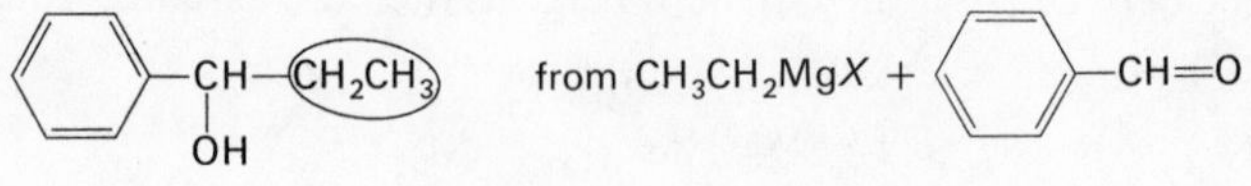

f. $CH_2=CH-CHCH_3$ from $CH_2=CHMgX + CH_3CH=O$
         |
        OH

or

$CH_2=CH-CH-CH_3$ from $CH_3MgX + CH_2=CH-CH=O$
         |
        OH

    Vinyl Grignard reagents, though a bit more difficult to prepare than simple alkyl Grignard reagents, are known. Either pair of reagents will work.

10.10. a.

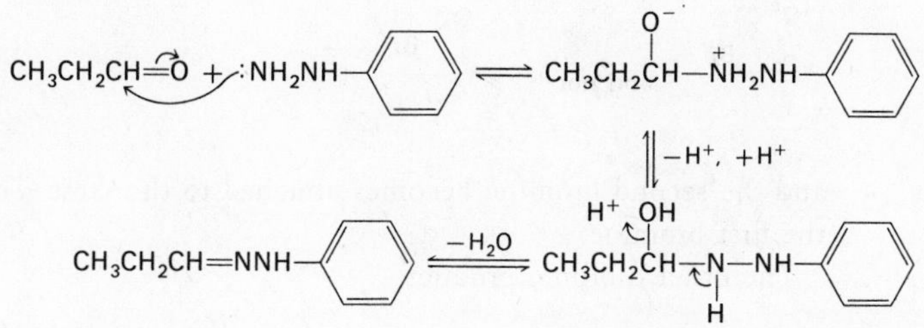

b.

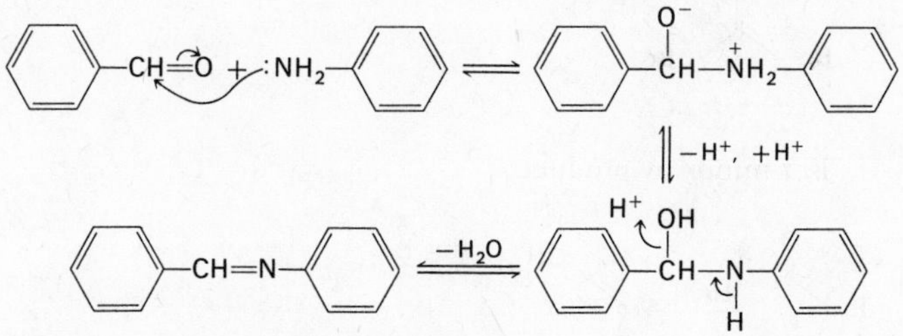

10.11. a. An aldol condensation occurs (Section 10.12).

$$2\ CH_3CH_2CH=O \xrightarrow[\text{heat}]{OH^-} CH_3CH_2\underset{\underset{CH_3}{|}}{\overset{\overset{OH}{|}}{CH}}CHCH=O \quad (\text{Eq. }10.56;\ R = CH_3)$$

  b. Halogenation occurs, α to the carbonyl group (Section 10.11c).

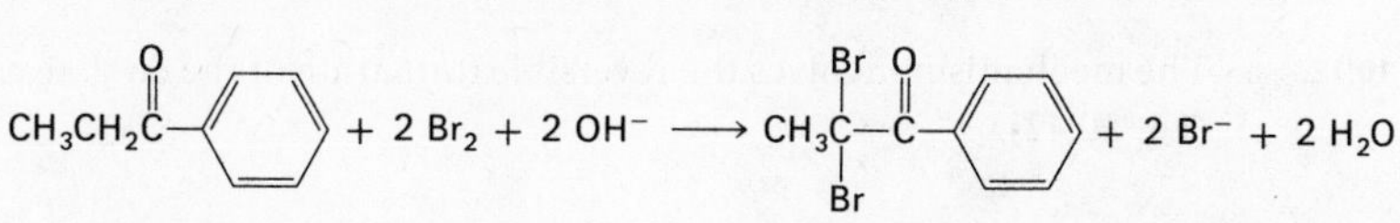

  c. The second halogen enters preferentially on the same side of the carbonyl group as the first:

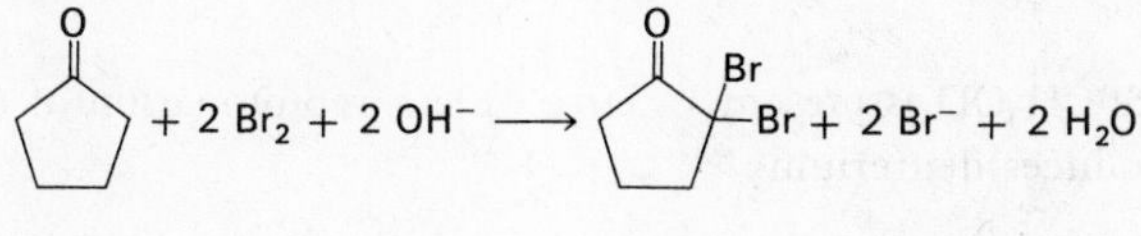

The reason for this preference is that in the monobromination product,

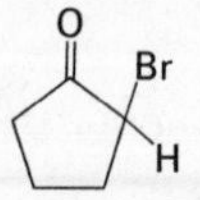

the acidity of the α-hydrogen adjacent to the bromine is enhanced by its electron-withdrawing inductive effect. Consequently the enolate that forms is mainly

and not

and the second bromine becomes attached to the same α-carbon as the first bromine.

The other dibromo product

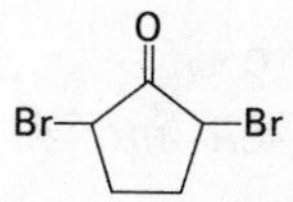

is a minor by-product.

d.

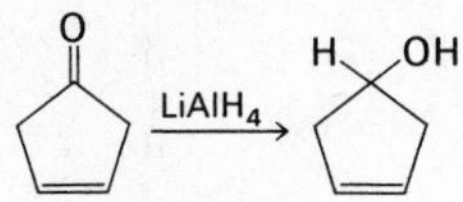

The carbonyl group is reduced without reduction of the carbon–carbon double bond (Eq. 10.40).

e. 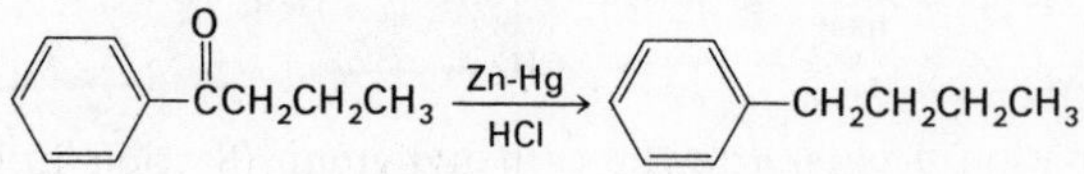   (Eq. 10.41)

10.12. a. The mechanism involves the reversible formation of the enolate anion (Eq. 10.42).

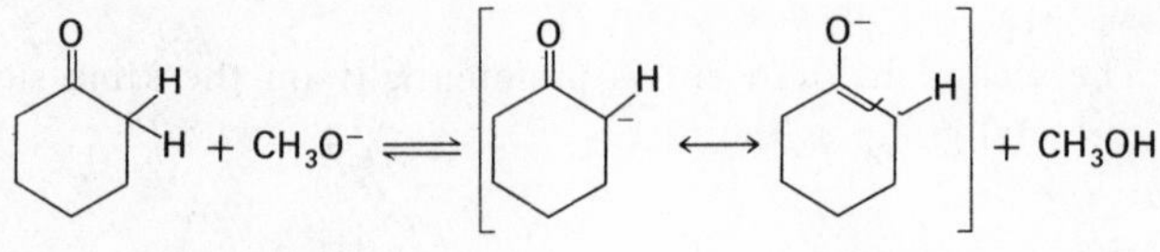

Since CH_3OD is present in large excess, reprotonation of the anion introduces deuterium:

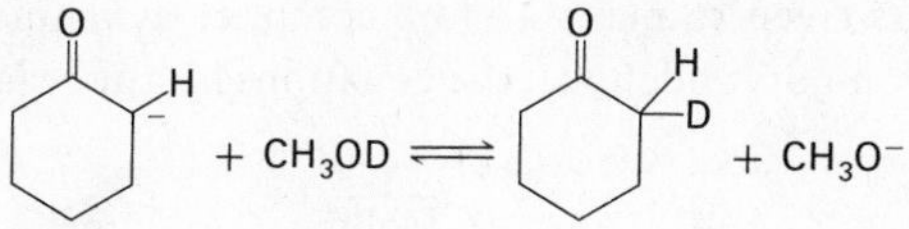

Repetition of this process leads to replacement of the remaining H's on the α-carbons. Since enolization involves only the α-protons, only these are exchanged. The four hydrogens at carbons 2 and 6 are exchanged, whereas the hydrogens attached to carbons 3, 4, and 5 are unaffected. This is a useful way of introducing deuterium in specific positions in an organic molecule.

b. In this case, reaction begins by protonation of the carbonyl carbon. The enol is then formed by loss of an α-hydrogen. Reversal of these two steps accomplishes the exchange.

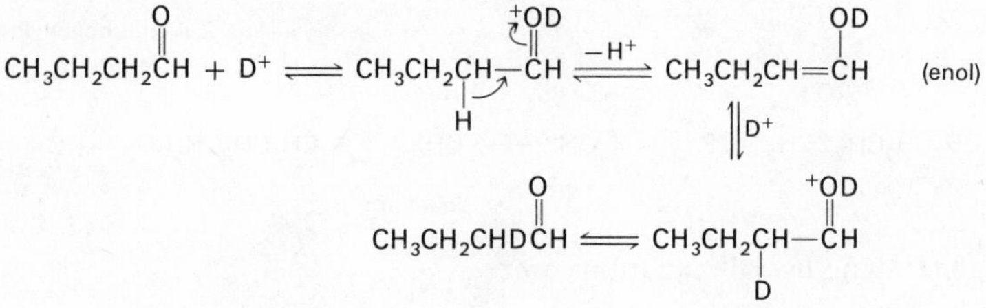

Repeat to exchange the second α-hydrogen.

10.13. Working backwards, compound **C** must contain a carbonyl group (gives a crystalline product with 2,4-dinitrophenylhydrazine–Section 10.9). Furthermore, it must be a methyl ketone, since it gives a positive iodoform test. Therefore **C** must have the partial structure

$$CH_3-\underset{\underset{O}{\|}}{C}-C_3H_7$$

Two possibilities are

$$CH_3-\underset{\underset{O}{\|}}{C}-CH_2CH_2CH_3 \quad \text{and} \quad CH_3-\underset{\underset{O}{\|}}{C}-CH(CH_3)_2$$

Compound **B** must therefore be the corresponding secondary alcohol, since it is oxidized to **C** with chromic acid (Section 7.6e). Possibilities for **B** are

$$CH_3\underset{\underset{OH}{|}}{C}HCH_2CH_2CH_3 \quad \text{and} \quad CH_3\underset{\underset{OH}{|}}{C}HCH(CH_3)_2$$

Since **B** is formed from $CH_3MgBr + $ **A**, **A** must be either

$$O=CHCH_2CH_2CH_3 \quad \text{or} \quad O=CHCH(CH_3)_2$$

Insufficient information is given to make a more complete assignment of the structures. Selecting **A** = *n*-butyraldehyde, the equations for the reactions are:

$$CH_3CH_2CH_2CH{=}O + CH_3MgBr \longrightarrow CH_3CH_2CH_2\overset{\overset{\displaystyle O^- \overbrace{MgBr}^{+}}{|}}{C}HCH_3$$

$$\downarrow H_3O^+$$

$$CH_3CH_2CH_2\overset{\displaystyle O}{\underset{\displaystyle \|}{C}}CH_3 \xleftarrow[H^+]{CrO_3} CH_3CH_2CH_2\overset{\overset{\displaystyle OH}{|}}{C}HCH_3$$

$$CH_3CH_2CH_2\overset{\displaystyle O}{\underset{\displaystyle \|}{C}}CH_3 + NH_2NH{-}\underset{\displaystyle NO_2}{\overset{\displaystyle NO_2}{\bigcirc}}{-}NO_2 \longrightarrow \underset{\displaystyle CH_3CH_2CH_2\overset{\displaystyle \|}{C}CH_3}{N{-}NH{-}}\underset{\displaystyle NO_2}{\overset{\displaystyle NO_2}{\bigcirc}}{-}NO_2 + H_2O$$

crystalline 2,4-dinitrophenylhydrazone

$$CH_3CH_2CH_2\overset{\displaystyle O}{\underset{\displaystyle \|}{C}}CH_3 + 3\,I_2 + 4\,OH^- \longrightarrow CHI_3 + CH_3CH_2CH_2CO_2^- + 3\,I^- + 3\,H_2O$$

iodoform

10.14. The overall equations are:

$$2\,CH_3CH_2CH_2CH{=}O \xrightarrow[\text{heat}]{OH^-} CH_3CH_2CH_2\overset{\overset{\displaystyle OH}{|}}{C}\underset{\underset{\displaystyle CH_2CH_3}{|}}{H}CHCH{=}O$$

(Eq. 10.56)

$$\downarrow \substack{H_2/Ni \\ (Eq.\ 10.37)}$$

$$CH_3CH_2CH_2\overset{\overset{\displaystyle OH}{|}}{C}\underset{\underset{\displaystyle CH_2CH_3}{|}}{H}CHCH_2OH$$

"6–12"

The steps in the mechanism of the first step are:

$$CH_3CH_2CH_2CH{=}O + {}^-OH \rightleftharpoons CH_3CH_2\overset{-}{C}H{-}CH{=}O + H_2O$$

$$\Big\| \; CH_3CH_2CH_2CH{=}O$$

$$OH^- + CH_3CH_2CH_2\overset{\overset{\displaystyle OH}{|}}{C}\underset{\underset{\displaystyle CH_2CH_3}{|}}{H}CHCH{=}O \xrightleftharpoons{H_2O} CH_3CH_2CH_2\overset{\overset{\displaystyle O^-}{|}}{C}H{-}\underset{\underset{\displaystyle CH_2CH_3}{|}}{C}H{-}CH{=}O$$

10.15. a. Reaction begins by formation of the enolate anion of acetaldehyde (the benzaldehyde, having no α-hydrogen, cannot form an enolate); this anion then attacks the carbonyl group of benzaldehyde.

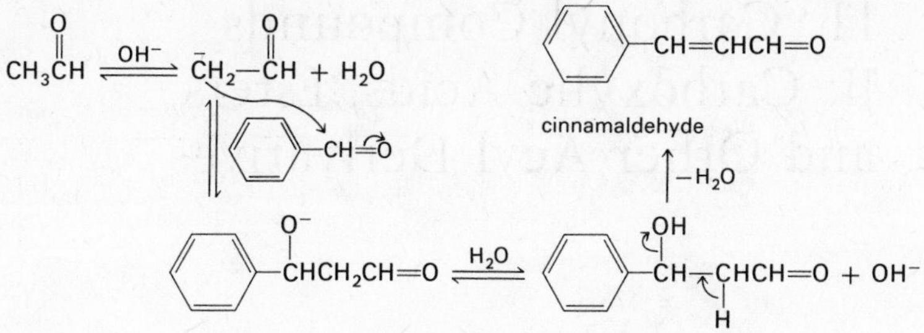

b. 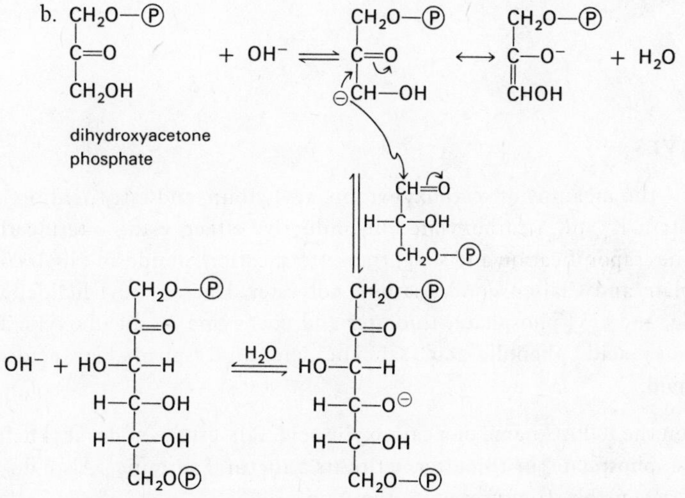 dihydroxyacetone phosphate

10.16. a. The reagents are ethylene glycol (HOCH$_2$CH$_2$OH) and H$^+$; compare with Eq. 10.12.

b. The reagent is chromic acid; compare with Eq. 7.30.

c. The reagent is sodium acetylide, HC≡C$^-$Na$^+$; compare with Eq. 10.30.

d. The reagent is dilute acid, to hydrolyze the ketal; compare with Eq. 10.15.

Although one might expect only Enovid to be formed, its double bond isomer Norlutin is also formed, through an acid-catalyzed enolization (acid is the reagent used to hydrolyze the ketal).

Enovid

Norlutin

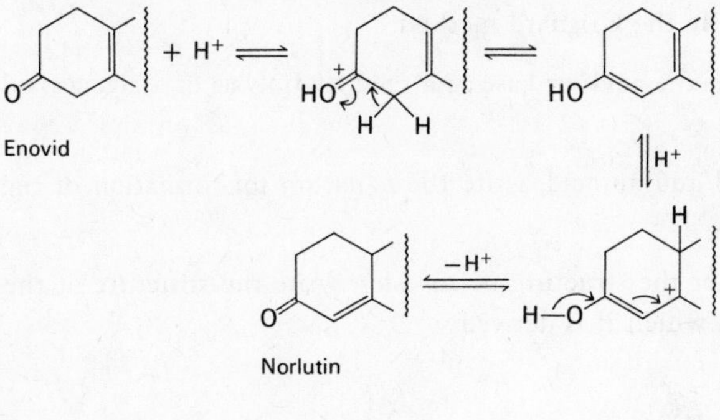

11. Carbonyl Compounds II: Carboxylic Acids, Esters, and Other Acyl Derivatives

OBJECTIVES

1. Know the meaning of: carboxyl group, acyl group, and fatty acid; ionization constant K_a, pK_a; carboxylate ion; inductive effect; ester, esterification, and lactone; saponification and soap; transesterification; amide and hydrazide; ester enolate and Claisen condensation; polyester, Dacron, acyl halide, acid anhydride, and acyl phosphate; thioester and coenzyme A; dicarboxylic acid and hydroxy acid; phenolic acid, salicylic acid, and aspirin; keto acid and pyruvic acid.

2. Given the IUPAC name of a carboxylic acid, salt, ester, amide, acyl halide, anhydride, phosphate, or thioester, write its structural formula. Also, do the converse (given the structure, write the name).

3. Know the common names of the monocarboxylic acids listed in Table 11.1.

4. Know the common names of the dicarboxylic acids listed in Table 11.2.

5. Write the resonance structures of the carboxylate ion.

6. Given a carboxylic acid and a base, write the equation for the neutralization reaction.

7. Given two or more carboxylic acids with closely related structures, rank them in order of increasing (or decreasing) acidities and pK_a's.

8. Given a carboxylic acid, write an equation for its synthesis by hydrolysis of a nitrile (cyanide) or by the Grignard method.

9. Write the steps in the acid- or base-catalyzed hydrolysis of a given alkyl cyanide (nitrile).

10. Given an alcohol and an acid, write the equation for formation of the corresponding ester.

11. Given the name or the structure of an ester, write the structure of the alcohol and acid from which it is derived.

12. Write the steps in the mechanism for the acid-catalyzed esterification of a given carboxylic acid with a given alcohol.

13. Write an equation for the reaction of a given ester with aqueous base (saponification).

14. Write an equation for the reaction of a given ester with ammonia, hydrazine, or lithium aluminum hydride.

15. Write the steps in the mechanism for any of the reations listed under Objective 13 or 14.

16. Given a particular ester, write the structure of the β-keto ester obtained from its self-condensation (Claisen condensation).

17. Write the steps in the mechanism of a particular Claisen condensation.

18. Draw the structure of a polyester obtained from a given dicarboxylic acid and diol.

19. Given a particular acid halide or anhydride, write an equation for its preparation from an acid.

20. Write the equation for the reaction of a given acid halide or anhydride with a given nucleophile (especially with water, an alcohol, or ammonia).

ANSWERS TO THE EXERCISES AND PROBLEMS

11.1. a. $CH_3CH_2CO_2H$

f. $\begin{array}{c} CO_2H \\ | \\ CO_2H \end{array}$

b. $\overset{3}{C}H_3\overset{2}{C}H_2\overset{}{C}H\overset{1}{C}H_2CO_2H$ with CH_3 branch

The carboxyl carbon is number 1.

g. benzene ring with CO_2H and CO_2H (ortho)

c. $CH_3CH_2CHCO_2H$ with Cl branch

h. HCO_2H

d. CH_3—(benzene ring)—CO_2H

i. cyclobutane ring with $\begin{array}{c} H \\ CO_2H \end{array}$

e. (benzene ring) —CO_2H with HO

j. $\overset{\gamma}{C}H_3\overset{\beta}{C}H\overset{\alpha}{C}H_2CO_2H$ with Br branch

Greek letters begin with the carbon atom adjacent to the carboxyl carbon.

11.2. a. 4-methylpentanoic acid

b. 3-bromo-2-methylbutanoic acid

c. ortho-nitrobenzoic acid

d. 2-phenylpropanoic acid (or α-phenylpropionic acid)

e. acrylic acid (or propenoic acid)

f. cyclohexanecarboxylic acid

g. 2,2-difluoropropanoic acid (or α,α-difluoropropionic acid)

h. 2-naphthoic acid (or β-naphthoic acid)

i. 3-methylpentanedioic acid (or 3- or β-methylglutaric acid)

j. tetrachloroterephthalic acid

11.3. The factors that affect acidity of carboxylic acids are discussed in Section 11.2b.

a. CH_2ClCO_2H; both substituents, Cl and Br, are approximately the same distance from the carboxyl group, but Cl is more electronegative than Br.

b. o-Bromobenzoic acid; the bromine is closer to the carboxyl group, and is an electron-withdrawing substituent. Compare the pK_a's of the corresponding chloro acids, given in Table 11.3.

c. CF_3CO_2H; fluorine is more electronegative than chlorine.

d. Benzoic acid; methoxyl is an electron-releasing substituent, when in the para position, and may destabilize the anion due to structures such as

that bring two negative charges near one another.

e. $CH_3CHClCO_2H$; the chlorine, which is electron withdrawing, is closer to the carboxyl group.

11.4. a. $CH_3CH_2CH_2CH_2OH \xrightarrow{Na_2Cr_2O_7} CH_3CH_2CH_2CO_2H$ **(Eqs. 7.26 and 10.3)**

b. $CH_3CH_2CH_2OH \xrightarrow[\text{(Eq. 7.13)}]{HBr} CH_3CH_2CH_2Br$

$CH_3CH_2CH_2Br \xrightarrow[\text{(Eq. 9.14)}]{NaCN} CH_3CH_2CH_2CN \xrightarrow[\substack{H^+ \\ \text{(Eq. 11.6)}}]{H_2O} CH_3CH_2CH_2CO_2H$

$CH_3CH_2CH_2Br \xrightarrow{Mg} CH_3CH_2CH_2MgBr \xrightarrow[\text{2. }H_2O]{\text{1. }CO_2} CH_3CH_2CH_2CO_2H$ **(Eq. 11.7)**

c. Cl—⟨benzene ring⟩—CH_3 $\xrightarrow[\text{heat}]{KMnO_4}$ Cl—⟨benzene ring⟩—CO_2H **(Eq. 5.18)**

d. $CH_2{=}CH_2$ $\xrightarrow{Br_2}$ $\underset{\underset{Br}{|}}{CH_2}{-}\underset{\underset{Br}{|}}{CH_2}$ $\xrightarrow[\substack{\text{a double} \\ S_N2 \text{ displacement}}]{NaCN}$ $\underset{\underset{CN}{|}}{CH_2}{-}\underset{\underset{CN}{|}}{CH_2}$ $\xrightarrow[H^+]{H_2O}$

$$\underset{\underset{CO_2H}{|}}{CH_2}{-}\underset{\underset{CO_2H}{|}}{CH_2} \quad \textbf{(Eq. 11.6)}$$

succinic acid

e. ⟨cyclopentane⟩ $\xrightarrow[\substack{\text{light} \\ (\text{Eq. 3.4})}]{Cl_2}$ ⟨cyclopentane with H and Cl⟩ $\xrightarrow[\substack{\text{2. } CO_2 \\ \text{3. } H_2O,\ H^+}]{\text{1. Mg}}$ ⟨cyclopentane with H and CO_2H⟩ **(Eq. 11.7)**

chlorocyclopentane

f. $\underset{\underset{O}{\diagdown\!\diagup}}{CH_2{-}CH_2}$ $\xrightarrow[\substack{H^+ \\ (\text{Eq. 8.11})}]{CH_3OH}$ $CH_3OCH_2CH_2OH$ $\xrightarrow[\substack{(\text{Eqs. 7.26} \\ \text{and 10.3})}]{Na_2Cr_2O_7}$ $CH_3OCH_2CO_2H$

11.5. a. Follow Eq. 11.5, with $R = CH_3CH_2CH_2{-}$. The mechanism for the last step, hydrolysis of the amide, can be pictured as follows:

$$CH_3CH_2CH_2\overset{\overset{\displaystyle O}{\|}}{C}NH_2 + H{-}\ddot{O}{-}H \longrightarrow CH_3CH_2CH_2\overset{\overset{\displaystyle OH}{|}}{\underset{\underset{H}{\overset{\displaystyle \ddot{O}^+}{|}}{H}}{C}}{-}\ddot{N}H_2 \underset{\longleftarrow}{\overset{-H^+,\ +H^+}{\rightleftharpoons}}$$

$$CH_3CH_2CH_2{-}\overset{\overset{\displaystyle O}{|}\overset{\displaystyle H}{}}{\underset{\underset{OH}{|}}{C}}{-}\overset{+}{N}H_3 \xrightarrow{-H^+} CH_3CH_2CH_2\overset{\overset{\displaystyle O}{\|}}{C}{-}OH + :NH_3 \overset{H^+}{\rightleftharpoons} NH_4^+$$

b. Follow Eq. 11.4, with $R = $ ⟨benzene ring⟩${-}CH_2{-}$. The mechanism for the

last step, hydrolysis of the amide, can be pictured as follows:

$$⟨benzene⟩{-}\overset{\overset{\displaystyle O}{\|}}{C}{-}NH_2 + {}^-{:}\ddot{O}H \longrightarrow ⟨benzene⟩{-}\underset{\underset{OH}{|}}{\overset{\overset{\displaystyle O}{|}}{C}}{-}\ddot{N}H_2 \longrightarrow$$

$$⟨benzene⟩{-}\overset{\overset{\displaystyle O}{\|}}{C}{-}OH + {:}\ddot{N}H_2^- \rightleftharpoons ⟨benzene⟩{-}\overset{\overset{\displaystyle O}{\|}}{C}{-}O^- + {:}NH_3$$

c. Follow Eq. 11.7, with $R = CH_3CH_2CH_2{-}$.

11.6. Follow Eq. 11.12, with $R =$ — and $R' = CH_3$.

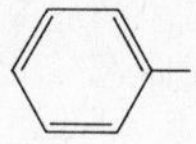

11.7. a. $CH_3\underset{\underset{Cl}{|}}{\overset{\overset{O}{\parallel}}{C}}HC\!-\!O^-Na^+$

d. $H\overset{\overset{O}{\parallel}}{C}\!-\!OCH_2CH_3$

b. $\left(CH_3\overset{\overset{O}{\parallel}}{C}\!-\!O^-\right)_2Ca^{2+}$

e.

c. $CH_3\overset{\overset{O}{\parallel}}{C}\!-\!OCH(CH_3)_2$

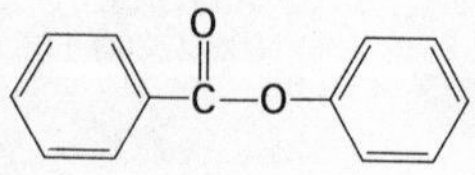

f. 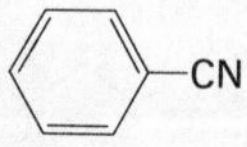 ⬡—CN (gives *benz*oic acid on hydrolysis; therefore *benzo*nitrile.)

11.8. See Section 11.2c for salt nomenclature, and Section 11.6 for ester nomenclature.

a. Calcium butanoate

d. Methyl trifluoroacetate

b. Phenyl isobutyrate, or

e. Methyl formate

    phenyl 2-methylpropanoate

f. Isopropyl propionate, or

c. Sodium *p*-toluate

    isopropyl propanoate.

11.9. a. See Section 4.2 for the definition of an isoprene unit. The compound is made of two isoprene units (in heavy lines) linked together as shown by the dotted lines.

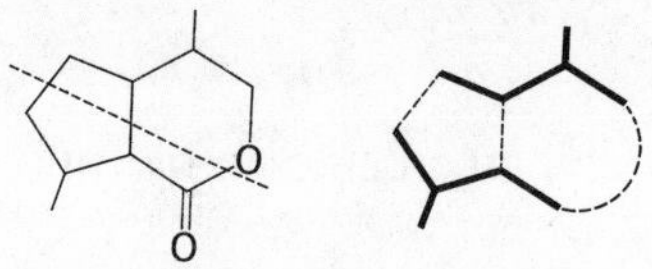

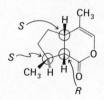

b. Review Section 6.4b for the *R–S* convention. Nepatalactone has three chiral centers:

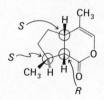

11.10. a.

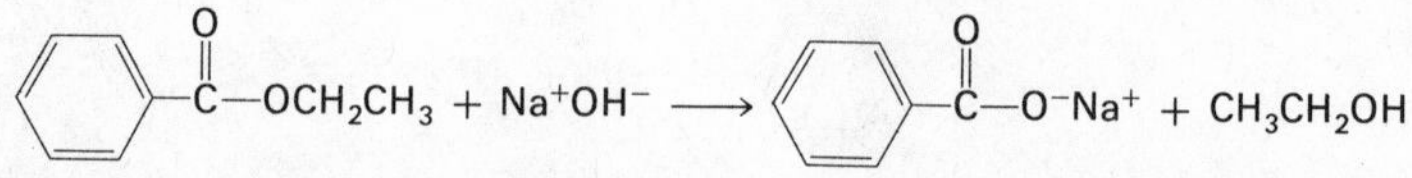

(Eq. 11.15, where $R =$ phenyl and $R' =$ ethyl)

b. 2 $\langle\!\!\!\bigcirc\!\!\!\rangle$ $\overset{O}{\underset{\|}{C}}$—OCH$_2CH_3$ + HOCH$_2$CH$_2$OH $\xrightarrow[\text{heat}]{H^+}$

$\langle\!\!\!\bigcirc\!\!\!\rangle$ $\overset{O}{\underset{\|}{C}}$—OCH$_2CH_2$O—$\overset{O}{\underset{\|}{C}}$ $\langle\!\!\!\bigcirc\!\!\!\rangle$ + 2 CH$_3$CH$_2$OH

(Eq. 11.18, R = phenyl, R' = ethyl, R''OH = ethylene glycol)

c. $\langle\!\!\!\bigcirc\!\!\!\rangle$ $\overset{O}{\underset{\|}{C}}$—OCH$_2CH_3$ + H$_2$NNH$_2$ $\longrightarrow$

$\langle\!\!\!\bigcirc\!\!\!\rangle$ $\overset{O}{\underset{\|}{C}}$—NHNH$_2$ + CH$_3$CH$_2$OH **(Eq. 11.20)**

d. $\langle\!\!\!\bigcirc\!\!\!\rangle$ $\overset{O}{\underset{\|}{C}}$—OCH$_2CH_3$ $\xrightarrow{\text{LiAlH}_4}$ $\langle\!\!\!\bigcirc\!\!\!\rangle$—CH$_2$OH + CH$_3CH_2$OH **(Eq. 11.21)**

11.11. a. Follow Eqs. 11.16 and 11.17, with R = CH$_3$CH$_2$— and R' = CH$_3$.

CH$_3$CH$_2$$\overset{O}{\underset{\|}{C}}$—OCH$_3$ + OH$^-$ $\rightleftharpoons$ CH$_3$CH$_2$—$\overset{O^-}{\underset{\underset{OH}{|}}{C}}OCH_3$ $\rightleftharpoons$

CH$_3$CH$_2$$\overset{O}{\underset{\|}{C}}$—OH + $^-$OCH$_3$ $\rightleftharpoons$ CH$_3$CH$_2$$\overset{O}{\underset{\|}{C}}$—O$^-$ + CH$_3$OH

b. ClCH$_2$$\overset{O}{\underset{\|}{C}}$—OCH$_3$ + :NH$_3$ $\longrightarrow$ ClCH$_2$$\overset{O^-}{\underset{\underset{^+NH_3}{|}}{C}}$—OCH$_3$ $\rightleftharpoons$

ClCH$_2$$\overset{O-H}{\underset{\underset{NH_2}{|}}{C}}OCH_3$ $\longrightarrow$ ClCH$_2$$\overset{O}{\underset{\|}{C}}NH_2$ + CH$_3$OH

11.12. Follow the pattern of Eq. 11.25. In the first step, the base (ethoxide ion) removes the α-proton of the ester; consequently, it is the α-carbon that acts as a nucleophile toward a second ester molecule.

CH$_3$CH$_2$CO$_2$C$_2$H$_5$ + Na$^+$$^-OC_2H_5$ $\rightleftharpoons$ CH$_3$$\overset{-}{C}HCO_2C_2H_5$ + C$_2$H$_5$OH
$\qquad\qquad\qquad\qquad\qquad\qquad$ Na$^+$

CH$_3$CH$_2$$\overset{O}{\underset{\|}{C}}OC_2H_5$ + $\overset{Na^+}{\underset{\underset{CH_3}{|}}{\overset{-}{C}H}}CO_2C_2H_5$ $\rightleftharpoons$ CH$_3$CH$_2$$\overset{O^-Na^+}{\underset{\underset{OC_2H_5}{|}}{C}}$—$\overset{}{\underset{\underset{CH_3}{|}}{C}}HCO_2C_2H_5$

Na$^+$$^-OC_2H_5$ + CH$_3$CH$_2$$\overset{O}{\underset{\|}{C}}$—$\underset{\underset{CH_3}{|}}{C}HCO_2C_2H_5$ $\rightleftharpoons$

The product reacts immediately with the Na$^+$$^-OC_2H_5$ present to form the enolate salt, which is converted to the desired ketoester by acidification at the end of the reaction.

$$CH_3CH_2\overset{\overset{O}{\|}}{C}-\overset{\overset{Na^+}{\underset{\underset{CH_3}{|}}{C}}}{}-CO_2C_2H_5 \xrightarrow{H^+} CH_3CH_2\overset{\overset{O}{\|}}{C}\overset{\underset{\underset{CH_3}{|}}{C}H}{}CO_2C_2H_5$$

11.13. If the ester contains 2% of the meta isomer, then in 100 units there are, on the average, two meta units. These send the chain off twice at angles of 60°. These angles arise from the geometry of the benzene ring.

para (linear)   meta (bent)

It is clear that the resulting polymer has a very different shape from that of Dacron made with pure dimethyl terephthalate. The need for high-purity starting materials in polymerization reactions is critical in controlling the properties of the resulting polymers.

11.14. a. The carbonyl group in esters is less reactive than the carbonyl group of ketones because of the resonance possibility:

This delocalizes to the "ether" oxygen some of the positive charge usually associated with the carbonyl carbon atom:

The carbonyl carbon in esters is therefore less susceptible to nucleophilic attack than the carbonyl carbon of ketones.

b. Compare

In both, a dipole in the direction shown enhances the positive charge on the carbonyl carbon, making it more susceptible to nucleophilic attack than the carbonyl group of an ester or acid. But Cl is more electronegative than O; therefore the acyl chlorides are usually more reactive toward nucleophiles than are the acid anhydrides.

c. In benzoyl chloride the positive charge on the carbonyl carbon can be delocalized in the aromatic ring:

$$\text{C}_6\text{H}_5-\overset{\overset{\textstyle O}{\|}}{\text{C}}-\text{Cl} \longleftrightarrow \overset{\overset{\textstyle O^-}{|}}{\text{C}^{\pm}}-\text{Cl} \longleftrightarrow \overset{\overset{\textstyle O^-}{|}}{\text{C}}-\text{Cl}$$

Such delocalization is not possible in cyclohexanecarbonyl chloride or any other aliphatic acid chloride. For this reason aryl acid chlorides are usually less reactive toward nucleophiles than aliphatic acid chlorides.

11.15. a. Reaction begins by nucleophilic attack on the carbonyl group.

$$CH_3\overset{O}{\underset{}{C}}-Cl + H-\ddot{O}-H \longrightarrow CH_3\overset{O^-}{\underset{\underset{H}{|}}{\overset{|}{C}}}\underset{Cl}{-}\overset{..+}{O}-H \xrightarrow{-Cl^-} CH_3-\overset{O}{\overset{\|}{C}}-\overset{..+}{O}-H$$

$$\Updownarrow \sim H^+ \qquad\qquad -H^+ \Updownarrow +H^+$$

$$CH_3\overset{O-H}{\underset{Cl}{\overset{|}{C}}}-OH \xrightarrow{-HCl} CH_3-\overset{O}{\overset{\|}{C}}-OH$$

The details of proton addition and removal are not known. This comment applies to all the equations in this problem; only one of several plausible paths that follow the initial nucleophilic attack is shown.

b.

$$C_6H_5-\overset{O}{\overset{\|}{C}}-Cl + CH_3\ddot{O}H \longrightarrow C_6H_5-\overset{O^-}{\underset{Cl}{\overset{|}{C}}}-\overset{H}{\underset{CH_3}{\overset{..+}{O}}}$$

$$\downarrow -Cl^-$$

$$C_6H_5-\overset{O}{\overset{\|}{C}}OCH_3 \xrightleftharpoons{-H^+} C_6H_5-\overset{O}{\overset{\|}{C}}-\overset{H}{\underset{CH_3}{\overset{..+}{O}}}$$

c. To conserve space, we abbreviate 1-pentanol as $C_5H_{11}OH$.

$$CH_3\overset{O}{\overset{\|}{C}}-O-\overset{O}{\overset{\|}{C}}CH_3 + H\ddot{O}-C_5H_{11} \longrightarrow CH_3\overset{O^-}{\overset{|}{C}}-O\overset{O}{\overset{\|}{C}}CH_3 \rightleftharpoons$$
$$\underset{H\;\;C_5H_{11}}{\overset{O^+}{|}}$$

$$CH_3\overset{O-H}{\underset{OC_5H_{11}}{\overset{|}{C}}}O\overset{O}{\overset{\|}{C}}CH_3 \longrightarrow CH_3\overset{O}{\overset{\|}{C}}-OC_5H_{11} + CH_3\overset{O}{\overset{\|}{C}}-OH$$

d. The sulfur acts as a nucleophile and attacks the carbonyl group.

$$CH_3\overset{O}{\overset{\|}{C}}-OPO_3^{2-} + CoA-\ddot{S}H \longrightarrow CH_3\overset{O^-}{\overset{|}{C}}-OPO_3^{2-} \rightleftharpoons$$

with $\overset{+}{S}$ attached, H and CoA below

$$CH_3\overset{O-H}{\overset{|}{\underset{S-CoA}{C}}}-OPO_3^{2-} \longrightarrow CH_3\overset{O}{\overset{\|}{C}}-S-CoA + OPO_3^{3-} + H^+$$

11.16. a. $CH_3CH_2CH_2\overset{O}{\overset{\|}{C}}-OH + PCl_5 \longrightarrow CH_3CH_2CH_2\overset{O}{\overset{\|}{C}}-Cl + HCl + POCl_3$

(Eq. 11.28)

b. $CH_3CH_2CH_2\overset{O}{\overset{\|}{C}}-Cl + CH_3\overset{O}{\overset{\|}{C}}-O^-Na^+ \longrightarrow CH_3CH_2CH_2\overset{O}{\overset{\|}{C}}-O-\overset{O}{\overset{\|}{C}}CH_3 + Na^+Cl^-$

(Eq. 11.35)

c. $CH_3CH_2\overset{O}{\overset{\|}{C}}-O-\overset{O}{\overset{\|}{C}}CH_2CH_3 + CH_3OH \longrightarrow CH_3CH_2\overset{O}{\overset{\|}{C}}-OCH_3 + CH_3CH_2CO_2H$

(Eq. 11.36)

d. Analogous to Eq. 11.15 but with a thioester:

$$CH_3\overset{O}{\overset{\|}{C}}-SCH_2CH_3 + Na^+OH^- \longrightarrow CH_3\overset{O}{\overset{\|}{C}}-O^-Na^+ + CH_3CH_2SH$$

Notice that these are the products that would be formed by nucleophilic attack of hydroxide ion on the carbonyl carbon of the thioester.

$\left(\text{The products are } not\ CH_3\overset{O}{\overset{\|}{C}}-S^-Na^+ \text{ and } CH_3CH_2OH\right).$

e. Ester formation occurs intramolecularly, to give a lactone (compare with Eq. 11.13).

$$CH_3\underset{:OH}{CH}CH_2CH_2\overset{O}{\overset{\|}{C}}-OH \longrightarrow$$

$$\begin{array}{c} CH_3-CH-CH_2 \\ H-\overset{+}{O}\quad CH_2 \\ \underset{-O}{C}\;OH \end{array} \rightleftharpoons$$

$$\begin{array}{c} CH_3-CH-CH_2 \\ O\quad CH_2 \\ C \\ H-O\;OH \end{array} \xrightarrow{-H_2O} \begin{array}{c} CH_3-CH-CH_2 \\ O\quad CH_2 \\ C \\ O \end{array}$$

11.17. *cis*-1,2-Cyclopropanecarboxylic acid forms a cyclic anhydride:

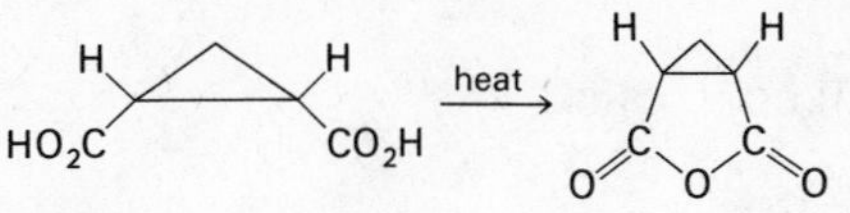

(cf. Eq. 11.42)

The trans isomer cannot form a cyclic anhydride (cf. Eq. 11.43); it may form a polymeric anhydride.

When the ring is larger, the monomeric anhydride is possible for both isomers:

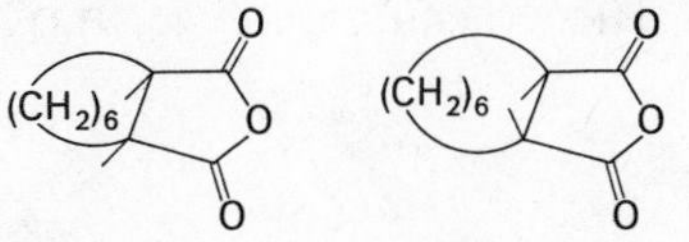

cis-anhydride   *trans*-anhydride

Six methylene (CH_2) groups are more than sufficient for being fused either cis or trans relative to the five-membered anhydride ring.

11.18. The method combines the formation of a cyanohydrin (Section 10.8a) with the hydrolysis of a cyanide to an acid (Section 11.4a). Compare with Eq. 10.21.

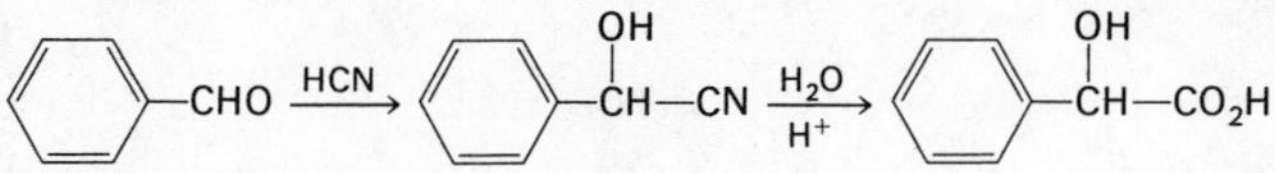

benzaldehyde
cyanohydrin

11.19. The substance is an acid, so the formula $C_4H_8O_3$ can therefore be represented as C_3H_7O—COOH. The reaction with acetyl chloride suggests that the remaining oxygen is present as a hydroxyl group, since alcohols are known to react with acetyl chloride to form esters. The fact that the acid loses water on heating ($C_4H_8O_3 \rightarrow C_4H_6O_2$) tends to support the presence of an alcohol function, with a hydrogen on the adjacent carbon(s). The positive iodoform test suggests that the alcohol must be present as

CH_3CH- (Section 10.11c)
  |
  OH

A satisfactory structure is

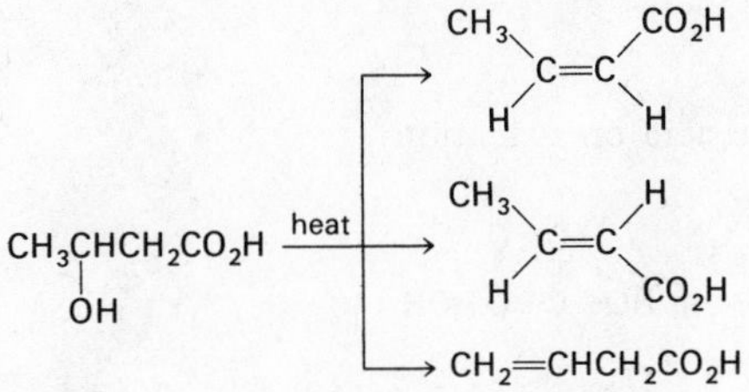

Equations for the tests are

$$CH_3CHCH_2CO_2H + CH_3\overset{O}{\underset{}{C}}Cl \longrightarrow CH_3CHCH_2CO_2H + HCl$$
$$\underset{OH}{} \qquad\qquad\qquad \underset{\underset{\underset{O}{\parallel}}{OCCH_3}}{}$$

$$CH_3CHCH_2CO_2H + 4\,I_2 + 7\,Na^+OH^- \longrightarrow$$
$$\underset{OH}{}$$

$$CHI_3 + 5\,Na^+I^- + Na^+{}^-O_2CCH_2CO_2{}^-Na^+ + 6\,H_2O$$

11.20. Since salicylic acid

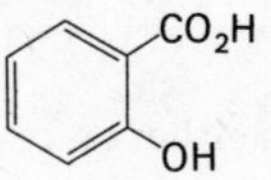

is an oxidation product, (A) must have a formula

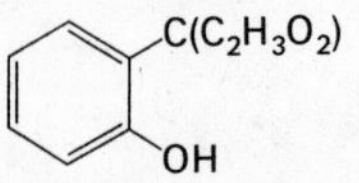

Since the side chain includes a carboxyl group (the compound is said to be a phenolic *acid*), the structure can be further refined to

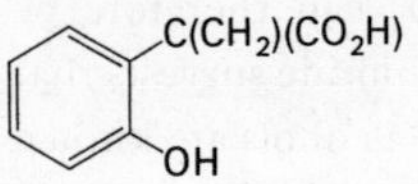

The two possibilities are

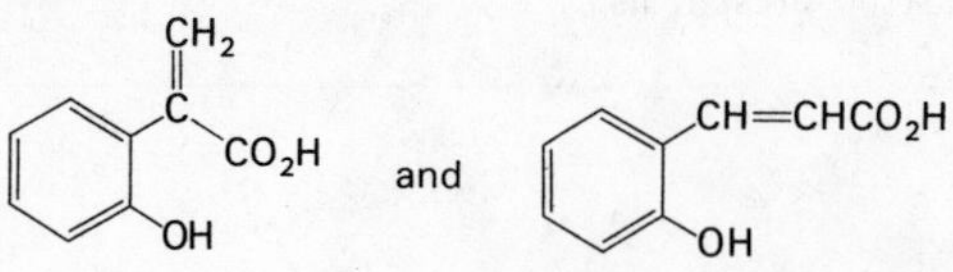

and

cis or trans

Only the second of these gives oxalic acid on oxidation:

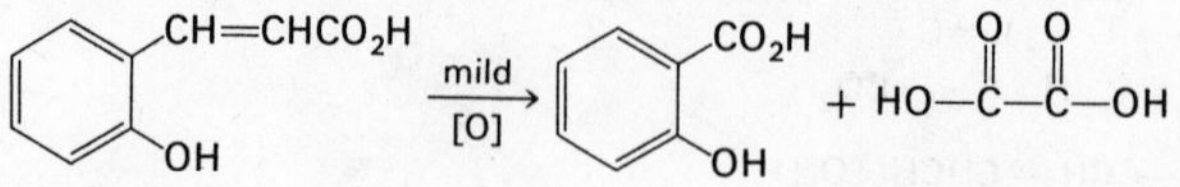

Therefore the structures of (A) are the *cis*- and *trans-o*-hydroxycinnamic acids. Of these, the cis isomer easily loses water to form a lactone; the trans cannot, because the carboxyl and hydroxyl groups are too far apart.

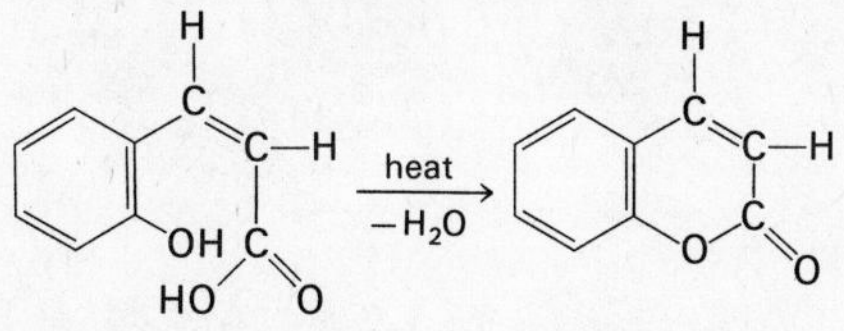

cis

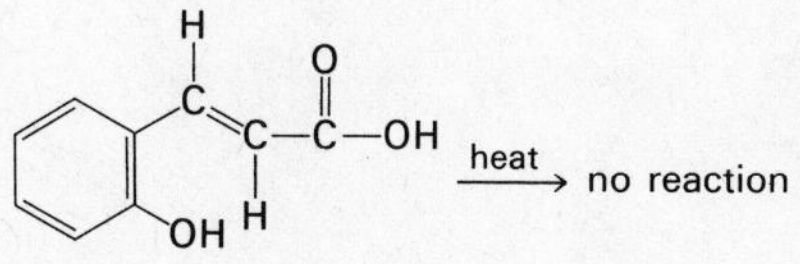

trans

12. Lipids

OBJECTIVES

1. Know the meaning of: lipid, fat, oil, and wax; glyceride; hydrogenolysis; saponification number, iodine number, soap, and micelle; synthetic detergent; lipase; coenzyme A, FAD, and NAD$^+$; phospholipid; prostaglandin; steroid; squalene and mevalonic acid; steroidal hormone, estrogen, and androgen.

2. Given the name of a glyceride, write its structure; also do the converse.

3. Given the name or structure of a carboxylic acid, write the formula for the corresponding glyceride.

4. Given the name or structure of a glyceride, write the equation for its saponification.

5. Given the name or structure of an unsaturated glyceride, write equations (including catalysts) for its hydrogenation and hydrogenolysis.

6. Explain in terms of structure the difference between a fat and a vegetable oil.

7. Calculate the saponification and iodine numbers of a given fat or oil.

8. Describe the structural features essential for a good soap or detergent.

9. Explain, with the aid of a diagram (see Figures 12.7 and 12.8), how a soap emulsifies fats and oils.

10. Explain, with the aid of equations, what happens when an ordinary soap is used in hard water, and how synthetic detergents overcome this difficulty.

11. Write equations for the biological oxidation of a saturated carboxylic acid to a carboxylic acid with two fewer carbon atoms (Figure 12.9).

12. Write equations for the biosynthesis of a saturated carboxylic acid with two more carbon atoms than a given carboxylic acid (Section 12.5b).

13. Draw the structure of a prostaglandin.

14. Draw the structure of a steroid.

ANSWERS TO THE EXERCISES AND PROBLEMS

12.1. Use Table 12.1 as a nomenclature guide.

    a. $CH_3(CH_2)_{14}CO_2^-K^+$

    b. $[CH_3(CH_2)_7CH=CH(CH_2)_7CO_2^-]_2Mg^{2+}$

    f.
$$CH_2-O-\overset{\overset{\displaystyle O}{\|}}{C}(CH_2)_{12}CH_3$$

    c.
$$CH_2-O-\overset{\overset{\displaystyle O}{\|}}{C}(CH_2)_{10}CH_3$$
$$CH-O-\overset{\overset{\displaystyle O}{\|}}{C}(CH_2)_{10}CH_3$$
$$CH_2-O-\overset{\overset{\displaystyle O}{\|}}{C}(CH_2)_{10}CH_3$$

$$CH-O-\overset{\overset{\displaystyle O}{\|}}{C}(CH_2)_{12}CH_3$$
$$CH_2-O-\overset{\overset{\displaystyle O}{\|}}{C}(CH_2)_{12}CH_3$$

    d.
$$CH_2-O-\overset{\overset{\displaystyle O}{\|}}{C}CH_2CH_2CH_3$$
$$CH-O-\overset{\overset{\displaystyle O}{\|}}{C}(CH_2)_{14}CH_3$$
$$CH_2-O-\overset{\overset{\displaystyle O}{\|}}{C}(CH_2)_7CH=CH(CH_2)_7CH_3$$

    e. $CH_3(CH_2)_4CH=CHCH_2CH=CH(CH_2)_7\overset{\overset{\displaystyle O}{\|}}{C}-O-(CH_2)_{13}CH_3$

12.2. a. glyceryl tripalmitate (or tripalmitin or tripalmitoylglycerol)

    b. β-stearo-α,α'-dimyristin (or 2-stearoyldimyristoylglycerol)

    c. myristyl linoleate

    d. glyceryl oleylstearyllaurate (or 1-oleoyl-2-stearoyllauroylglycerol)

12.3. Saponification:

$$CH_2-O-\overset{\overset{\displaystyle O}{\|}}{C}(CH_2)_7CH=CHCH_2CH=CHCH_2CH=CHCH_2CH_3$$
$$CH-O-\overset{\overset{\displaystyle O}{\|}}{C}(CH_2)_7CH=CHCH_2CH=CHCH_2CH=CHCH_2CH_3 + 3\ NaOH \xrightarrow[\text{(Eq. 12.1)}]{}$$
$$CH_2-O-\overset{\overset{\displaystyle O}{\|}}{C}(CH_2)_7CH=CHCH_2CH=CHCH_2CH=CHCH_2CH_3$$

$$\begin{array}{l} CH_2OH \\ CHOH \\ CH_2OH \end{array} + 3\ CH_3CH_2CH=CHCH_2CH=CHCH_2CH=CH(CH_2)_7CO_2^-Na^+$$

Hydrogenation:

$$CH_2-O-\overset{\overset{O}{\|}}{C}(CH_2)_7CH=CHCH_2CH=CHCH_2CH=CHCH_2CH_3$$

$$CH-O-\overset{\overset{O}{\|}}{C}(CH_2)_7CH=CHCH_2CH=CHCH_2CH=CHCH_2CH_3 + 9\ H_2 \xrightarrow[\text{Heat}]{\text{Ni}}$$

$$\text{(Eq. 12.4)}$$

$$CH_2-O-\overset{\overset{O}{\|}}{C}(CH_2)_7CH=CHCH_2CH=CHCH_2CH=CHCH_2CH_3$$

$$CH_2-O-\overset{\overset{O}{\|}}{C}(CH_2)_{16}CH_3$$

$$CH-O-\overset{\overset{O}{\|}}{C}(CH_2)_{16}CH_3$$

$$CH_2-O-\overset{\overset{O}{\|}}{C}(CH_2)_{16}CH_3$$

Hydrogenolysis:

$$CH_2-O-\overset{\overset{O}{\|}}{C}(CH_2)_7CH=CHCH_2CH=CHCH_2CH=CHCH_2CH_3$$

$$CH-O-\overset{\overset{O}{\|}}{C}(CH_2)_7CH=CHCH_2CH=CHCH_2CH=CHCH_2CH_3 + 6\ H_2 \xrightarrow[\text{chromite}]{\text{zinc}}$$

$$\text{(Eq. 12.3)}$$

$$CH_2-O-\overset{\overset{O}{\|}}{C}(CH_2)_7CH=CHCH_2CH=CHCH_2CH=CHCH_2CH_3$$

$$\begin{array}{l} CH_2OH \\ CHOH + 3\ CH_3CH_2CH=CHCH_2CH=CHCH_2CH=CH(CH_2)_7CH_2OH \\ CH_2OH \end{array}$$

12.4. Saponification number is defined as the number of milligrams of KOH required to hydrolyze 1 g of a fat. Since 3 mol KOH is required for every mole of fat (Eq. 12.1), $3 \times 56 = 168$ g KOH is required per mole of fat. Therefore (1/mol wt of fat) $\times$ 168 g KOH is needed to hydrolyze 1 g of fat. To convert to milligrams of KOH, multiply by 1000; the correct formula is

$$\text{Saponification no.} = \frac{168,000}{\text{mol wt of fat}}$$

a. $\dfrac{168,000}{302} = 556$

b. $\dfrac{168,000}{806} = 208$

It is clear that saponification number varies inversely with molecular weight.

12.5. Iodine number is defined as the number of grams of iodine that combine with 100 g of a fat.

a. Glyceryl trioleate has a molecular weight of 884; it reacts with 3 mol of I_2, since it contains three double bonds. The atomic weight of iodine is 127. Therefore, 884 g of glyceryl trioleate reacts with $3 \times 254 = 762$ g of iodine. Therefore, 100 g of the fat reacts with $100/884 \times 762 = 86.2$ g of iodine. Therefore, the *iodine number* of glyceryl trioleate is 86.2.

b. The reasoning is as described in part a. The molecular weight of the fat is 872; it reacts with 9 mol iodine. Therefore, the iodine number of this glyceride is $(100/872 \times 2286 = 262.1$.

From the answers to parts a and b, we see that the iodine number increases with an increase in degree of unsaturation.

12.6. The essentials of soap and detergent design are discussed in Sections 12.4b and 12.4d.

12.7. Fruit juices may be acidic because of the presence of citric and other acids. Ordinary soaps are not very effective in acidic water because of the reaction shown in Eq. 12.5.

12.8. The calcium and magnesium ions present in hard water form insoluble salts with ordinary soaps (Eq. 12.6). In contrast, the calcium and magnesium salts of sulfate or sulfonate detergents (Section 12.4d) are water soluble. Nonacidic syndets, such as the esters of polyols or the tetraalkylammonium ions, are also not affected by these metallic ions.

12.9. $CH_3(CH_2)_7CH{=}CH_2 +$

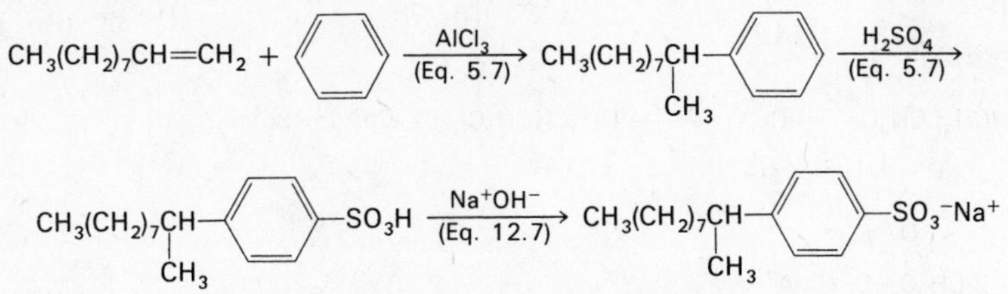

12.10. The first steps are analogous to Eq. 8.11, and the last steps are analogous to Eq. 12.8.

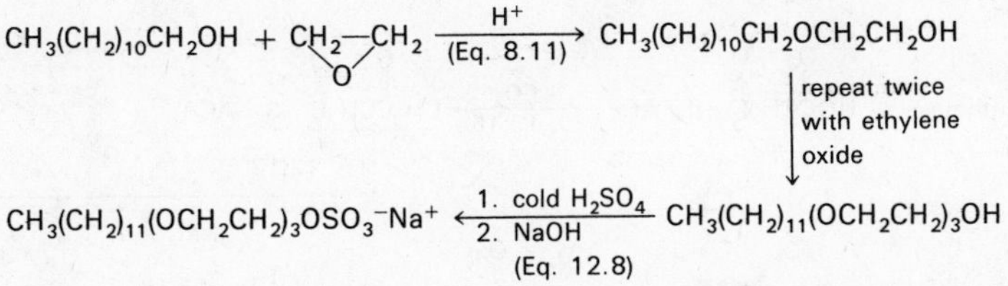

12.11 This early experiment very clearly supported the idea that fatty acids are metabolized in two-carbon units. If n is an even number, then the ultimate oxidation product obtained by oxidizing the chain two carbons at a time from the carboxyl end has to be phenylacetic acid, as seen in the following example:

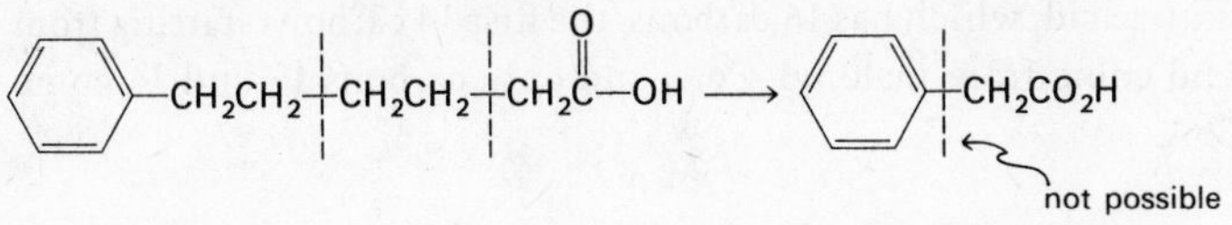

Further oxidation is not possible, since it requires breaking a bond to the benzene ring. If n is odd, the product of a similar oxidation procedure is benzoic acid.

$$\langle\!\!\!\bigcirc\!\!\!\rangle\!-CH_2\!\!+\!\!CH_2CH_2\!\!+\!\!CH_2CH_2\!\!+\!\!CH_2\overset{\displaystyle O}{\overset{\|}{C}}\!\!-OH \longrightarrow \langle\!\!\!\bigcirc\!\!\!\rangle\!-CO_2H$$

These results are consistent with present theory, as expressed in Figure 12.9.

12.12. In the first step, the acid is esterified with coenzyme A (Eq. 12.9).

$$CH_3CH_2CH_2CO_2H + CoA\!-\!SH \underset{ATP}{\overset{enzyme}{\rightleftharpoons}} CH_3CH_2CH_2\overset{\displaystyle O}{\overset{\|}{C}}\!-\!S\!-\!CoA + H_2O$$

Then the steps outlined in Figure 12.9 are followed.

$$CH_3CH_2CH_2\overset{\displaystyle O}{\overset{\|}{C}}\!-\!S\!-\!CoA \xrightarrow{FAD} CH_3CH\!=\!CH\!-\!\overset{\displaystyle O}{\overset{\|}{C}}\!-\!S\!-\!CoA \quad (trans)$$

$$\downarrow H\!-\!OH$$

$$CH_3\overset{\displaystyle O}{\overset{\|}{C}}CH_2\overset{\displaystyle O}{\overset{\|}{C}}\!-\!S\!-\!CoA \xleftarrow{NAD^+} CH_3\overset{}{\underset{OH}{CH}}CH_2\overset{\displaystyle O}{\overset{\|}{C}}\!-\!S\!-\!CoA$$

$$\downarrow CoA\!-\!SH$$

$$2\ CH_3\overset{\displaystyle O}{\overset{\|}{C}}\!-\!S\!-\!CoA$$

12.13. The pertinent equations are 12.16, 12.17, and 12.18. These equations are abbreviated below; the portions coming from malonyl-CoA are underlined.

$$CH_3\overset{\displaystyle O}{\overset{\|}{C}}\!-\!S\!-\!synthetase + HO\underline{CCH_2}\overset{\displaystyle O}{\overset{\|}{}}\!-\!S\!-\!ACP \xrightarrow[Eq.\ 12.16]{-CO_2} CH_3\overset{\displaystyle O}{\overset{\|}{C}}\underline{CH_2}\overset{\displaystyle O}{\overset{\|}{C}}\!-\!S\!-\!ACP$$

$$\downarrow Eq.\ 12.17$$

$$CH_3CH_2CH_2\overset{\displaystyle O}{\overset{\|}{C}}\underline{CH_2}\overset{\displaystyle O}{\overset{\|}{C}}\!-\!S\!-\!ACP \xleftarrow[Eq.\ 12.16]{repeat} CH_3CH_2CH_2\overset{\displaystyle O}{\overset{\|}{C}}\!-\!S\!-\!synthetase \xleftarrow{Eq.\ 12.18} CH_3CH_2CH_2\overset{\displaystyle O}{\overset{\|}{C}}\!-\!S\!-\!AC$$

$$\downarrow Eq.\ 12.17$$

$$CH_3CH_2\underline{CH_2CH_2}\overset{\displaystyle O}{\overset{\|}{C}}\!-\!S\!-\!ACP \xrightarrow{Eq.\ 12.18} CH_3CH_2CH_2CH_2\overset{\displaystyle O}{\overset{\|}{C}}\!-\!S\!-\!synthetase,\ and\ so\ on.$$

Clearly, in palmitic acid, which has 16 carbons, the first 14 carbons starting from the carboxyl end come from malonyl-CoA, and only carbons 15 and 16 come from acetyl–CoA.

12.14. The answer is actually shown in outline form in the final three steps of the answer to Question 12.13.

$$CH_3CH_2CH_2\overset{O}{\underset{\|}{C}}-S-\text{synthetase} + HO\overset{O}{\underset{\|}{C}}CH_2\overset{O}{\underset{\|}{C}}-S-ACP \xrightarrow{\text{Eq. 12.16}}$$

$$CH_3CH_2CH_2\overset{O}{\underset{\|}{C}}-CH_2\overset{O}{\underset{\|}{C}}-S-ACP + CO_2 + \text{synthetase}-SH$$

NADPH (Eq. 12.17)

$$CH_3CH_2CH_2CH=\overset{O}{\underset{\|}{C}}-S-ACP \xleftarrow[\text{(Eq. 12.17)}]{\text{Enzyme}} CH_3CH_2CH_2\overset{OH}{\underset{|}{C}}HCH_2\overset{O}{\underset{\|}{C}}-S-ACP$$

$$\xrightarrow{\text{NADPH}} CH_3CH_2CH_2CH_2CH_2\overset{O}{\underset{\|}{C}}-S-ACP \xrightarrow{\text{Eq. 12.18}} CH_3CH_2CH_2CH_2CH_2\overset{O}{\underset{\|}{C}}-S-\text{synthetase}$$

12.15. Since the chain is built up two carbons at a time from the carboxyl end, carbons 2, 4, 6, 8, 10, 12, 14, and 16 contain ^{14}C, and the odd-numbered carbons contain ordinary ^{12}C.

$$\overset{*}{C}H_3CH_2\overset{*}{C}H_2CH_2\overset{*}{C}H_2CH_2\overset{*}{C}H_2CH_2\overset{*}{C}H_2CH_2\overset{*}{C}H_2CH_2\overset{*}{C}H_2CH_2\overset{*}{C}H_2CO_2H$$

12.16.

$$CH_3\overset{O}{\underset{\|}{C}}-SR + HO\overset{O}{\underset{\|}{C}}-\overset{\ominus}{C}H-\overset{O}{\underset{\|}{C}}-SR' \rightleftharpoons CH_3-\overset{O^{\ominus}}{\underset{|}{C}}-\overset{|}{C}H-\overset{O}{\underset{\|}{C}}-SR'$$

with SR, CO₂H below

$$\| -SR^{\ominus}$$

$$CH_3\overset{O}{\underset{\|}{C}}CH_2\overset{O}{\underset{\|}{C}}-SR' + CO_2 \longleftarrow CH_3-\overset{O}{\underset{\|}{C}}-\overset{|}{C}H-\overset{O}{\underset{\|}{C}}-SR'$$

with CO₂H below

(R = synthetase, R' = ACP)

The first two steps involve the usual attack of a nucleophile at an ester carbonyl group, to displace, in this case, SR. The product is a β-keto acid (Section 11.11d), which readily decarboxylates (compare with Eqs. 11.49 and 11.50).

12.17. Compare the general formula for a fat or oil (i.e., a glyceride) in Eq. 12.1 with the general formula for a wax (a simple ester with long carbon chains, as in Section 12.7).

$$C_{15}H_{31}\overset{O}{\underset{\|}{C}}-OC_{30}H_{61} + Na^+OH^- \longrightarrow C_{15}H_{31}CO_2{}^-Na^+ + C_{30}H_{61}OH$$

sodium palmitate   myricyl alcohol

12.18. Use the second formula in Section 12.9 as a guide.

a. Equatorial   c. Equatorial

b. Equatorial   d. Equatorial

The β bonds at C1, C3, and C7 (the odd-numbered carbons) are equatorial (α are axial); the α bonds at C2, C4, and C6 (even-numbered carbons) are equatorial (β are axial).

12.19.

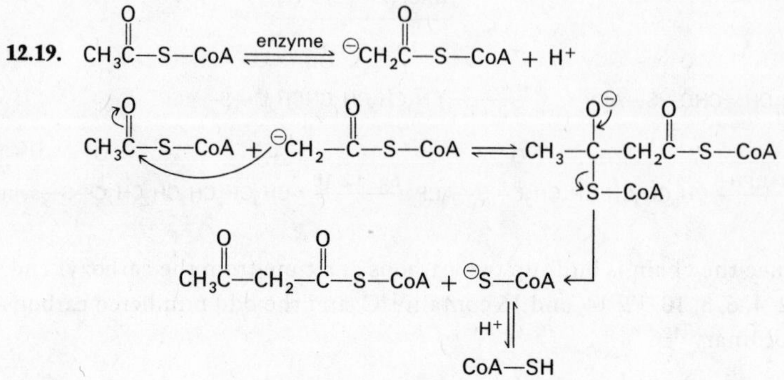

$$CH_3\overset{O}{\underset{||}{C}}-S-CoA \xrightleftharpoons{enzyme} {}^{\ominus}CH_2\overset{O}{\underset{||}{C}}-S-CoA + H^+$$

The reaction is a Claisen condensation of two thioesters (see Eq. 11.24).

12.20. The reaction bears some similarity to both the aldol (Section 10.12) and Claisen (Section 11.8) condensations. An α-hydrogen is removed from the ester, and the resulting anion attacks the ketone carbonyl group of acetoacetyl–CoA.

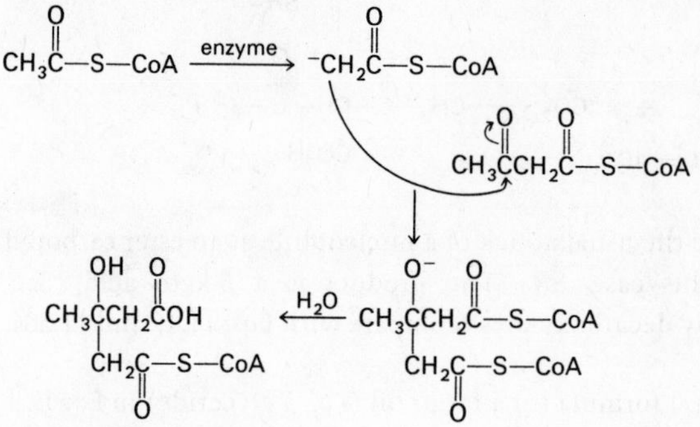

12.21. Mevalonic acid:

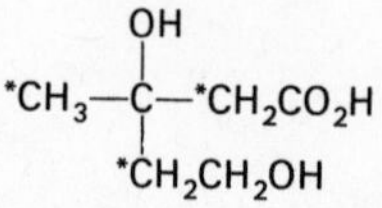

$$\begin{array}{c} \overset{OH}{|} \\ {}^*CH_3-C-{}^*CH_2CO_2H \qquad {}^* = {}^{14}C \\ | \\ {}^*CH_2CH_2OH \end{array}$$

The label distribution can be deduced from Eqs. 12.22 and 12.23.

Squalene:

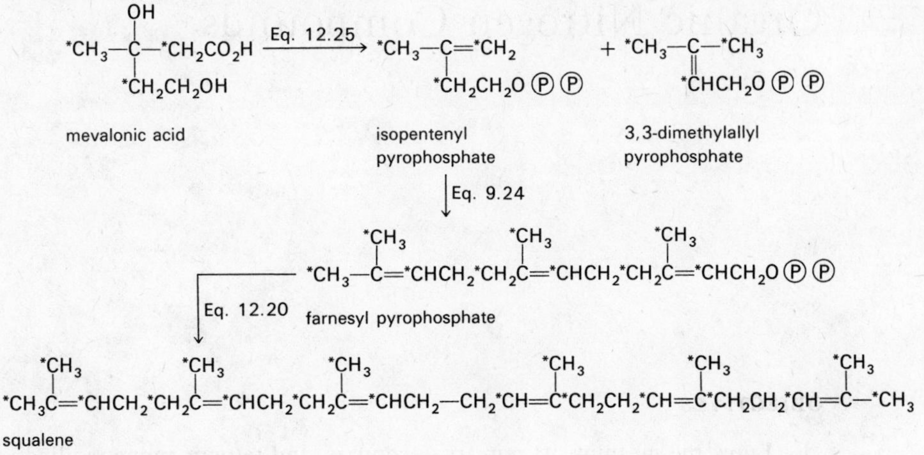

$$\overset{\text{OH}}{\underset{\text{*CH}_2\text{CH}_2\text{OH}}{\text{*CH}_3-\overset{|}{\underset{|}{\text{C}}}-\text{*CH}_2\text{CO}_2\text{H}}} \xrightarrow{\text{Eq. 12.25}} \underset{\text{*CH}_2\text{CH}_2\text{O} \textcircled{P} \textcircled{P}}{\text{*CH}_3-\text{C}=\text{*CH}_2} \quad + \quad \underset{\text{*CHCH}_2\text{O} \textcircled{P} \textcircled{P}}{\text{*CH}_3-\overset{\|}{\text{C}}-\text{*CH}_3}$$

mevalonic acid   isopentenyl   3,3-dimethylallyl
                         pyrophosphate   pyrophosphate

↓ Eq. 9.24

$$\text{*CH}_3-\overset{\text{*CH}_3}{\overset{|}{\text{C}}}=\text{*CHCH}_2\text{*CH}_2\overset{\text{*CH}_3}{\overset{|}{\text{C}}}=\text{*CHCH}_2\text{*CH}_2\overset{\text{*CH}_3}{\overset{|}{\text{C}}}=\text{*CHCH}_2\text{O} \textcircled{P} \textcircled{P}$$

Eq. 12.20   farnesyl pyrophosphate

↓

$$\overset{\text{*CH}_3}{\underset{}{\text{*CH}_3\text{C}}}=\text{*CHCH}_2\text{*CH}_2\overset{\text{*CH}_3}{\overset{|}{\text{C}}}=\text{*CHCH}_2\text{*CH}_2\overset{\text{*CH}_3}{\overset{|}{\text{C}}}=\text{*CHCH}_2-\text{CH}_2\text{*CH}=\text{C*CH}_2\text{CH}_2\text{*CH}=\overset{\text{*CH}_3}{\overset{|}{\text{C}}}\text{*CH}_2\text{CH}_2\text{*CH}=\overset{\text{*CH}_3}{\overset{|}{\text{C}}}-\text{*CH}_3$$

squalene

13. Amines, Amides, and Related Organic Nitrogen Compounds

OBJECTIVES

1. Know the meaning of: primary, secondary, and tertiary amine; aniline; dissociation constant K_b of an amine; alkaloid; quaternary ammonium compound; choline; acylation of an amine; carboxamide and sulfonamide; nitrosamine; diazonium ion and diazotization; azo coupling and azo compound; diamine, polyamide, Nylon, and lactam; pyrrolidine, piperidine, pyridine, quinoline, isoquinoline, and indole; porphyrin; imidazole; amide and imide; 1°, 2°, and 3° amides; analgesic, barbiturate, and penicillin.

2. Given the structure of an amine, identify it as primary, secondary, or tertiary.

3. Given the structure of an amine, name it. Also, given the name of an amine, write its structural formula.

4. Explain the effect of hydrogen-bonding on the boiling points of amines and on their solubility in water.

5. Write an equation for the dissociation of an amine in water.

6. Draw the important contributors to the resonance hybrid for an aromatic amine.

7. Given the structures of several amines, rank them in order of relative basicity.

8. Account for the difference in basicity between an aliphatic and an aromatic amine.

9. Write an equation for the reaction of a given amine of any class with a strong acid. Also, write an equation for the reaction of an amine salt with a strong base.

10. Explain, with the aid of equations, how you can separate an amine from a mixture containing neutral and/or acidic compounds.

11. Write an equation for the reaction between ammonia or an amine of any class and an alkyl halide.

12. Write an equation for the reaction of a given primary or secondary amine with an acid anhydride.

13. Write the steps in the mechanism for acylation of a primary or secondary amine.

14. Write an equation for the reaction of a primary or secondary amine with an aryl sulfonyl halide.

15. Write equations for the reaction of a given primary, secondary, or tertiary amine with nitrous acid.

16. Write an equation for the diazotization of a given primary aromatic amine.

17. Write equations for the reaction of an aromatic diazonium salt with: aqueous base, $Cu_2X_2(X = Cl, Br)$, and $Cu_2(CN)_2$.

18. Write an equation for the coupling of an aromatic diazonium salt with a phenol or aromatic amine.

19. Write an equation for the formation of a polyamide from a diamine and a dicarboxylic acid or acid derivative.

20. Write an equation for the formation of Nylon 6—6 and Nylon 6.

21. Write an equation for the reaction of a heterocyclic amine with a strong inorganic acid.

22. Draw the resonance contributors for protonated imidazole, and explain why it is basic.

23. Given the structure of an amide, name it; also do the converse.

24. Draw the principal resonance contributors to an amide, and explain why rotation around the C—N bond is restricted.

25. Write an equation for the hydrolysis of a given amide.

ANSWERS TO THE EXERCISES AND PROBLEMS

13.1. Many correct answers are possible; only one example is given in each case.

a. CH_3NH_2 methylamine

b.   pyrrolidine

c.   N,N-dimethylaniline

d.   tetramethyl-ammonium chloride

e. 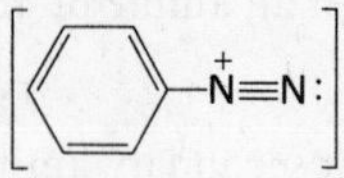 $\left[\overset{+}{N}\equiv N: \right] Cl^-$ benzenediazonium chloride

h. 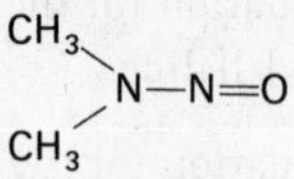 $\begin{array}{c} CH_3 \\ \diagdown \\ N-N=O \\ \diagup \\ CH_3 \end{array}$ N-nitrosodimethylamine

f. 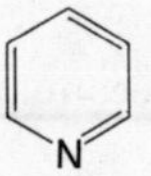 pyridine

i. 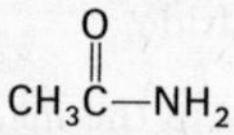 $CH_3\overset{\displaystyle O}{\overset{\|}{C}}-NH_2$ acetamide

g. 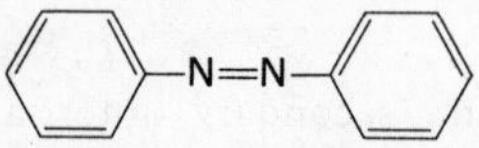 $\diagdown$ N=N $\diagup$ azobenzene

j. 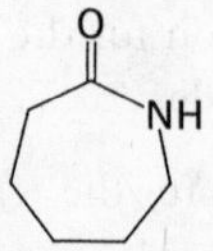 caprolactam

13.2. a. 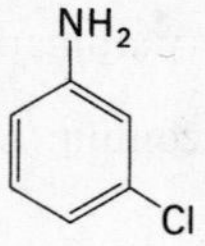 $\begin{array}{c} NH_2 \end{array}$ ... Cl

f. $\begin{array}{c} CH_3CH-CH_2 \\ | | \\ NH_2 NH_2 \end{array}$

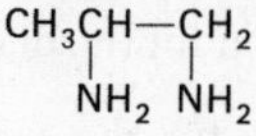

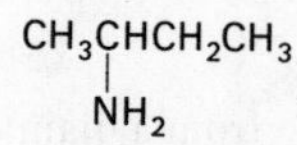

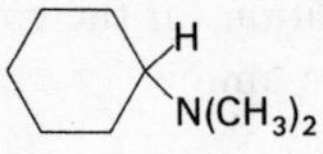

b. $\begin{array}{c} CH_3CHCH_2CH_3 \\ | \\ NH_2 \end{array}$

g. cyclohexyl $\overset{\displaystyle H}{\underset{}{N(CH_3)_2}}$

c. $\begin{array}{c} CH_3CHCH_2CH_2CH_2CH_3 \\ | \\ NH_2 \end{array}$

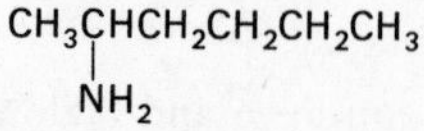

h. $(CH_3CH_2)_4N^+Br^-$

d. 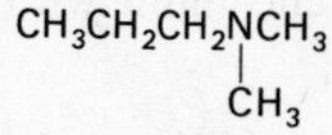 $\begin{array}{c} CH_3CH_2CH_2NCH_3 \\ | \\ CH_3 \end{array}$

i. 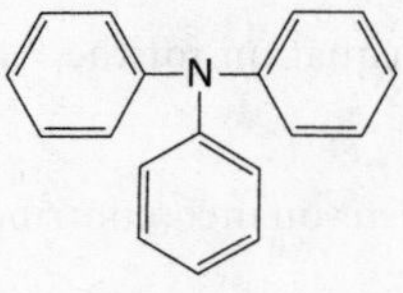 triphenyl amine

e. 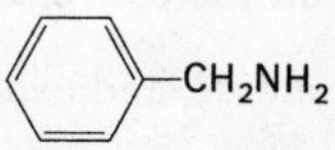 $\diagup$ —CH_2NH_2

j. 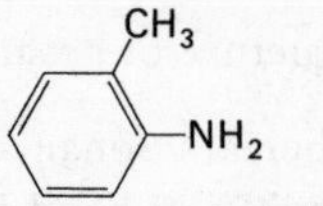 $\begin{array}{c} CH_3 \\ | \\ \diagup —NH_2 \end{array}$

13.3.
a. *p*-bromoaniline
b. methylisopropylamine
c. methyldiethylamine
d. tetramethylammonium chloride
e. 4-amino-2-butanol

f. 2-methylaminoethanol
g. benzenediazonium hydrogen sulfate
h. 2-aminonaphthalene
i. cyclopentylamine
j. 1,3-diaminopropane

13.4. $CH_3CH_2CH_2CH_2NH_2$ *n*-butylamine (primary)

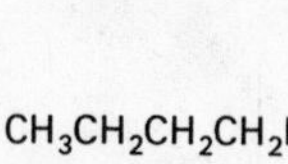

$\begin{array}{c} CH_3CH_2CHCH_3 \\ | \\ NH_2 \end{array}$ *sec*-butylamine (primary)

$CH_3CHCH_2NH_2$ $\quad\;\vert$ $\quad CH_3$	isobutylamine (primary)
$(CH_3)_3CNH_2$	*t*-butylamine (primary)
$CH_3CH_2CH_2NHCH_3$	methyl-*n*-propylamine (secondary)
$CH_3CHNHCH_3$ $\quad\;\vert$ $\quad CH_3$	methyl-*i*-propylamine (secondary)
$CH_3CH_2NHCH_2CH_3$	diethylamine (secondary)
$CH_3—N—CH_2CH_3$ $\qquad\vert$ $\quad\; CH_3$	dimethylethylamine (tertiary)

13.5. a. Perhaps the question is best answered by explaining why aniline is a weaker base than cyclohexylamine. In aniline, the unshared electron pair on the nitrogen is delocalized to the aromatic ring (Section 13.3).

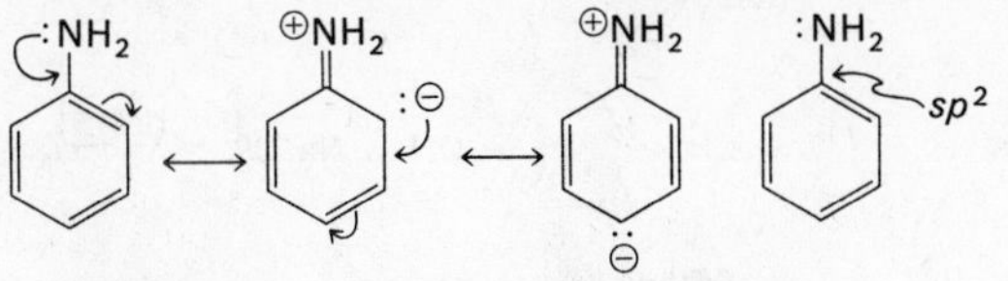

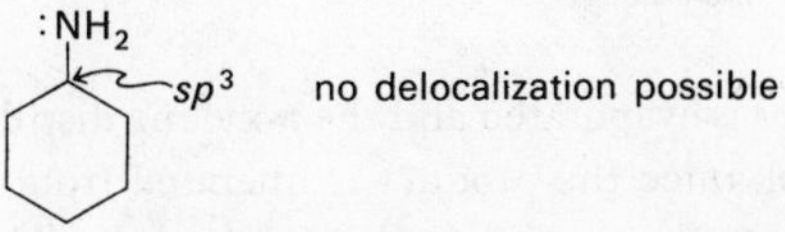

No analogous delocalization is possible with cyclohexylamine. Second, in aniline an sp^2-hybridized carbon is attached to the nitrogen, whereas in cyclohexylamine the carbon attached to nitrogen is sp^3 hybridized. Since an sp^2 carbon is more electron-withdrawing than an sp^3 carbon, electron density is withdrawn from the nitrogen more in aniline than in cyclohexylamine. This decreases the availability of the unshared electrons to a proton; that is, it decreases the basicity of the nitrogen.

b. The nitro group is electron withdrawing; electron density is thus withdrawn from the amino nitrogen, making it less basic toward a proton.

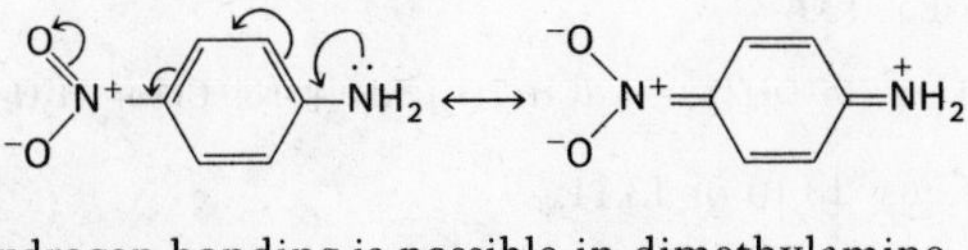

13.6. Hydrogen-bonding is possible in dimethylamine, but not in trimethylamine:

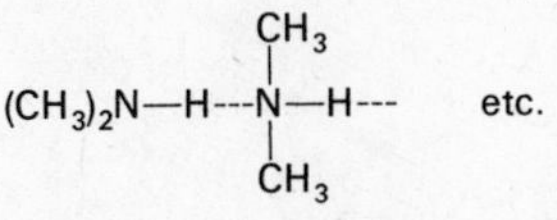

Energy is required to break these hydrogen bonds, to vaporize dimethylamine.

13.7. The mixture might first be dissolved in an inert, low-boiling solvent such as ether. The following scheme describes a separation procedure.

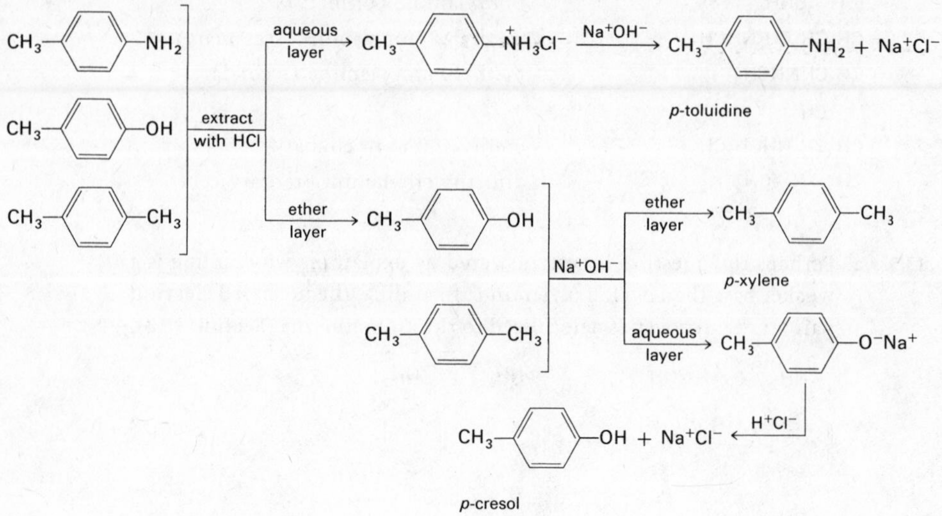

p-toluidine

p-xylene

p-cresol

In the case of *p*-xylene, the ether is evaporated and the *p*-xylene distilled. In the case of *p*-toluidine and *p*-cresol, once the product is liberated from the corresponding salt, it is extracted from the water by ether; the ether is then evaporated and the desired product is distilled.

The order of extraction—acid first, then base—can be reversed.

13.8.   a. Compare with Eq. 13.3.

b. Compare with Eq. 13.5.

$$(CH_3CH_2)_3N + H\!-\!OSO_3H \longrightarrow (CH_3CH_2)_3\overset{+}{N}H + \overset{-}{O}SO_3H$$

c. Compare with Eq. 13.6.

$$(CH_3CH_2)_2\overset{+}{N}H_2Cl^- + Na^+OH^- \longrightarrow (CH_3CH_2)_2NH + Na^+Cl^- + H_2O$$

d. Compare with Eqs. 13.10 or 13.11.

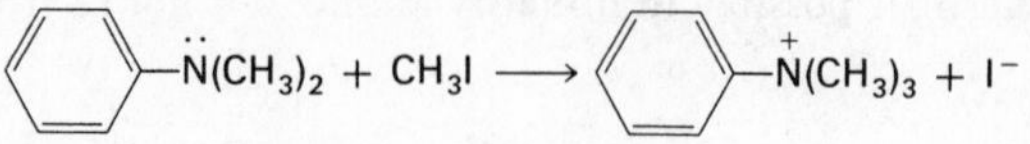

e. Compare with Eq. 9.10.

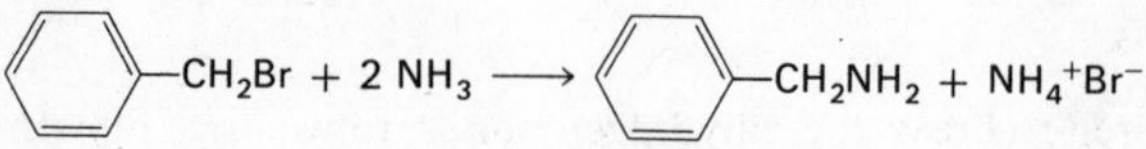

Amines, Amides, and Related Organic Nitrogen Compounds

13.9. The reaction involves an S_N2 ring opening of ethylene oxide; see Eq. 8.12.

$$(CH_3)_3N\colon \;+\; CH_2\!-\!CH_2 \xrightarrow{\text{base}} (CH_3)_3\overset{+}{N}CH_2CH_2O^-$$

$$\Big\Downarrow H_2O$$

$$[(CH_3)_3\overset{+}{N}CH_2CH_2OH]OH^-$$

choline

13.10. Consider the possibilities for hydrogen-bonding in each case. In the tertiary ammonium base, the hydroxide ion can form a hydrogen bond with the trimethylammonium ion; this is not possible with the quarternary ammonium base. Consequently, the hydroxide ion is freer in the latter case.

$$CH_3-\overset{\overset{\displaystyle CH_3}{|}}{\underset{\underset{\displaystyle CH_3}{|}}{\overset{+}{N}}}-H\cdots\overset{-}{O}H$$

$$CH_3-\overset{\overset{\displaystyle CH_3}{|}}{\underset{\underset{\displaystyle CH_3}{|}}{\overset{+}{N}}}-CH_3 \;\; OH^-$$

13.11. The reaction begins with nucleophilic attack by the amine on the carbonyl group of the anhydride.

$$CH_3\overset{O}{\overset{\|}{C}}O\overset{O}{\overset{\|}{C}}CH_3 + H_2NCH_2CH_3 \longrightarrow CH_3\overset{\overset{\displaystyle O^-}{|}}{\underset{\underset{\displaystyle OCCH_3}{\|O}}{C}}-\overset{+}{N}H_2CH_2CH_3 \xrightarrow{\sim H^+}$$

$$CH_3-\overset{\overset{\displaystyle O-H}{|}}{\underset{\underset{\displaystyle OCCH_3}{\|O}}{C}}-NHCH_2CH_3 \xrightarrow{-HOAc} CH_3\overset{O}{\overset{\|}{C}}-NHCH_2CH_3$$

Even though the resulting amide has an unshared electron pair on nitrogen, it does not react with a second mole of acetic anhydride to become diacylated:

$$CH_3\overset{O}{\overset{\|}{C}}O\overset{O}{\overset{\|}{C}}CH_3 + CH_3\overset{O}{\overset{\|}{C}}NHCH_2CH_3 \xrightarrow{\;\times\!\!\!\to\;} \left(CH_3\overset{O}{\overset{\|}{C}}\right)_2\!\!-\!NCH_2CH_3$$

The reason is that amides are poor nucleophiles because the unshared electron pair on the nitrogen is delocalized (Section 13.8):

$$CH_3\overset{O}{\overset{\|}{C}}-NHCH_2CH_3 \longleftrightarrow CH_3\overset{\overset{\displaystyle O^-}{|}}{C}=\overset{+}{N}HCH_2CH_3$$

13.12. Orinase is a sulfonamide; it is also a substituted urea.

$$CH_3-\!\!\left\langle\!\!\bigcirc\!\!\right\rangle\!\!-\overset{\overset{\displaystyle O}{\|}}{\underset{\underset{\displaystyle O}{\|}}{S}}\!-\!NH\!-\!\overset{\overset{\displaystyle O}{\|}}{C}\!-\!NHCH_2CH_2CH_2CH_3 \xrightarrow[\text{heat}]{\text{NaOH}}$$

sulfonamide — urea

$$CH_3-\!\!\left\langle\!\!\bigcirc\!\!\right\rangle\!\!-SO_3^-Na^+ + NH_3 + CO_2 + H_2NCH_2CH_2CH_2CH_3$$

Complete hydrolysis results in cleavage of all three bonds, indicated with dashed lines.

13.13. The amines are 1°, 2°, and 3°, respectively. The reactions of amines with nitrous acid are described in Section 13.4c.

$$(CH_3)_2CHNH_2 + HONO \xrightarrow{0°} (CH_3)_2CHOH + N_2\uparrow + H_2O \qquad \textbf{(Eqs. 13.22 and 13.23)}$$

A gas will be evolved.

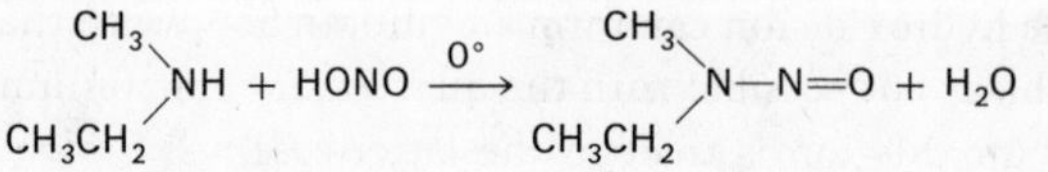

$$\qquad \textbf{(Eq. 13.21)}$$

A yellow oily upper layer will appear.

$$(CH_3)_3N + HONO \xrightarrow{0°} \text{no observable reaction}$$

13.14. These equations illustrate the reactions in Sections 13.5a and 13.5b.

a.

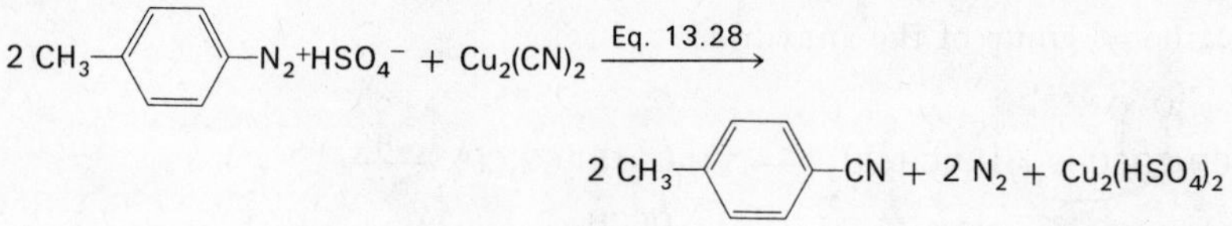

b.

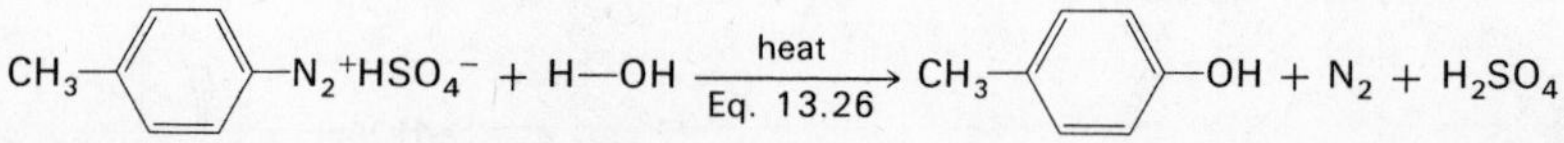

c.

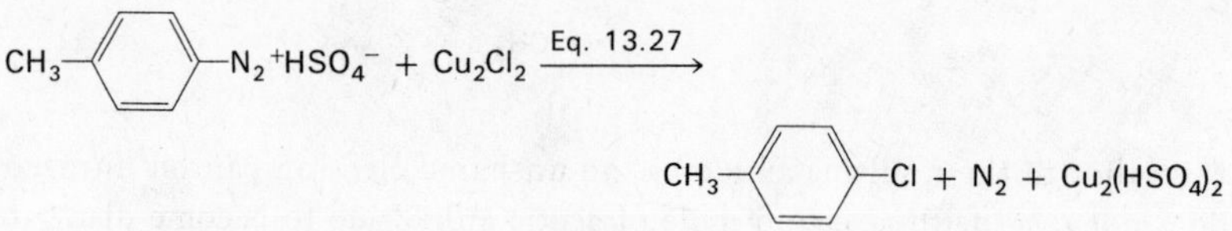

d.

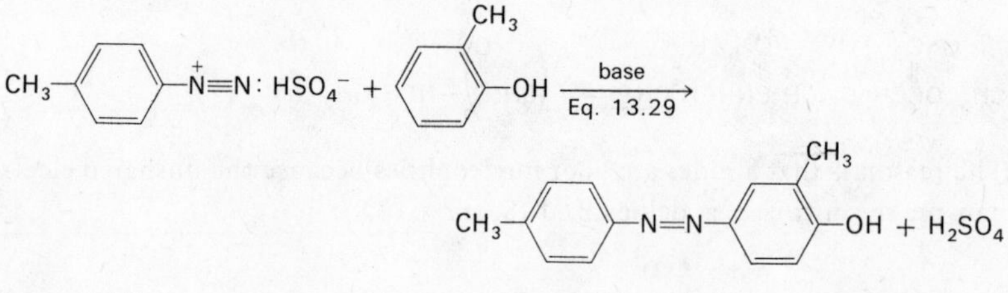

e.

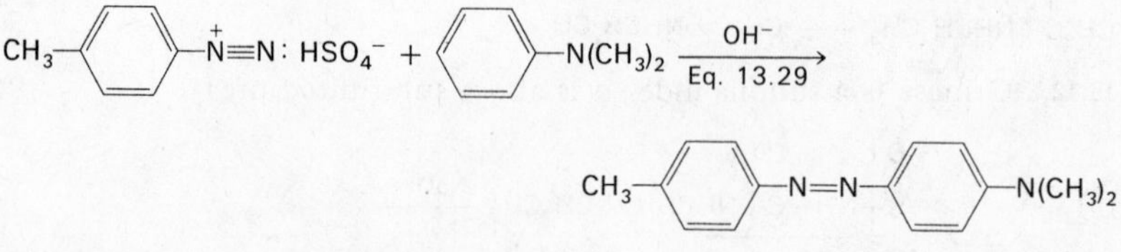

13.15. Benzidine can be diazotized at each end; it can then couple with 2 mol of the aminosulfonic acid. Coupling occurs ortho to the amino group, since the para position is blocked by the sulfonic acid group.

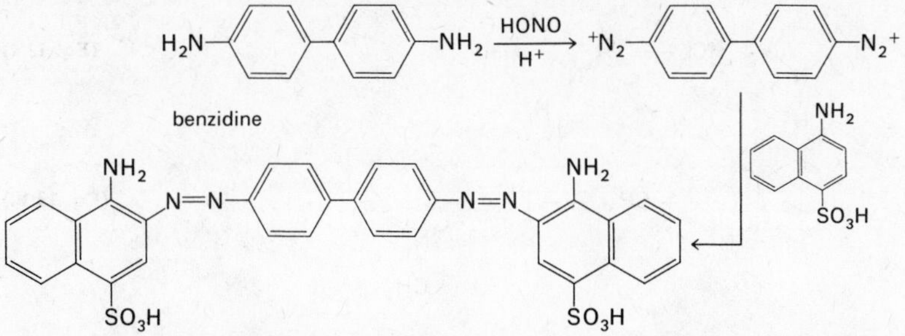

H_2N—⬡—⬡—NH_2 $\xrightarrow[H^+]{HONO}$ $^+N_2$—⬡—⬡—$N_2{}^+$

benzidine

(naphthalene structure with NH$_2$, N=N—⬡—⬡—N=N, NH$_2$, SO$_3$H groups; and separate naphthalene with NH$_2$ and SO$_3$H)

13.16. 1,4 Addition of chlorine to 1,3-butadiene gives a dihalide in which both chlorines are allylic and therefore quite easily displaced by nucleophiles. Reaction with sodium cyanide gives the dinitrile.

$$CH_2{=}CH{-}CH{=}CH_2 + Cl_2 \longrightarrow \underset{Cl}{CH_2}{-}CH{=}CH{-}\underset{Cl}{CH_2}$$

$$NCCH_2CH{=}CHCH_2CN \xleftarrow{NaCN}$$

The double bond can now be hydrogenated to give the saturated nitrile. Hydrolysis of the dinitrile gives adipic acid, whereas reduction gives hexamethylenediamine.

$$NCCH_2CH{=}CHCH_2CN \xrightarrow{H_2}{Ni} NCCH_2CH_2CH_2CH_2CN$$

$$\underset{\text{adipic acid}}{HO{-}\overset{O}{C}(CH_2)_4\overset{O}{C}{-}OH} \xleftarrow[H^+]{H_2O} \quad \xrightarrow[N_2]{H_2} \underset{\text{hexamethylenediamine}}{H_2N{-}(CH_2)_6{-}NH_2}$$

13.17. The ring structures are all given in Section 13.7.

a. 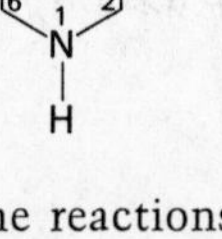 (pyrrolidine ring, numbered 1–5, with N–H and CH$_3$)

c. 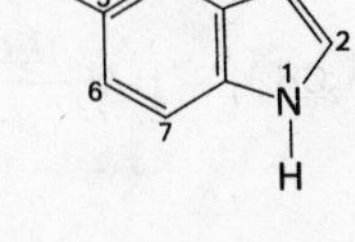 (pyridine ring, numbered 1–6, with CH$_3$ at 2, 4, and 6 positions)

b. (piperidine ring, numbered 1–6, with H, Cl at 4, N–H)

d. (indole ring, numbered 1–7, with HO at 5, N–H)

13.18. The reactions of heterocyclic amines with acid, alkyl halides, nitrous acid, or acylating agents are entirely analogous to those of aliphatic or aromatic amines.

a. 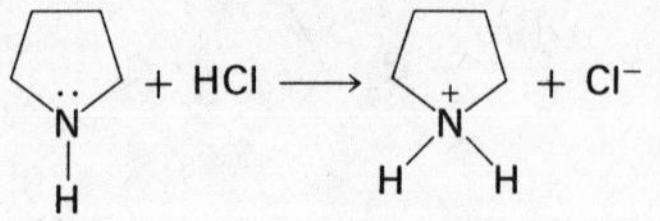 [pyrrolidine] + HCl ⟶ [pyrrolidinium] + Cl⁻   **(Eq. 13.4)**

b. 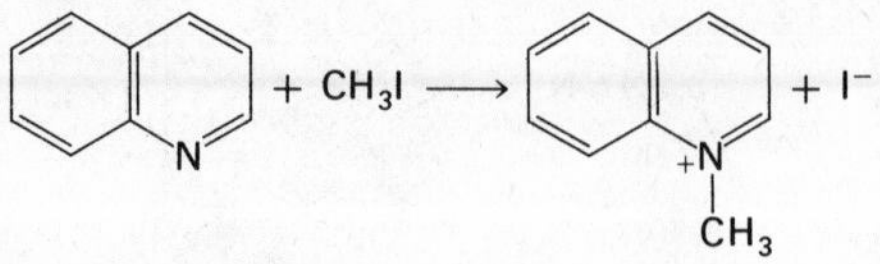 [quinoline] + CH_3I ⟶ [N-methylquinolinium] + I⁻   **(Eq. 13.10)**

c. 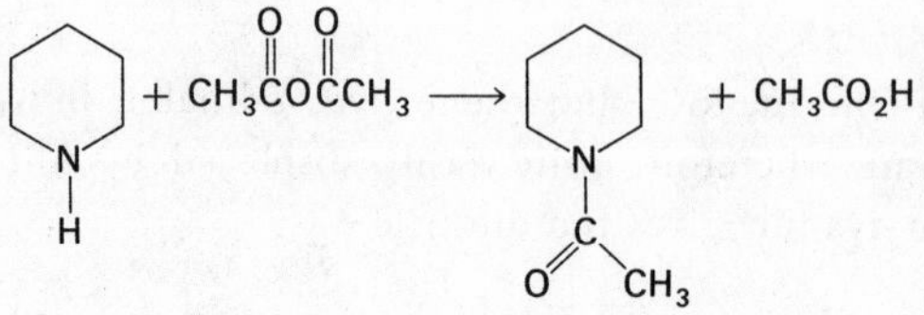 [piperidine] + $CH_3\overset{O}{\overset{\|}{C}}O\overset{O}{\overset{\|}{C}}CH_3$ ⟶ [N-acetylpiperidine] + CH_3CO_2H **(Eq. 13.13)**

d. 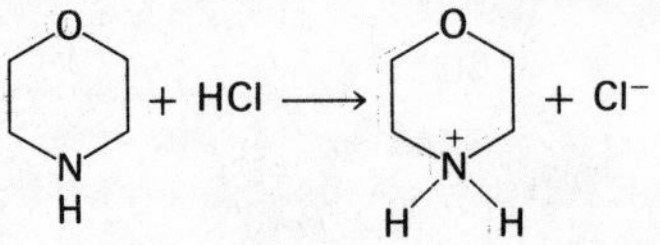 [morpholine] + HCl ⟶ [morpholinium] + Cl⁻   **(Eq. 13.3)**

The nitrogen is more basic than the oxygen (that is, amines are more basic than ethers).

13.19. The nomenclature of amides is described in Section 13.8.

a. $CH_3CH_2\overset{O}{\overset{\|}{C}}NH_2$

b. $\underset{\underset{Cl}{|}}{CH_2}CH_2CH_2\overset{O}{\overset{\|}{C}}NH_2$

c. 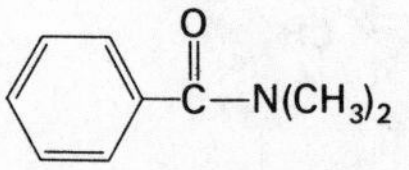 [benzene]$-\overset{O}{\overset{\|}{C}}-N(CH_3)_2$

d. 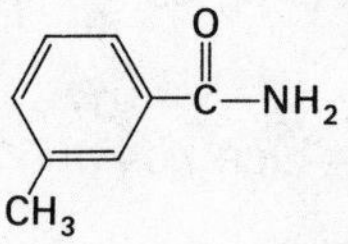 [benzene with CH_3]$-\overset{O}{\overset{\|}{C}}-NH_2$

e. 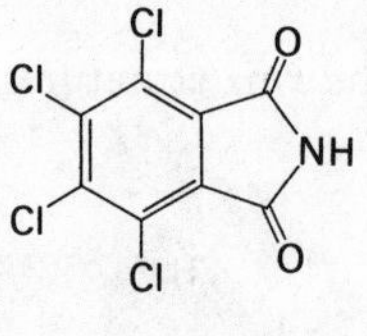 [tetrachloroisoindole-1,3-dione structure with Cl, Cl, Cl, Cl and NH]

13.20. The general equation for hydrolysis of an amide is shown in Eq. 13.37. If the hydrolysis is carried out in alkaline medium, the acid is present as its salt. If the hydrolysis is carried out in an acidic medium, the amine is protonated.

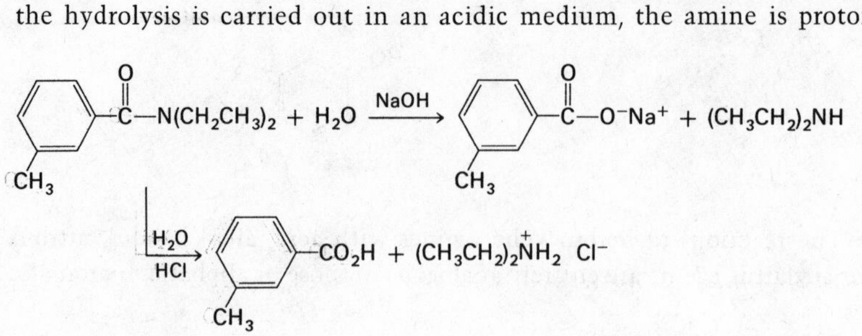

[aryl]$-\overset{O}{\overset{\|}{C}}-N(CH_2CH_3)_2 + H_2O \xrightarrow{NaOH}$ [aryl]$-\overset{O}{\overset{\|}{C}}-O^-Na^+ + (CH_3CH_2)_2NH$

$\xrightarrow[HCl]{H_2O}$ [aryl]$-CO_2H + (CH_3CH_2)_2\overset{+}{N}H_2 \ Cl^-$

13.21. a. Demerol contains an ester group that should be hydrolyzed by base (Section 11.7a).

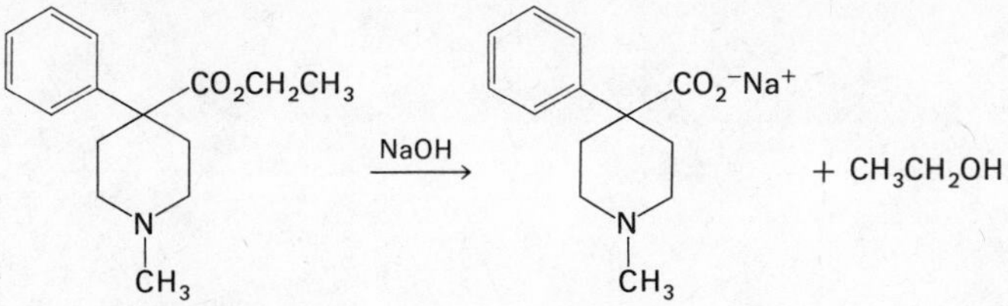

$$+ CH_3CH_2OH$$

b. Methadone contains a tertiary amine group that should be protonated in acid (Eq. 13.5).

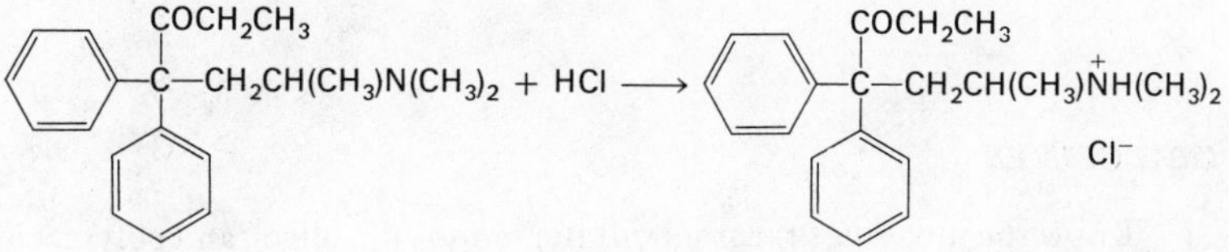

c. Amphetamine is a primary amine that should be acetylated (Eq. 13.13) by acetic anhydride.

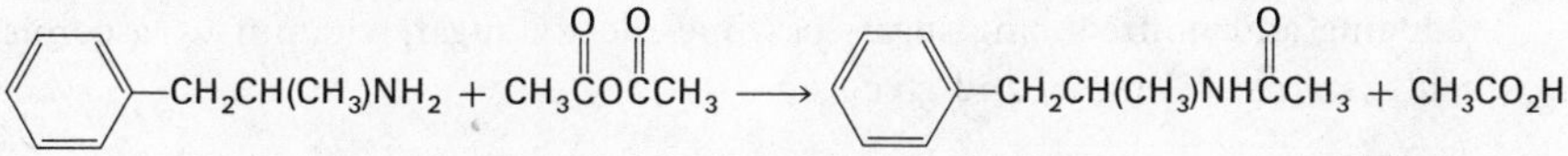

d. Epinephrine has two phenolic hydroxyl groups. Treatment with base and then methyl iodide should convert these hydroxyl groups to methyl ethers, in a Williamson synthesis (Eq. 9.7).

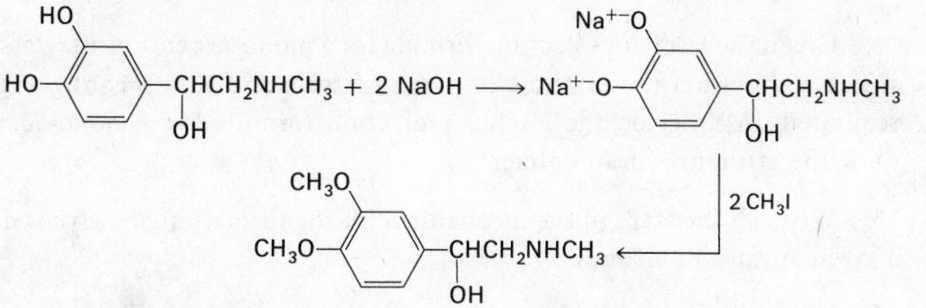

14. Carbohydrates

OBJECTIVES

1. Know the meaning of: carbohydrate; mono-, di-, oligo-, and polysaccharide; tri-, tetr-, pent-, and hexose; aldose and ketose; glyceraldehyde and dihydroxyacetone; D- and L-sugar; epimers; anomeric center; α- and β-configuration; furanose and pyranose; mutarotation; glycoside; glycosidic linkage; reducing and nonreducing sugar; osazone; deoxy sugar; vitamin C (ascorbic acid); starch, cellulose, and glycogen.

2. Draw the Fischer projection formulas for glucose, mannose, galactose, and fructose.

3. Draw the cyclic structures (Haworth projection and conformational structure) for α-D- and β-D-glucose and the corresponding methyl glucosides.

4. Given the Fischer projection formula for a monosaccharide, draw its cyclic structure in either the furanose or pyranose form and α- or β-configuration, as requested. Also, given the Fischer projection formula for a monosaccharide, draw the structure of an epimer.

5. Write all the steps in the mechanism for the formation of a glycoside from a given sugar and alcohol.

6. Write all the steps in the mechanism for the hydrolysis of a given glycoside to the corresponding sugar and alcohol.

7. Given the formula for a D-sugar, write the formula for the corresponding L-sugar.

8. Write all the steps in the mechanism for the hydrolysis of a given disaccharide to the component monosaccharides.

9. Given the structure of a sugar, tell whether it is reducing or nonreducing.

10. Given the structure of a sugar, write the structure of the corresponding osazone.

11. Given the structure of a sugar, write equations for its reaction with each of the following reagents: acetic anhydride, bromine water, hydrogen cyanide, and Tollens' or Fehling's reagent.

12. Given the structure of a sugar, write the structure of the product obtained by treating it with base and dimethyl sulfate.

13. Write structures for the repeating structural units in starch and cellulose.

14. Given the structure of cellulose, write equations for the formation of cellulose nitrate or cellulose acetate.

ANSWERS TO THE EXERCISES AND PROBLEMS

14.1. These definitions, usually with examples, are given in the following sections of the text:

    a. 14.1

    b. 14.1

    c. 14.1, 14.2

    d. 14.1, 14.6

    e. 14.1, 14.10

    f. 14.3b

    g. 14.3b

    h. 14.5

    i. 14.7b

    j. 14.7a

14.2. D-Sugars have the same configuration at the carbon atom adjacent to the primary alcohol function as D(+)-glyceraldehyde (which is R).

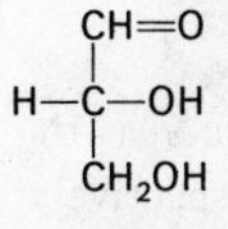

$$
\begin{array}{lll}
\text{CH=O} & \text{CHO} & \text{CH}_2\text{OH} \\
\text{H—C—OH} & \text{(CHOH)}_n & \text{C=O} \\
\text{CH}_2\text{OH} & \text{H—C—OH} & \text{(CHOH)}_n \\
\text{D(+)-glyceraldehyde} & \text{CH}_2\text{OH} & \text{H—C—OH} \\
 & \text{a D-aldose} & \text{CH}_2\text{OH} \\
 & & \text{a D-ketose}
\end{array}
$$

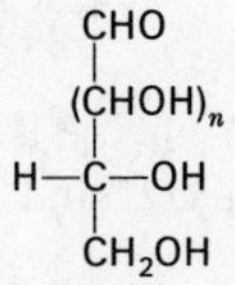

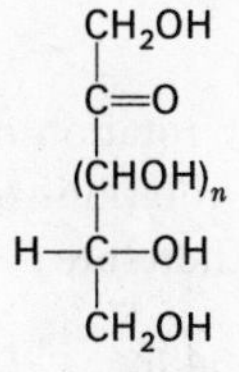

14.3. Epimers are stereoisomers that differ in configuration at one carbon atom and have identical configurations at all other carbon atoms.

D-ribose ⎫
⎬ epimers at C2
D-arabinose ⎭

D-ribose ⎫
⎬ epimers at C3
D-xylose ⎭

D-arabinose ⎫
⎬ epimers at C3
D-lyxose ⎭

D-xylose ⎫
⎬ epimers at C2
D-lyxose ⎭

14.4. a. See Eq. 14.3 and Section 14.3b.

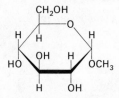

b. Using Table 14.1 as a guide, compare the configuration at each carbon of gulose with that of glucose.

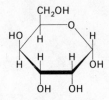

c. See Section 14.3b and Table 14.1.

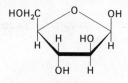

14.5. At equilibrium the specific rotation of D-glucose is $+52°$, whereas the pure α and β forms have specific rotations of $+112°$ and $+19°$, respectively. The % β form at equilibrium is therefore

$$\frac{112 - 52}{112 - 19} \times 100 = \frac{60}{93} \times 100 = 64.5\%.$$

14.6. a. Consult Table 14.1 for the Fischer projection formula of D-mannose. The L isomer is enantiomeric with the D isomer.

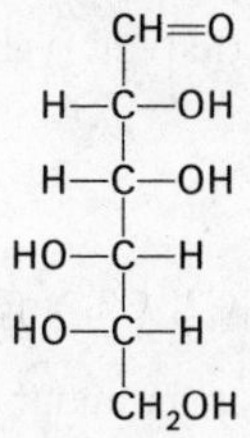

$$
\begin{array}{c}
\text{CH}{=}\text{O} \\
\text{H}{-}\text{C}{-}\text{OH} \\
\text{H}{-}\text{C}{-}\text{OH} \\
\text{HO}{-}\text{C}{-}\text{H} \\
\text{HO}{-}\text{C}{-}\text{H} \\
\text{CH}_2\text{OH}
\end{array}
$$

L-mannose

b. See Section 14.4 for the Fischer projection formula of D-fructose.

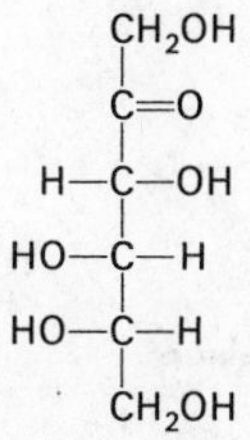

$$
\begin{array}{c}
\text{CH}_2\text{OH} \\
\text{C}{=}\text{O} \\
\text{H}{-}\text{C}{-}\text{OH} \\
\text{HO}{-}\text{C}{-}\text{H} \\
\text{HO}{-}\text{C}{-}\text{H} \\
\text{CH}_2\text{OH}
\end{array}
$$

L-fructose

14.7.

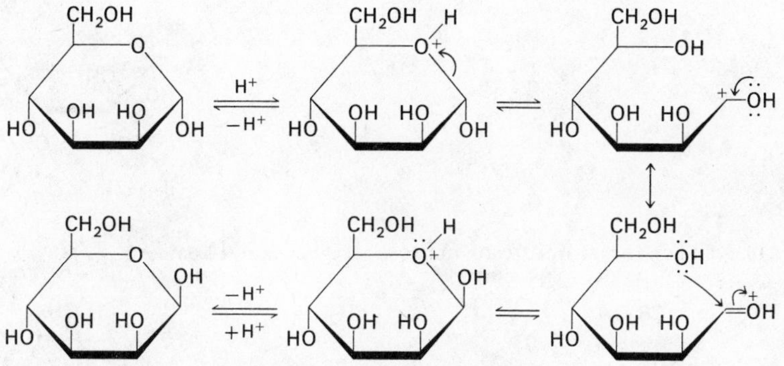

14.8. The structure is

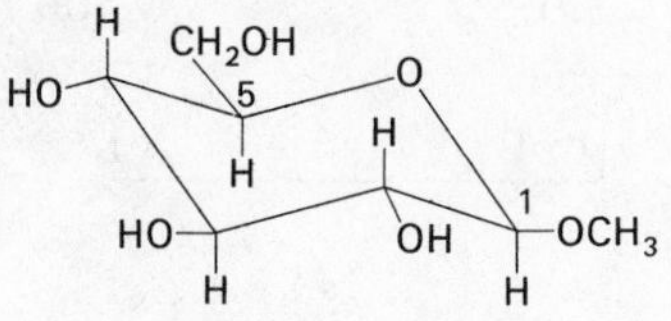

Methyl refers to the name of the alkyl group attached to the oxygen at C1.

β refers to the configuration of the methoxyl group at C1 ("up," as shown).

D refers to the configuration at C5, which is the same as that of D-glyceraldehyde.

(+) means that the compound is dextrorotatory.

Gluco refers to glucose and indicates the configurations at C2, C3, and C4.

Pyranos indicates that the oxygen-containing heterocyclic ring is six-membered.

The suffix *ide* indicates that the compound is an acetal (a glyco*ide*).

14.9. The products are glucose and salicyl alcohol (see Eq. 14.4).

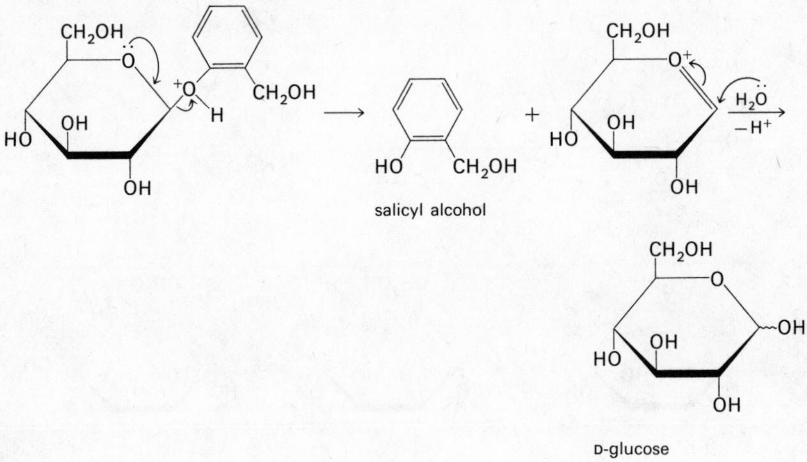

salicyl alcohol

D-glucose

14.10. a. For the structure of maltose, see Section 14.6a.

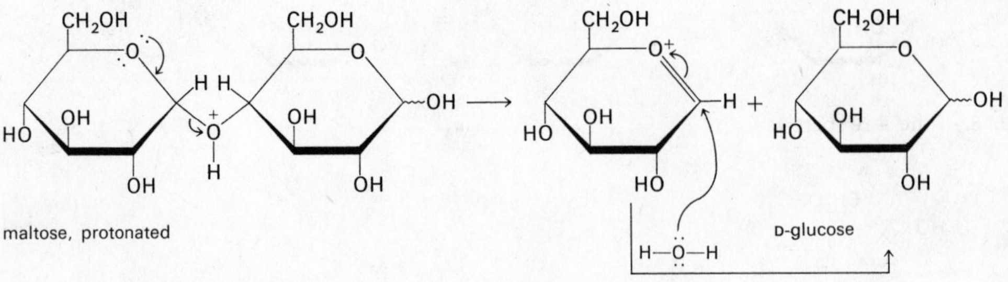

maltose, protonated

D-glucose

b. For the structure of lactose, see Section 14.6b.

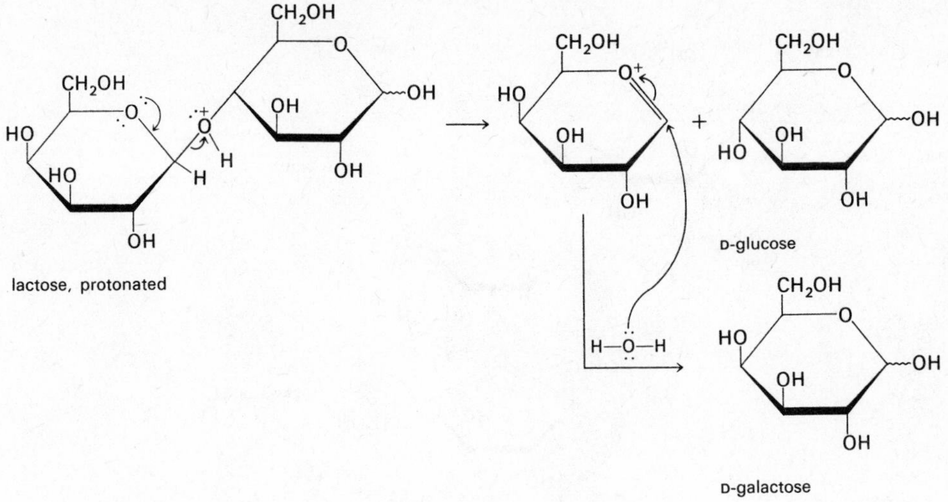

lactose, protonated

D-glucose

D-galactose

c. For the structure of sucrose, see Section 14.6c.

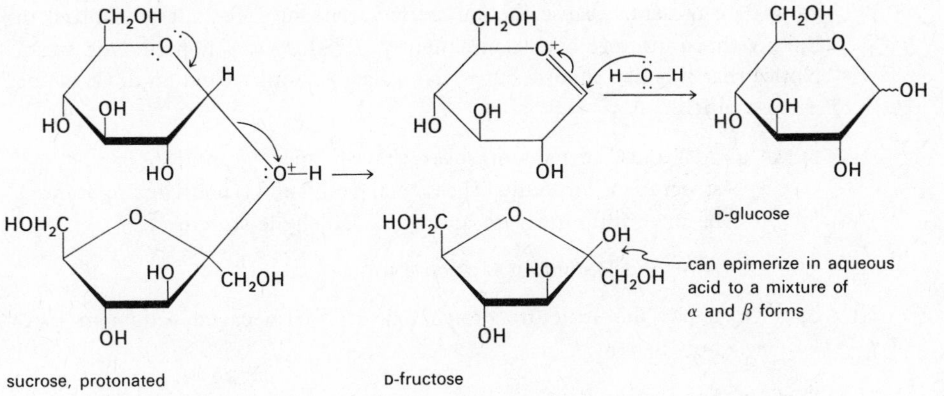

sucrose, protonated

D-fructose

D-glucose

can epimerize in aqueous acid to a mixture of α and β forms

The mechanism shown is one of two that are possible. The alternative would break the other glycoside bond to give glucose and the carbocation from the fructose unit. Both mechanisms undoubtedly occur simultaneously. The products, of course, are the same from both paths, namely a mixture of the α and β forms of D-glucose and D-fructose.

14.11.   a. Two moles of D-glucose.

b. The test is negative because no hemiacetal group is present.

c. Trehalose cannot form a methyl glycoside because no hemiacetal group is present.

14.12.

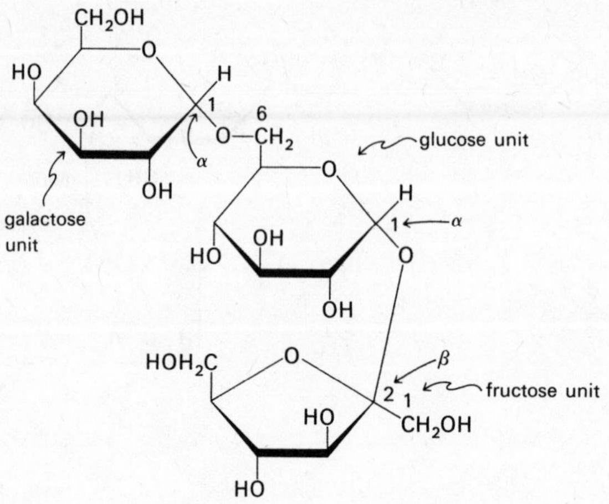

Complete hydrolysis gives D-galactose, D-glucose, and D-fructose. No hemiacetal groups are present because the anomeric carbon of each unit is involved in linking the units together. Consequently, raffinose is a nonreducing sugar. Notice that it is like sucrose but with a galactose unit tacked on to C6 of the glucose unit.

14.13. a. A, B, and C are reducing sugars (have hemiacetal groups as part of their structures). Structure D has acetal groups and is nonreducing (cannot be in equilibrium with an acyclic, aldehyde structure).

b. A, B, and D contain D-glucose units.

c. B has the structure designated; it is also called cellobiose (Section 14.6a).

14.14. a. See Eq. 14.13.

b. See Table 14.2.

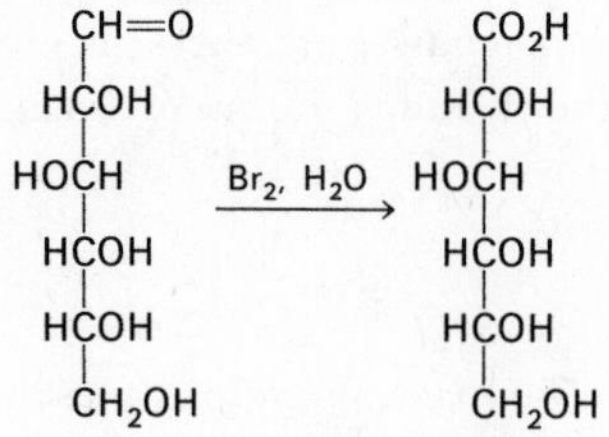

c. See Table 14.2.

$$
\begin{array}{c}
\text{CH=O} \\
\text{HCOH} \\
\text{HOCH} \\
\text{HCOH} \\
\text{HCOH} \\
\text{CH}_2\text{OH}
\end{array}
\;+\; H_2 \xrightarrow{\text{catalyst}}
\begin{array}{c}
\text{CH}_2\text{OH} \\
\text{HCOH} \\
\text{HOCH} \\
\text{HCOH} \\
\text{HCOH} \\
\text{CH}_2\text{OH}
\end{array}
$$

sorbitol

d. Compare with Table 10.3.

$$
\begin{array}{c}
\text{CH=O} \\
\text{HCOH} \\
\text{HOCH} \\
\text{HCOH} \\
\text{HCOH} \\
\text{CH}_2\text{OH}
\end{array}
\;+\; NH_2OH \longrightarrow
\begin{array}{c}
\text{CH=NOH} \\
\text{HCOH} \\
\text{HOCH} \\
\text{HCOH} \\
\text{HCOH} \\
\text{CH}_2\text{OH}
\end{array}
\;+\; H_2O
$$

glucose oxime

e. See Eq. 14.3.

f.

$$
\begin{array}{c}
\text{CH=O} \\
\text{HCOH} \\
\text{HOCH} \\
\text{HCOH} \\
\text{HCOH} \\
\text{CH}_2\text{OH}
\end{array}
\;+\; HCN \longrightarrow
\begin{array}{c}
\text{CN} \\
\overset{*}{\text{HCOH}} \\
\text{HCOH} \\
\text{HOCH} \\
\text{HCOH} \\
\text{HCOH} \\
\text{CH}_2\text{OH}
\end{array}
\quad\text{and/or}\quad
\begin{array}{c}
\text{CN} \\
\overset{*}{\text{HOCH}} \\
\text{HCOH} \\
\text{HOCH} \\
\text{HCOH} \\
\text{HCOH} \\
\text{CH}_2\text{OH}
\end{array}
$$

glucose cyanohydrin

A new chiral center (*) is generated in this reaction. Both epimers are formed, though not necessarily in equal amounts.

g. See Eq. 14.11.

h. Compare with Eq. 14.8.

$$
\begin{array}{c}
\text{CH=O} \\
\text{HCOH} \\
\text{HOCH} \\
\text{HCOH} \\
\text{HCOH} \\
\text{CH}_2\text{OH}
\end{array}
\;+\; 2\,Cu^{II} + 4\,OH^- \longrightarrow
\begin{array}{c}
\text{CO}_2\text{H} \\
\text{HCOH} \\
\text{HOCH} \\
\text{HCOH} \\
\text{HCOH} \\
\text{CH}_2\text{OH}
\end{array}
\;+\; Cu_2O + 2\,H_2O
$$

14.15. The first steps are shown in Table 14.1. Oxidation of D-erythrose gives *meso*-tartaric acid,

$$
\begin{array}{c}
\text{CHO} \\
\text{H}\!-\!\text{OH} \\
\text{H}\!-\!\text{OH} \\
\text{CH}_2\text{OH}
\end{array}
\quad\longrightarrow\quad
\begin{array}{c}
\text{CO}_2\text{H} \\
\text{H}\!-\!\text{OH} \\
\text{H}\!-\!\text{OH} \\
\text{CO}_2\text{H}
\end{array}
$$

D-erythrose   *meso*-tartaric acid
(optically inactive)

whereas analogous oxidation of D-threose gives an optically active tartaric acid:

$$
\begin{array}{c}
\text{CHO} \\
\text{HO}\!-\!\text{H} \\
\text{H}\!-\!\text{OH} \\
\text{CH}_2\text{OH}
\end{array}
\quad\longrightarrow\quad
\begin{array}{c}
\text{CO}_2\text{H} \\
\text{HO}\!-\!\text{H} \\
\text{H}\!-\!\text{OH} \\
\text{CO}_2\text{H}
\end{array}
$$

D-threose   optically active
(S,S) tartaric acid

In this way, we can readily assign structures to the two tetroses.

14.16. Use Table 14.1 as a guide.

Since D-ribose and D-arabinose have the same configurations at C3 and C4, they give the same osazone, with the structure

$$
\begin{array}{c}
\text{CH}\!=\!\text{NNHC}_6\text{H}_5 \\
\text{C}\!=\!\text{NNHC}_6\text{H}_5 \\
\text{HCOH} \\
\text{HCOH} \\
\text{CH}_2\text{OH}
\end{array}
$$

Similarly, D-xylose and D-lyxose give the identical osazone, with the structure

$$
\begin{array}{c}
\text{CH}\!=\!\text{NNHC}_6\text{H}_5 \\
\text{C}\!=\!\text{NNHC}_6\text{H}_5 \\
\text{HOCH} \\
\text{HCOH} \\
\text{CH}_2\text{OH}
\end{array}
$$

Using analogous reasoning, the eight D-hexoses in Table 14.1 give four osazones, with each of the following pairs giving the same osazone.

D-allose	D-glucose	D-gulose	D-galactose
D-altrose	D-mannose	D-idose	D-talose

14.17. The formula of L-galactose can be obtained from that of D-galactose in Table 14.1. Deoxy sugars are discussed in Section 14.9a.

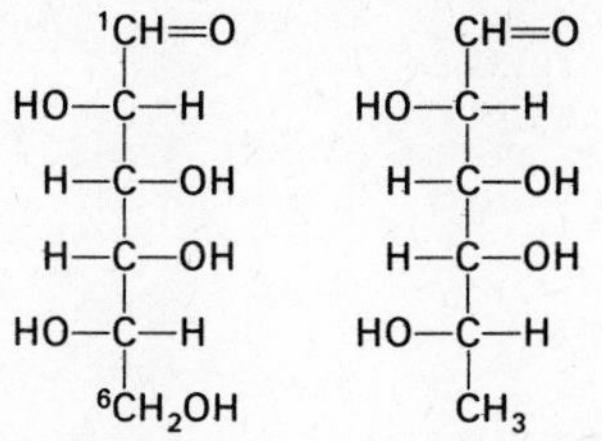

$$
\begin{array}{c}
^1\text{CH}=\text{O} \\
\text{HO}-\text{C}-\text{H} \\
\text{H}-\text{C}-\text{OH} \\
\text{H}-\text{C}-\text{OH} \\
\text{HO}-\text{C}-\text{H} \\
^6\text{CH}_2\text{OH}
\end{array}
\qquad
\begin{array}{c}
\text{CH}=\text{O} \\
\text{HO}-\text{C}-\text{H} \\
\text{H}-\text{C}-\text{OH} \\
\text{H}-\text{C}-\text{OH} \\
\text{HO}-\text{C}-\text{H} \\
\text{CH}_3
\end{array}
$$

L-galactose   L-fucose (6-deoxy-L-galactose)

14.18.

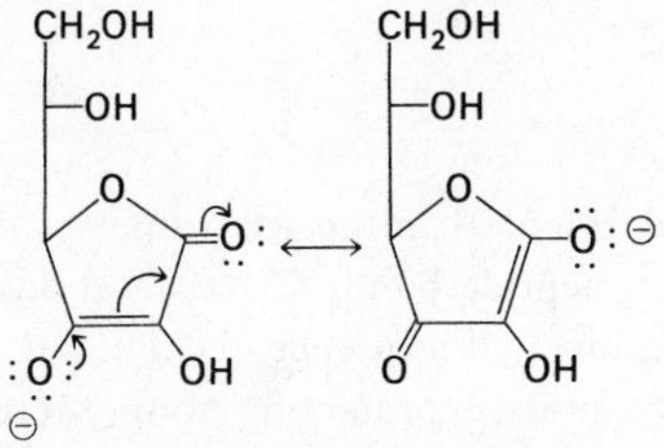

The negative charge can be almost equally spread over the two oxygen atoms.

15. Amino Acids and Proteins

1. Know the meaning of: α-amino acid, essential amino acid; dipolar ion and amphoteric; isoelectric point; ninhydrin; peptide bond; di-, tri-, and polypeptide; N- and C-terminal amino acid; amino-acid sequence; DNFB and DNP-amino acid; Edman degradation; carboxypeptidase; protecting group; Merrifield solid-phase technique; dicyclohexylcarbodiimide; t-butoxycarbonyl (BOC) group; primary, secondary, tertiary, and quaternary protein structure; pleated sheet and α-helix; enzyme.

2. Draw the general structure of an α-amino acid.

3. Learn the names, abbreviations, and structural formulas of as many of the amino acids in Table 15.1 as you can.

4. Given the structure of an amino acid, write the structure in the dipolar ion form.

5. Given a particular amino acid, draw its structure as a function of the pH of the medium.

6. Given the pK_a's of an amino acid, estimate the isoelectric pH.

7. Write the equation for the reaction of an amino acid (dipolar form) with strong acid or strong base.

8. Write the equation for the reaction of an amino acid with ninhydrin reagent.

9. Write the equations for the reaction of a given amino acid with (a) a given alcohol and H^+, and (b) acetic anhydride or another activated acyl derivative.

10. Given the structures of the component amino acids and the name of a di-, tri-, or polypeptide, draw its structure.

11. Write the equation for the hydrolysis of a given di- or polypeptide.

12. Write the equation for the reaction of an amino acid with 2,4-dinitrofluorobenzene.

13. Given the name or structure of a di- or polypeptide, and the fact that it has been treated with 2,4-dinitrofluorobenzene, write the structures of the hydrolysis products.

14. Given the DNP-derivative and hydrolysis products of an unknown polypeptide, deduce the structure of the original polypeptide.

15. Write the equations for carrying out an Edman degradation on a given tri- or polypeptide.

16. Write an equation for the protection of an amino acid with *t*-butoxycarbonyl chloride.

17. Describe the geometry of the peptide bond.

18. Compare the pleated-sheet and α-helix structures of proteins.

ANSWERS TO THE EXERCISES AND PROBLEMS

15.1. These definitions are given in the following sections of the text:

a. 15.6

b. 15.1a and Table 15.1

c. 15.1a and Table 15.1

d. 15.1a and Table 15.1

e. 15.2

f. 15.2

g. 15.1a and Figure 15.1

h. 15.6

i. 15.2

j. 15.1a

15.2.

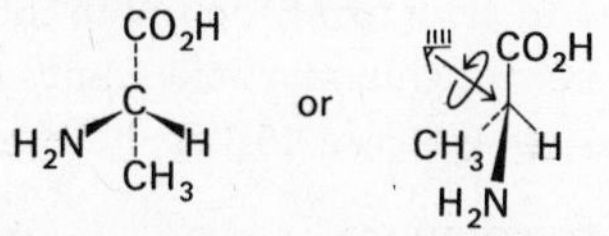

L-alanine

priority order: $NH_2 > CO_2H > CH_3 > H$

The configuration is *S*.

15.3. Compare with Eq. 15.2 ($R = CH_3$).

a. $CH_3\underset{NH_3{}^+}{CHCO_2{}^-} + H^+Cl^- \longrightarrow CH_3\underset{NH_3{}^+Cl^-}{CHCO_2H}$

b. $CH_3\underset{NH_3{}^+}{CHCO_2{}^-} + Na^+OH^- \longrightarrow CH_3\underset{NH_2}{CHCO_2{}^-Na^+} + H_2O$

15.4. Compare with Eq. 15.3.

$$HO_2CCH_2CH_2\underset{\overset{|}{+NH_3}}{C}HCO_2H + OH^- \xrightarrow{2.19} HO_2CCH_2CH_2\underset{\overset{|}{+NH_3}}{C}HCO_2^- + H_2O$$

$$4.25\Big|OH^-$$

$$^-O_2CCH_2CH_2\underset{\overset{|}{NH_2}}{C}HCO_2^- + H_2O \xleftarrow{\quad OH^- \quad}{9.67}\ ^-O_2CCH_2CH_2\underset{\overset{|}{+NH_3}}{C}HCO_2^- + H_2O$$

15.5. Compare with Eq. 15.4.

$$\underset{\overset{|}{+NH_2}}{\overset{NH_2}{C}}-NHCH_2CH_2CH_2\underset{\overset{|}{+NH_3}}{C}HCO_2H \xrightarrow[2.17]{OH^-} \underset{\overset{|}{+NH_2}}{\overset{NH_2}{C}}NHCH_2CH_2CH_2\underset{\overset{|}{+NH_3}}{C}HCO_2^- + H_2O$$

$$9.04\Big|OH^-$$

$$\underset{\overset{|}{NH}}{\overset{NH_2}{C}}NHCH_2CH_2CH_2\underset{\overset{|}{NH_2}}{C}HCO_2^- + H_2O \xleftarrow[12.48]{OH^-} \underset{\overset{|}{+NH_2}}{\overset{NH_2}{C}}NHCH_2CH_2CH_2\underset{\overset{|}{NH_2}}{C}HCO_2^- + H_2O$$

15.6. Follow the sequence in Eqs. 15.5 and 15.6, with

$$R = \langle\!\!\!\bigcirc\!\!\!\rangle-CH_2-$$

15.7. The isoelectric points of the three amino acids are expected to be: glycine (near neutral), arginine (basic), and glutamic acid (acidic). The actual values are pH 5.97, 10.76, and 3.22, respectively. See Section 15.4 for a discussion of amino-acid separation, which will help you solve this problem.

Since the resin contains sulfonic acid groups, the amino acids are protonated by the resin. Arginine, being most basic, is most easily protonated and most firmly bound to the resin. Glycine is next; and glutamic acid, with two carboxyl groups, is least readily protonated and therefore least firmly bound to the resin. The order of elution is the inverse of the above; glutamic acid comes off the column first, glycine next, and arginine last (see Figure 15.3).

15.8. a. $CH_3\underset{\overset{|}{NH_2}}{C}HCO_2H + CH_3CH_2OH \xrightarrow{H^+} CH_3\underset{\overset{|}{NH_2}}{C}HCO_2CH_2CH_3 + H_2O$ **(Eq. 15.7)**

b. $CH_3\underset{\overset{|}{NH_2}}{C}HCO_2H + (CH_3CO)_2O \longrightarrow CH_3\underset{\overset{|}{NHCCH_3}\atop\overset{||}{O}}{C}HCO_2H + CH_3CO_2H$ **(Eq. 13.13)**

c. $CH_3\underset{\overset{|}{NH_2}}{C}HCO_2H + \langle\!\!\!\bigcirc\!\!\!\rangle\overset{\overset{O}{||}}{C}-Cl \longrightarrow CH_3\underset{\overset{|}{NHC}\atop\overset{||}{O}\langle\!\!\bigcirc\!\!\rangle}{C}HCO_2H + HCl$ **(Eq. 11.32)**

d. 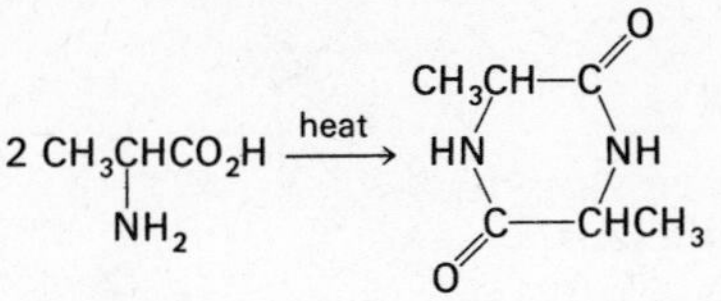 $2 \text{ CH}_3\text{CHCO}_2\text{H} \xrightarrow{\text{heat}}$

(the cyclic diketopiperazine structure with CH₃CH—C=O, HN, NH, C=O, CHCH₃)

(Eqs. 15.8, 15.9)

15.9. Use Table 15.1 for the structures of the component amino acids, and the structures in Section 15.6 as a guide. Here we write the structures in the neutral forms, recognizing, of course, that dipolar structures are possible and that the exact form depends on the solution's pH.

a.

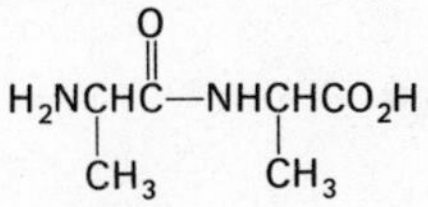

$$\text{H}_2\text{NCHC(=O)—NHCHCO}_2\text{H}$$
with CH₃ and CH₃ substituents

b.

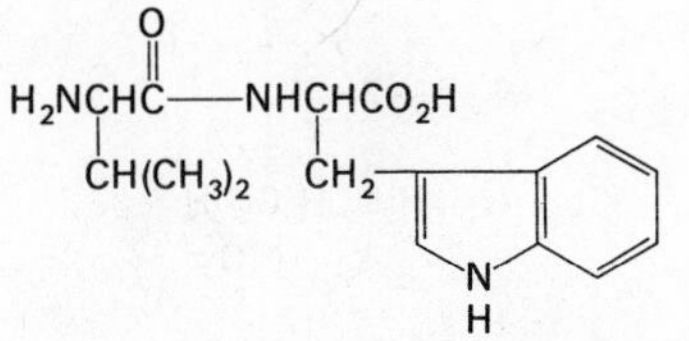

$$\text{H}_2\text{NCHC(=O)—NHCHCO}_2\text{H}$$
with CH(CH₃)₂ and CH₂–indole substituents

c.

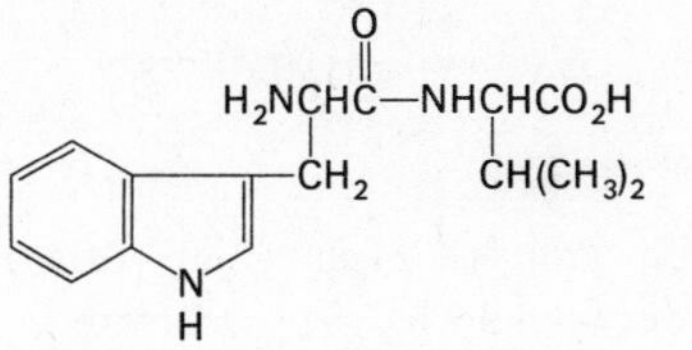

$$\text{H}_2\text{NCHC(=O)—NHCHCO}_2\text{H}$$
with CH₂–indole and CH(CH₃)₂ substituents

d.

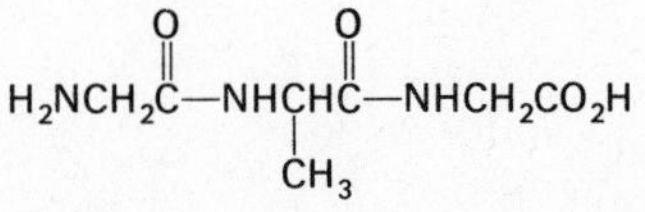

$$\text{H}_2\text{NCH}_2\text{C(=O)—NHCHC(=O)—NHCH}_2\text{CO}_2\text{H}$$
with CH₃ substituent

e.

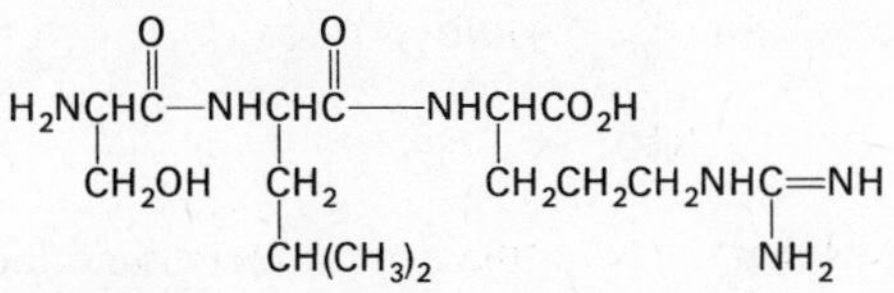

$$\text{H}_2\text{NCHC(=O)—NHCHC(=O)—NHCHCO}_2\text{H}$$
with CH₂OH, CH₂CH(CH₃)₂, and CH₂CH₂CH₂NHC(=NH)NH₂ substituents

f.

$$\text{H}_2\text{NCHC(=O)—NHCH}_2\text{C(=O)—NHCH}_2\text{C(=O)—NHCHCO}_2\text{H}$$
with CH₂–imidazole and CH₂CH₂CO₂H substituents

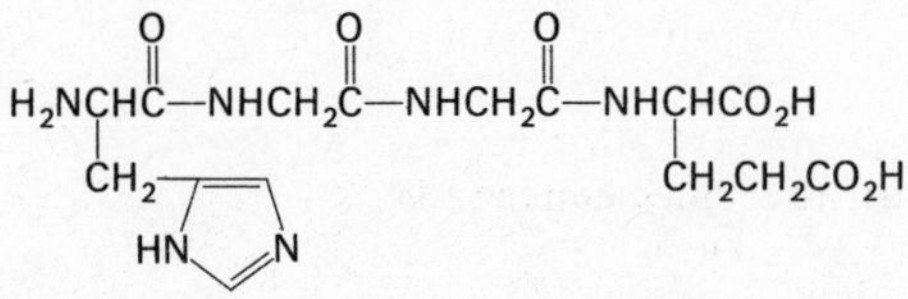

15.10. Altogether there are six possibilities:

Gly—Ala—Ser
Gly—Ser—Ala
Ala—Gly—Ser

Ala—Ser—Gly
Ser—Gly—Ala
Ser—Ala—Gly

The full structure of the last of these is

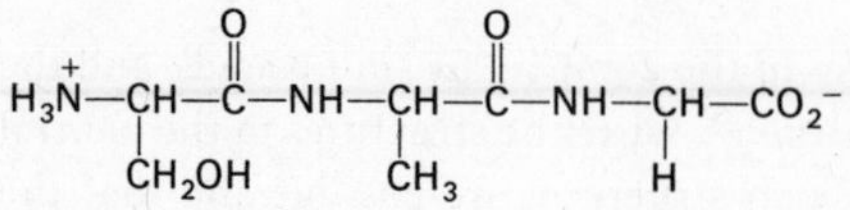

$$\overset{+}{H_3N}-\underset{\underset{CH_2OH}{|}}{CH}-\overset{\overset{O}{\|}}{C}-NH-\underset{\underset{CH_3}{|}}{CH}-\overset{\overset{O}{\|}}{C}-NH-\underset{\underset{H}{|}}{CH}-CO_2^-$$

15.11. The reaction is an example of nucleophilic aromatic substitution (Section 9.3). For a prototype, see Eq. 9.36.

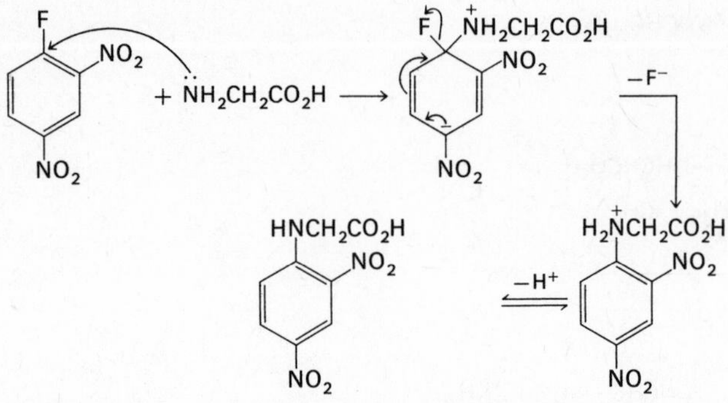

2,4-dinitrophenylglycine

15.12. Lysine contains two amino groups. Each group can react with 2,4-dinitrofluorobenzene. The product would be

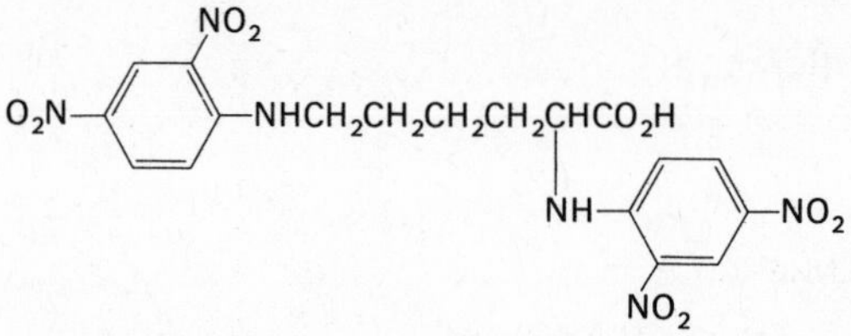

15.13. The first result tells us that the N-terminal amino acid is methionine; the structure at this point is

Met(2 Met, Ser, Gly)

From dipeptide D we learn that one sequence is

Ser—Met

From dipeptide C we learn that one sequence is

Met—Met

From tripeptide B we learn that one sequence is

Met(Met, Ser)

and in view of the result from dipeptide D, tripeptide B must be

Met—Ser—Met

Since two methionines must be adjacent (dipeptide C), the possibilities are

Met—Met—Ser—Met—Gly
and   Met—Ser—Met—Met—Gly

Tripeptide A allows a decision, since 2 Met's and one Gly must be joined together.

Therefore the correct structure is

Met—Ser—Met—Met—Gly

15.14. Follow the scheme in Figure 15.4, with $R_1 = CH_3$, $R_2 = H$, and $R_3 = (CH_3)_2CH$—. The resulting dipeptide is glycylvaline and the thiohydantoin has $R_1 = CH_3$:

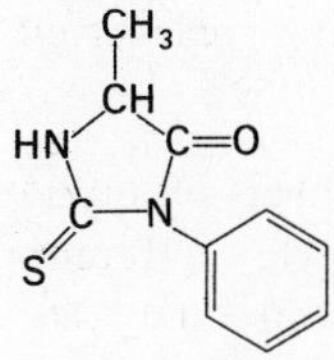

15.15. See Section 15.7b. Carboxypeptidase cleaves peptides one amino acid at a time from the C-terminal end:

Gly   and   Ala—Lys—Met—Leu—Phe—Lys—Tyr—Val—Arg

The arginine is cleaved next.

15.16. The overlapping sequences are easily discerned as shown:
Ala—Gly
    Gly—Val
    Gly—Val—Tyr
        Val—Tyr—Cys
            Tyr—Cys—Phe
                Cys—Phe—Leu
                    Phe—Leu—Try

The peptide must be Ala—Gly—Val—Tyr—Cys—Phe—Leu—Try, an octapeptide. The N-terminal acid is alanine, the C-terminal is tryptophan, and the name is alanylglycylvalyltyrosylcystylphenylalanylleucyltryptophan.

15.17.   a. This is an example of an S_N2 displacement. The carboxylate anion of the protected amino acid is the nucleophile, and the alkyl halide is a substituted (with the polymer backbone) benzyl chloride (review Section 9.1b).

b. Follow Eq. 15.14 with $R_1 = CH_3$. The reaction involves nucleophilic attack at the carbonyl group of the reagent (compare with Eqs. 11.32 and 11.27).

$$(CH_3)_3CO\overset{O}{\overset{\|}{C}}-Cl + H_2\overset{CH_3}{\overset{|}{N}}CHCO_2H \longrightarrow (CH_3)_3CO\overset{O^-}{\underset{Cl}{\overset{|}{C}}}-\overset{+}{N}H_2\overset{CH_3}{\overset{|}{C}}HCO_2H$$

$$(CH_3)_3CO\overset{O}{\overset{\|}{C}}-NH\overset{CH_3}{\overset{|}{C}}HCO_2H \xleftarrow{-HCl} (CH_3)_3CO\overset{O-H}{\underset{Cl}{\overset{|}{C}}}-NH\overset{CH_3}{\overset{|}{C}}HCO_2H$$

15.18. The principal factors in secondary protein structure are the planarity of the amide bond and hydrogen-bonding. Factors leading to tertiary structure are disulfide linkages, electrostatic interactions between functions on positive ($-\overset{+}{N}H_3$) and negative ($-CO_2^-$) groups, hydrogen bonds between functions on the R groups of amino acid side chains, and hydrophobic attractions between nonpolar alkyl side chains. Factors leading to quaternary structures are less well understood, but they include many of the above.

15.19. Although casein and silk fibroin have nearly equal numbers of amino acid residues (199 and 206 respectively), their constitution is very different. Over half the amino acids in silk fibroin have small R groups (Gly and Ala). Consequently, the pleated-sheet structure (Figure 15.9) is possible. But casein has only a small percentage of these amino acids; it does not have the pleated-sheet structure, but it is a globular protein.

15.20. The imidazole group in histidine can function both as an acid (proton donor) and base (proton acceptor), due to resonance stabilization of its cation and anion (review Eq. 13.36). For this reason it is a versatile catalytic group, as illustrated in Eq. 15.17.

16. Nucleotides and Nucleic Acids

OBJECTIVES

1. Know the meaning of: nucleic acid, nucleotide, and nucleoside; ribose and 2-deoxyribose; RNA and DNA; pyrimidine and purine bases; cytosine, thymine, uracil, adenine, and guanine; ribosides (adenosine, guanosine, cytidine, and uridine); deoxyribosides and thymidine; adenosine monophosphate (AMP), adenosine diphosphate (ADP), and adenosine triphosphate (ATP); CoA–SH, NAD, and FAD; T–A and C–G base pairs; double helix; messenger, ribosomal, and transfer RNA; codon and anticodon; transcription and translation.

2. Write a general scheme for the stepwise hydrolysis of a nucleic acid.

3. Given the name, draw the structure of any of the five common bases present in nucleic acids.

4. Draw the structures of the sugar moieties present in RNA and DNA.

5. Given the name, draw the structure of a specific nucleoside.

6. Write an equation for the hydrolysis of a specific nucleoside in acid. Write the steps in the reaction mechanism.

7. Given the name, draw the structure of a specific nucleotide.

8. Write an equation for the hydrolysis of a specific nucleotide by aqueous base.

9. Draw the structures of AMP, ADP, and ATP.

10. Draw the primary structure of a segment of an RNA or DNA chain.

11. Explain, with the aid of equations, why RNA (but not DNA) is readily hydrolyzed by dilute aqueous base.

12. Given the shorthand representation for a dinucleotide, write its full structure.

13. Explain why only pyrimidine–purine base pairing is permissible in the double-helix structure.

14. Explain, with the aid of structures, hydrogen-bonding's role in nucleic acid structure.

15. Explain the different functions of messenger, ribosomal, and transfer RNAs.

ANSWERS TO THE EXERCISES AND PROBLEMS

16.1. a. See the formulas for cytidine and adenosine, Section 16.3.

b. See the formula for adenosine-5'-phosphoric acid, Eq. 16.5.

c. See the formulas for thymidine and deoxyguanosine, Section 16.3.

d. Use Table 16.1, last column, as a guide.

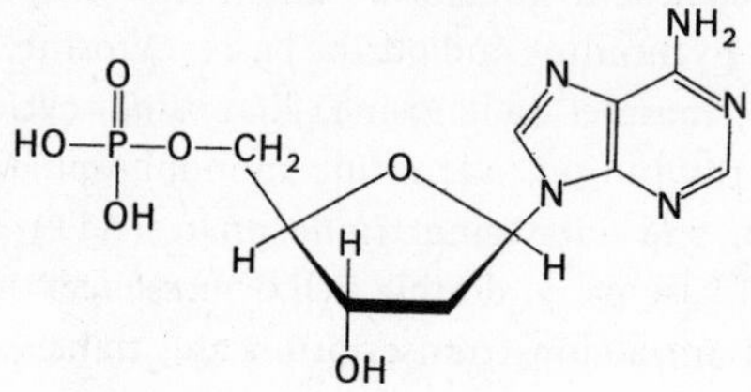

deoxyadenosine-5'-phosphoric acid
(dAMP)

e. See the formulas of cytosine, thymine, and uracil in Section 16.2.

f. See the formulas of adenine and guanine in Section. 16.2.

16.2. a. See Section 16.3.

b.

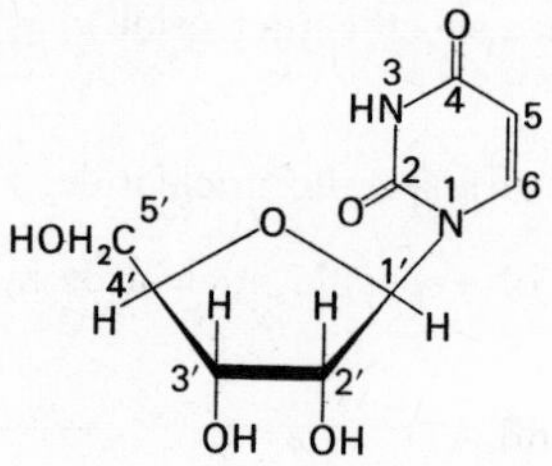

uridine

c.

d.

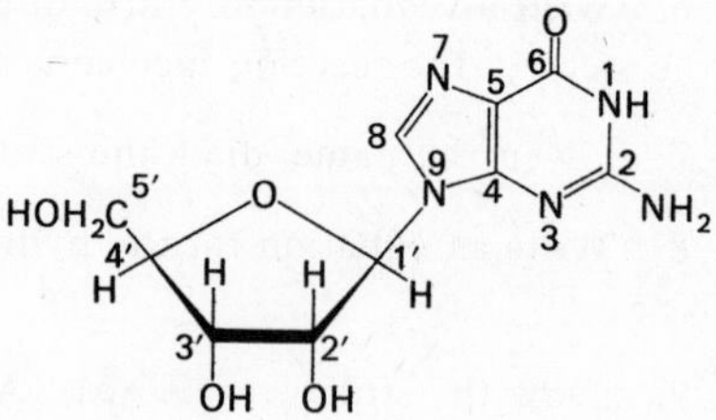

guanosine

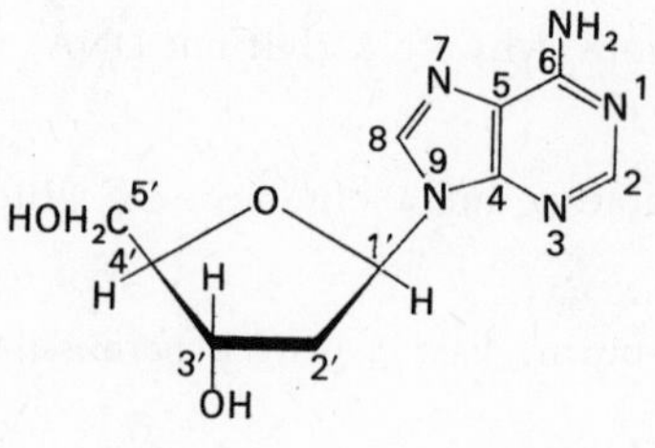

16.3. There is one additional tautomer involving the carbonyl group that is not immediately adjacent to the carbon–carbon double bond. Its structure is

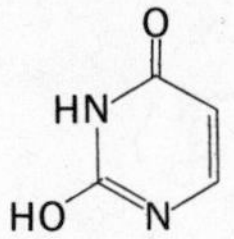

16.4. a.

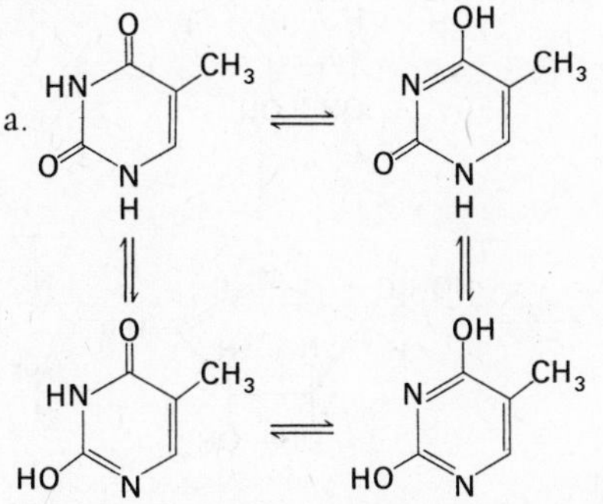

b. There are four possible tautomers in the pyrimidine portion of the molecule, and each of these can be paired with two possible tautomers in the imidazole portion of the molecule, for a total theoretical number of *eight* tautomers.

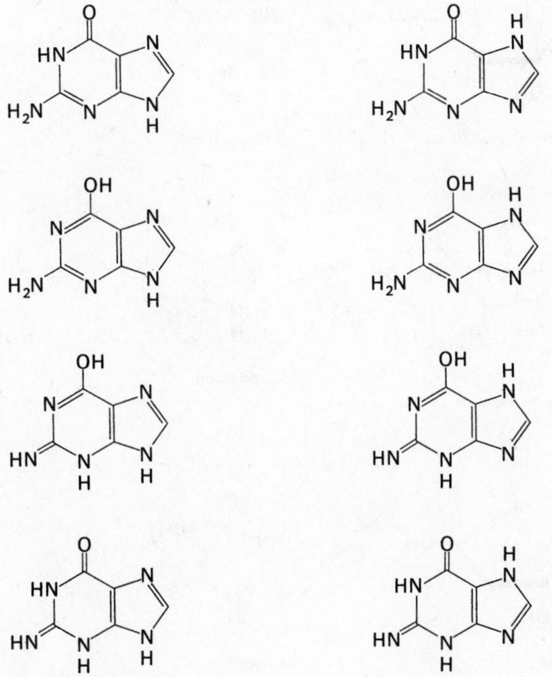

16.5. The mechanism is analogous to the hydrolysis of an acetal (reverse of Eq. 10.14; see also Section 14.5).

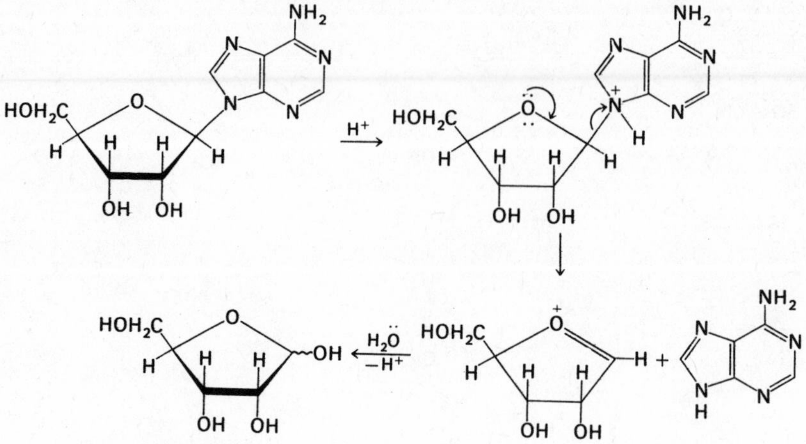

D-ribose (α and β)

adenine

16.6. In each case, hydrolysis of the nucleoside gives the corresponding sugar and base.

a.

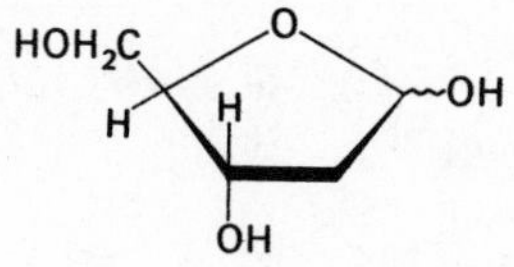

2-deoxyribose (α and β)

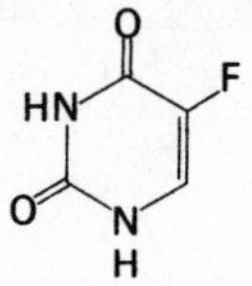

and

5-fluorouracil

b.

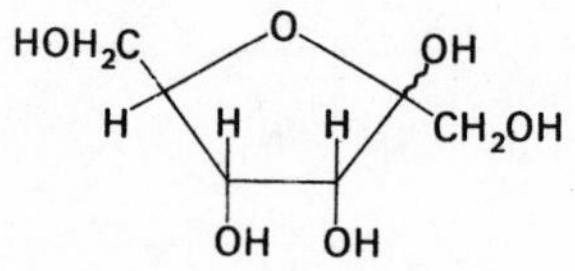

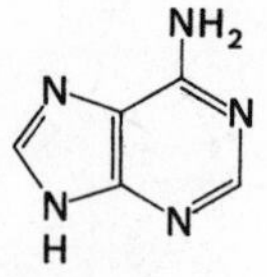

D-psicose
(The keto sugar may equilibrate with pyranose forms.)

and

adenine

c.

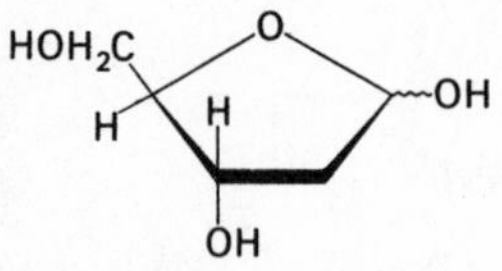

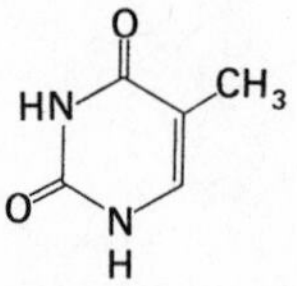

2-deoxyribose

and

thymine

16.7. a.

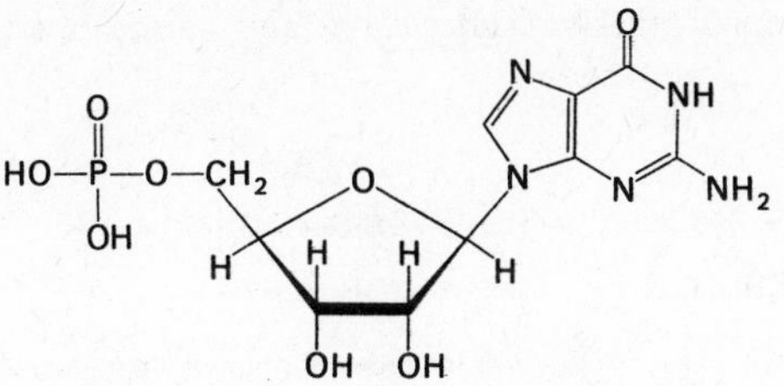

b.

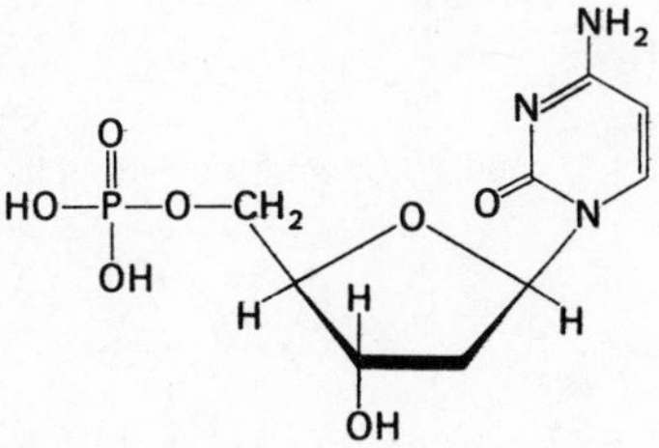

c.

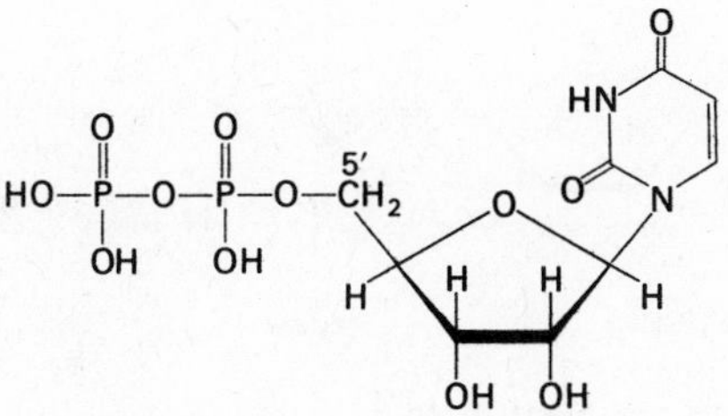

d. The name is deoxyguanosine 5'-triphosphate.

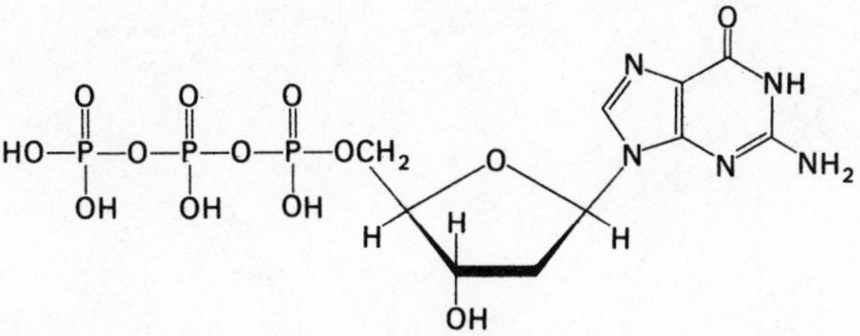

16.8. The reaction involves an S_N2 displacement of phosphate by hydroxide.

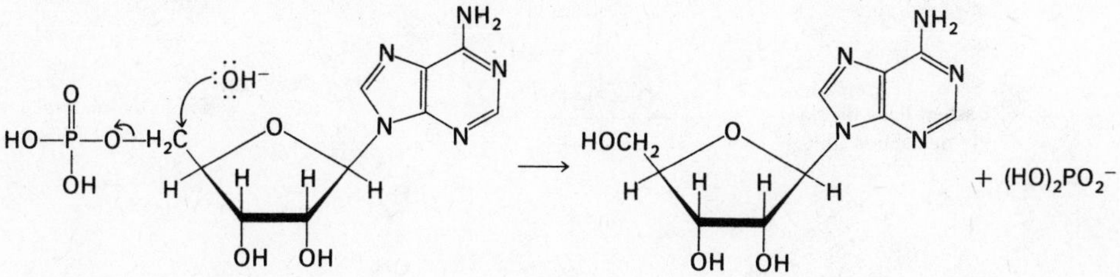

Actually, in strong base the two protons on the phosphoric-acid moiety of AMP may be fully ionized, in which case the inorganic phosphate released is PO_4^{3-}.

16.9. a. Hydrolysis occurs at all glycosidic, ester, and amide linkages. The products are

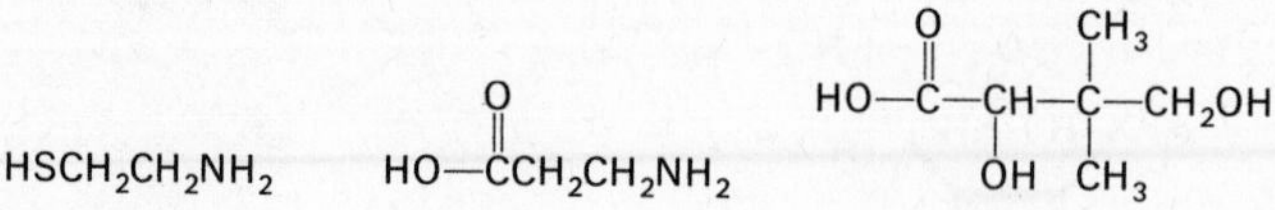

HSCH$_2$CH$_2$NH$_2$

2-aminoethanethiol

O
‖
HO—CCH$_2$CH$_2$NH$_2$

β-alanine

2,4-dihydroxy-3,3-dimethylbutanoic acid

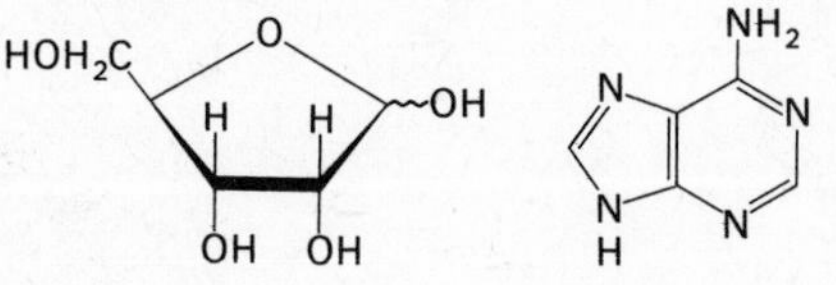

D-ribose   adenine   and phosphoric acid (3 mol)

b. Hydrolysis occurs at all glycosidic, ester, and amide linkages.

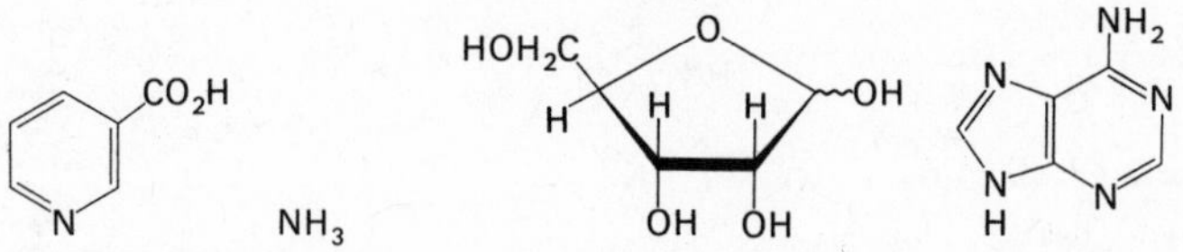

nicotinic acid   ammonia   D-ribose (2 mol)   adenine   and phosphoric acid (2 mol)

16.10. For the general structure, see Section 16.6.

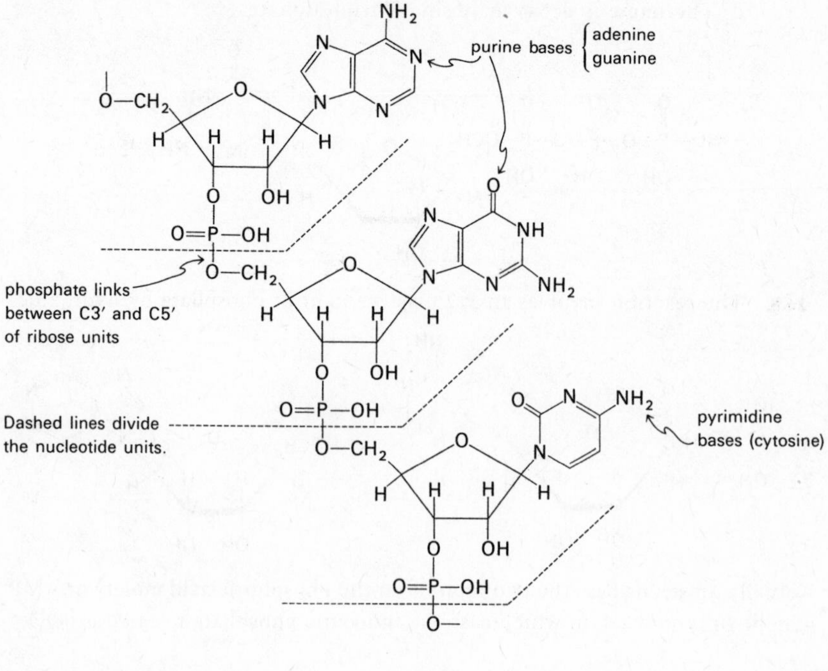

purine bases { adenine, guanine }

phosphate links between C3′ and C5′ of ribose units

Dashed lines divide the nucleotide units.

pyrimidine bases (cytosine)

16.11. For the meaning of these abbreviations, see Section 16.7.

a. pA = adenosine 5′-phosphoric acid (AMP); for its structure, see Eq. 16.5.

b. Ap = adenosine 3′-phosphoric acid.

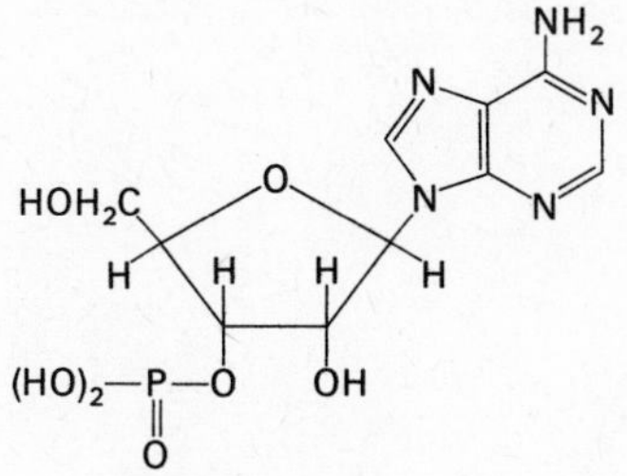

c. pAA ≡ P⌒⌒P⌒OH

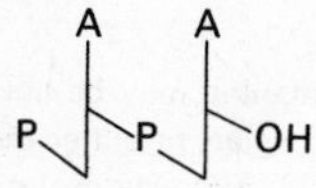

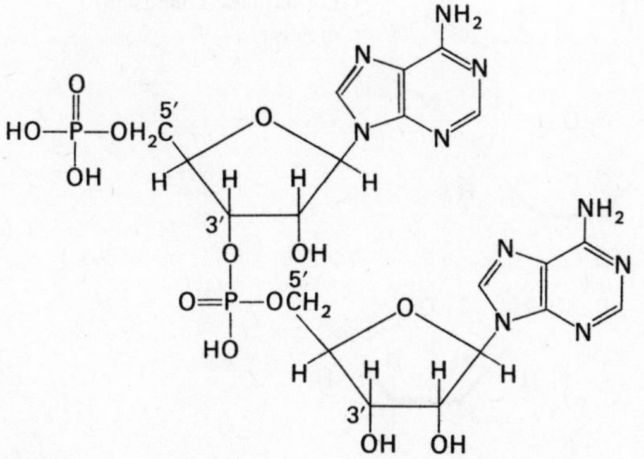

16.12. Possible structures are:

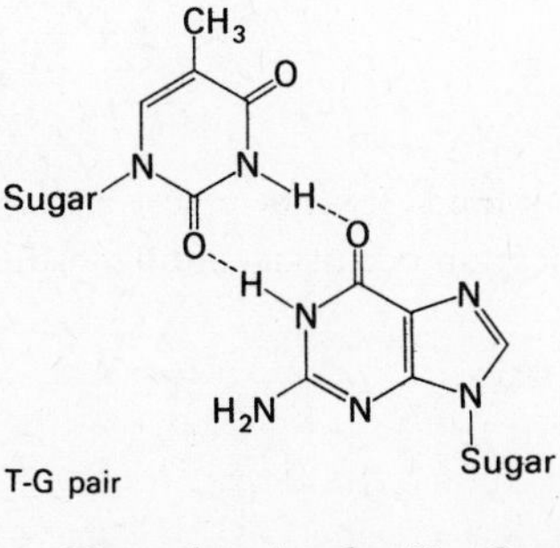

T-G pair

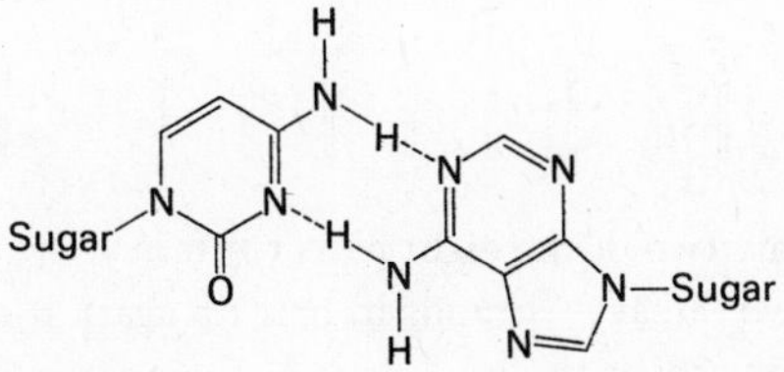

C-A pair

Note that in the T—G pair, one of the possible H–bonding sites that guanine uses in the C—G pair goes unused; similarly in the C—A pair, one of the bonding sites that cytosine uses in the C—G pair goes unused.

16.13. The complementary base pairs are T—A and G—C; in RNA, T is replaced by U. The sequence would be

—U—U—C—G—

16.14. There is a terminal —OH group that can form an ester with the amino acid (in this case, alanine):

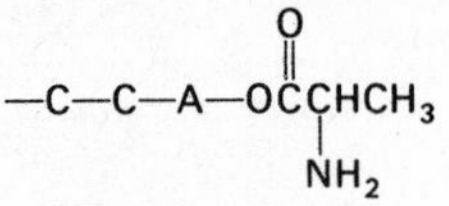

$$-C-C-A-O\overset{\overset{\displaystyle O}{\|}}{C}CHCH_3$$
$$\underset{NH_2}{|}$$

or in more detail

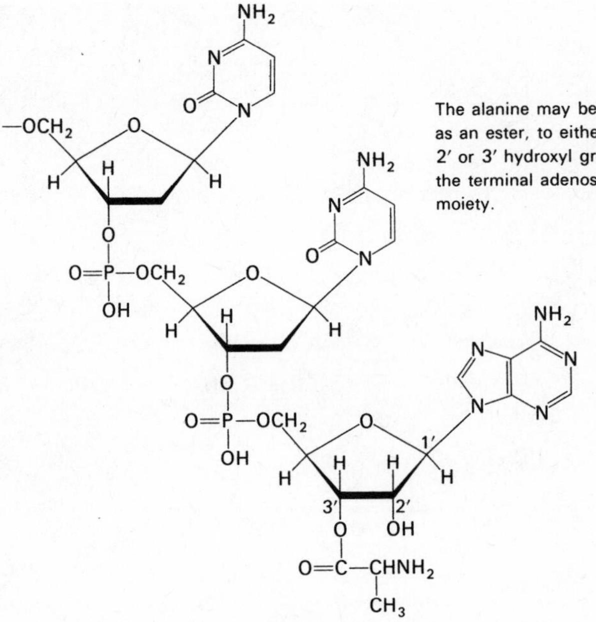

The alanine may be linked, as an ester, to either the 2′ or 3′ hydroxyl group of the terminal adenosine moiety.

16.15.

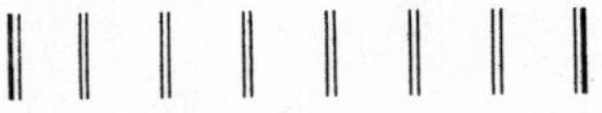

Only two of the eight pairs contain a "heavy" strand. It is never possible for the two "heavy" strands to pair up again if replication occurs according to the Watson–Crick theory.

Appendix
An Introduction to Spectroscopy

OBJECTIVES

1. Know the meaning of: nmr, chemical shift, TMS, δ, and spin-spin splitting; infrared spectrum, group frequency, and fingerprint region; mass spectrum, molecular ion, and fragmentation.

2. Given the nmr spectrum and the structure of a compound, use Table A.1 and the spin-spin splitting pattern to assign the peaks to particular protons.

3. Given the structure of a simple compound, predict the main features of its nmr spectrum.

4. Given the molecular formula and certain nmr and/or infrared data, deduce a plausible structure.

5. Given the structure of a simple compound and its mass spectrum, deduce plausible structures for the fragment ions.

ANSWERS TO THE EXERCISES AND PROBLEMS

A.1. The peaks are assigned as follows:

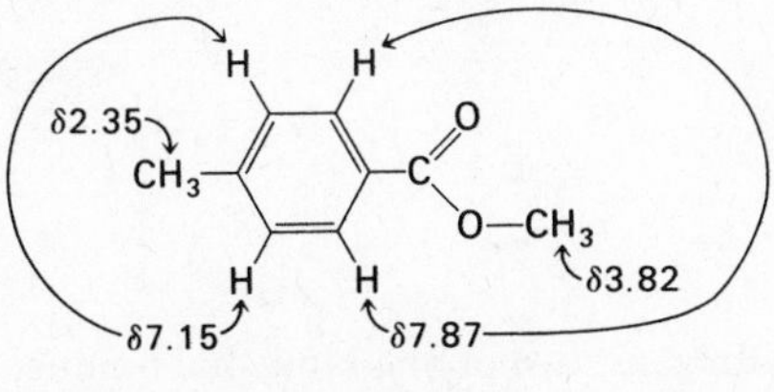

In general, aromatic protons come at lower field if they are adjacent to electron-withdrawing substituents; this is the basis for distinguishing between the two sets of aromatic protons.

A.2. The ir band at 1725 cm^{-1} is due to a carbonyl group, probably a ketone. The quartet-triplet pattern in the nmr spectrum suggests an ethyl group. The compound is 3-pentanone:

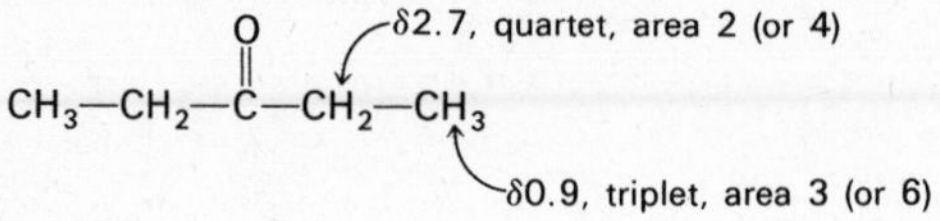

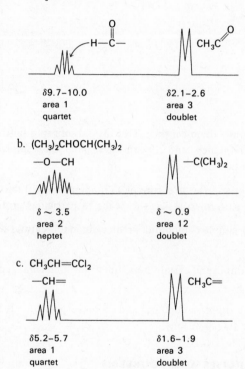

A.3. a. CH$_3$CHO

b. (CH$_3$)$_2$CHOCH(CH$_3$)$_2$

c. CH$_3$CH=CCl$_2$

A.4. The first compound must have nine equivalent hydrogens. The only possible structure is *t*-butyl bromide:

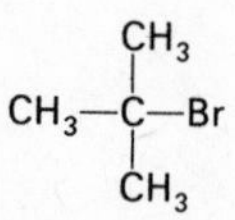

CH$_3$—C—Br with CH$_3$ groups

Its isomer has three different types of hydrogens, two of one kind, one unique, and six equivalent. The compound must be isobutyl bromide. The chemical shifts and spin-spin splitting pattern fit this structure:

$$\delta1.9, \text{complex, area 1}$$

$$(CH_3)_2\overset{|}{C}HCH_2Br$$

$\delta1.0,$ doublet, area 6 $\delta2.7,$ doublet, area 2

A.5. The absence of a band at 3500 cm^{-1} indicates that there are no hydroxyl groups. The absence of a band at 1720 cm^{-1} indicates that the compound is not an aldehyde or ketone. This suggests that the oxygen function is probably an ether. Possible structures are

$$CH_3OCH{=}CH_2 \qquad \underset{\underset{\displaystyle CH_2}{}}{\overset{\displaystyle O}{CH_2 \quad CH_2}} \qquad \overset{\displaystyle O}{CH_2{-}CH{-}CH_3}$$

An nmr spectrum would readily distinguish between these possibilities.

A.6. The mass of sulfur is twice that of oxygen. Consequently, bonds to sulfur vibrate with lower frequency than corresponding bonds to oxygen. The C=S vibrational frequency comes in the range 1050–1200 cm^{-1}.

A.7. These infrared data provide direct evidence for hydrogen bonding in alcohols. In dilute solution the alcohol molecules are isolated, being surrounded by inert solvent molecules. The sharp band at 3580 cm^{-1} is due to the O—H stretching frequency in an isolated ethanol molecule. As the concentration of ethanol is increased, alcohol molecules come in contact with one another and form hydrogen bonds. Hydrogen-bonded O—H is less "tight" than an isolated O—H and has a variable length (as the proton is transferred back and forth between oxygen atoms). Consequently, hydrogen-bonded O—H absorbs at a lower frequency and with a broader range (3250–3350 cm^{-1}) than the isolated O—H group.

A.8. The quartet-triplet pattern suggests that the 10 protons are present as two ethyl groups. This gives a partial structure $(CH_3CH_2)_2CO_3$. The chemical shift of the CH_2 groups ($\delta4.15$) suggests that they are attached to the oxygen atoms. Finally, the infrared band at 1745 cm^{-1} suggests a carbonyl function. The structure is diethyl carbonate:

$$CH_3CH_2O\overset{\overset{\displaystyle O}{\|}}{C}OCH_2CH_3$$

A.9. Cleavage on either side of the carbonyl group produces fragment ions with the indicated masses:

$$CH_3CH_2CH_2 \overset{\overset{\displaystyle O}{\|}}{\underset{43 \quad 85}{C}} CH_2CH_2CH_2CH_3 \qquad\qquad CH_3CH_2CH_2 \overset{\overset{\displaystyle O}{\|}}{\underset{71 \quad 57}{C}} CH_2CH_2CH_2CH_3$$

A.10. The nmr peak at δ7.4 with an area of 5 suggests that the compound may have a phenyl group, C_6H_5—. If so, this accounts for 77 of the 102 mass units. This leaves only 25 mass units, one of which must be a hydrogen (for the nmr peak at δ3.08). The other 24 units must be two carbon atoms, since the compound is a hydrocarbon (no other elements present except C and H). Phenylacetylene fits all the data:

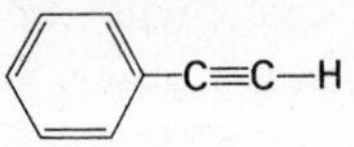

Study Review

In our textbook we describe the properties and reactions of each class of compounds. We purposely do *not* stress methods for synthesizing the various classes of organic compounds, because most students do not become synthetic organic chemists. Each reaction, however, not only describes the chemical behavior of the reactants, but also constitutes a synthetic method for obtaining the reaction products. We present here an outline of the main reactions discussed in the text, organized from the point of view of synthetic methods. Often a subject is best learned by approaching it from several directions, and we hope that this review helps you learn the important reactions. At the end of this section there are a few problems in synthesis to test your mastery of the reactions.

We also summarize the main types of reaction mechanisms.

SYNTHETIC METHODS

Each method is described in the section of the text that is indicated in parentheses. We have selected only the important synthetic methods, and each is illustrated with a general equation.

1. ALKANES AND CYCLOALKANES

   a. alkenes + H_2 (4.6a, 5.3)

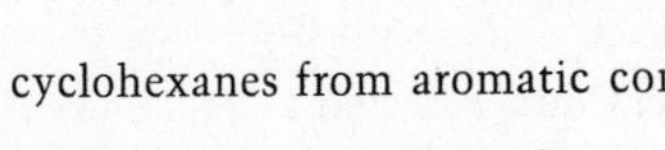

$$\text{C=C} + H_2 \xrightarrow[\text{catalyst}]{\text{Ni or Pt}} -\overset{|}{\underset{H}{C}}-\overset{|}{\underset{H}{C}}-$$

   b. cyclohexanes from aromatic compounds + H_2 (5.3, 5.6)

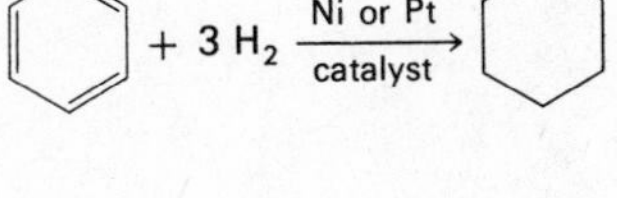

$$\bigcirc + 3\,H_2 \xrightarrow[\text{catalyst}]{\text{Ni or Pt}} \bigcirc$$

c. Grignard reagent + H_2O (or D_2O) (9.6b)

$$RMgX + H\text{—}OH \longrightarrow R\text{—}H + Mg(OH)X$$

d. reduction of thioketals (10.7)

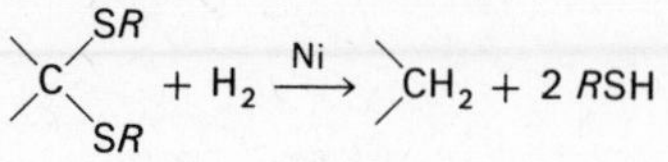

$$\underset{SR}{\overset{SR}{>}}\!C\!< + H_2 \xrightarrow{\ Ni\ } >\!CH_2 + 2\,RSH$$

e. Clemmensen reduction of $>\!C\!=\!O$ (10.10)

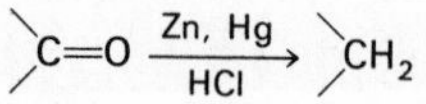

$$>\!C\!=\!O \xrightarrow[HCl]{Zn,\ Hg} >\!CH_2$$

2. ALKENES

a. alkynes + H_2 (4.6a)

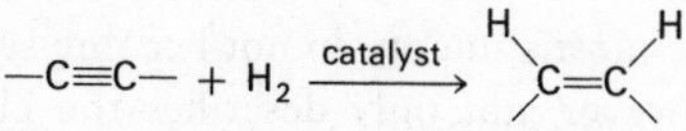

$$-C\!\equiv\!C- + H_2 \xrightarrow{\text{catalyst}} \underset{}{\overset{H\qquad H}{>\!C\!=\!C\!<}}$$

b. double bond isomerization (4.9a)

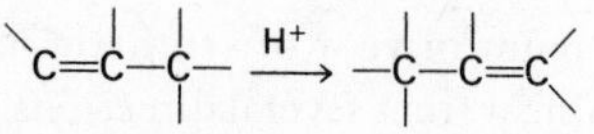

$$>\!C\!=\!C\!-\!C\!- \xrightarrow{H^+} -\!C\!-\!C\!=\!C\!<$$

c. alcohol dehydration (7.5a)

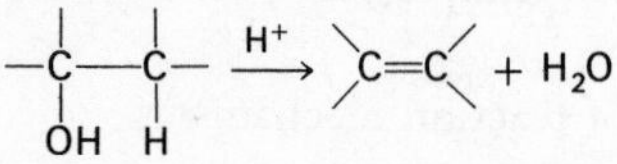

$$-\!\underset{OH}{C}\!-\!\underset{H}{C}\!- \xrightarrow{H^+} >\!C\!=\!C\!< + H_2O$$

d. elimination reaction; alkyl halide + strong base (9.2)

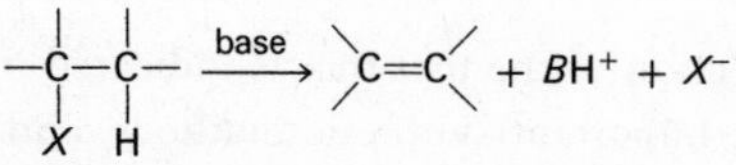

$$-\!\underset{X}{C}\!-\!\underset{H}{C}\!- \xrightarrow{\text{base}} >\!C\!=\!C\!< + BH^+ + X^-$$

3. ALKYNES

a. From acetylides and alkyl halides (4.9d, 9.1a)

$$R\text{—}C\!\equiv\!C\text{—}H \xrightarrow[NH_3]{NaNH_2} R\text{—}C\!\equiv\!C^{\ominus}\,Na^{\oplus} \xrightarrow{R'X} R\text{—}C\!\equiv\!C\text{—}R'$$

4. AROMATIC COMPOUNDS

a. alkylbenzenes by way of Friedel-Crafts reaction (5.5a, 12.4d)

$$R\text{—}X + Ar\text{—}H \xrightarrow{AlCl_3} R\text{—}Ar + HX$$

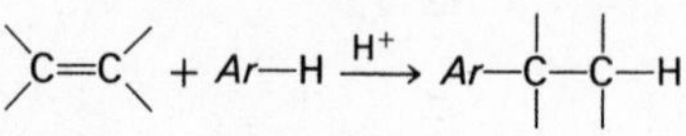

$$>\!C\!=\!C\!< + Ar\text{—}H \xrightarrow{H^+} Ar\text{—}\!C\!-\!C\!-\!H$$

b. aromatic nitro compounds, by nitration (5.5, 5.8b, 7.6c)

$$Ar-H + HONO_2 \xrightarrow{H^+} Ar-NO_2 + H_2O$$

c. aromatic sulfonic acids, by sulfonation (5.5a)

$$Ar-H + HOSO_3H \longrightarrow Ar-OSO_3H + H_2O$$

d. aromatic halogen compounds, by halogenation (5.2, 5.5)

$$Ar-H + X_2 \xrightarrow{FeX_3} Ar-X + HX \ (X = Cl, \ Br)$$

e. aromatic halogen compounds from diazonium salts (13.5a)

$$Ar-N_2^+ + Cu_2X_2 \longrightarrow Ar-X + N_2 \ (X = Cl, \ Br, \ I)$$

5. ALCOHOLS

a. hydration of alkenes (4.6a, 4.6b)

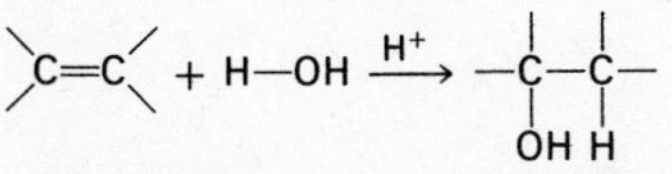

$$\text{C=C} + H-OH \xrightarrow{H^+} -\underset{OH}{\overset{|}{C}}-\underset{H}{\overset{|}{C}}-$$

b. alkyl halides + aqueous base (9.1b)

$$R-X + OH^- \longrightarrow R-OH + X^- \quad \text{(best for } R = \text{primary)}$$

c. Grignard reagent + a carbonyl compound (10.8b)

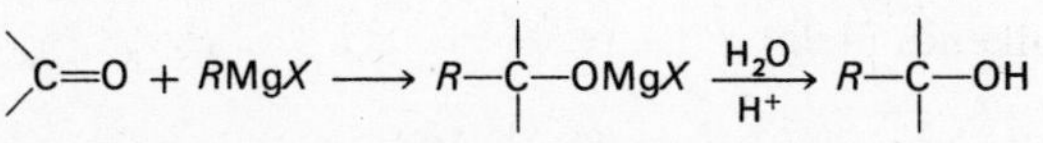

$$\text{C=O} + RMgX \longrightarrow R-\overset{|}{\underset{|}{C}}-OMgX \xrightarrow[H^+]{H_2O} R-\overset{|}{\underset{|}{C}}-OH$$

d. reduction of aldehydes or ketones (10.10)

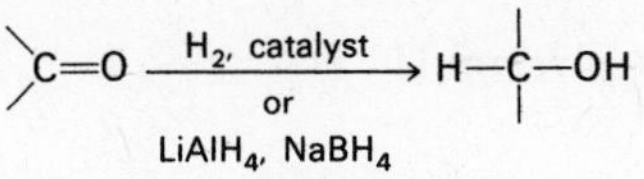

$$\text{C=O} \xrightarrow[\substack{or \\ LiAlH_4, \ NaBH_4}]{H_2, \ catalyst} H-\overset{|}{\underset{|}{C}}-OH$$

e. Grignard reagent + ethylene oxide (9.6b)

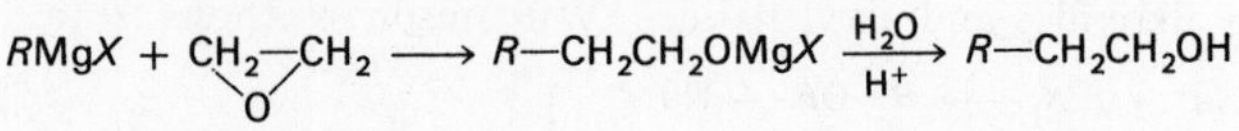

$$RMgX + \underset{O}{CH_2-CH_2} \longrightarrow R-CH_2CH_2OMgX \xrightarrow[H^+]{H_2O} R-CH_2CH_2OH$$

f. saponification of esters (11.7a)

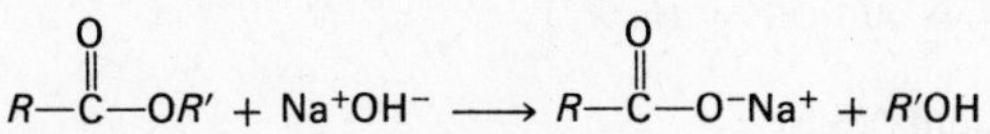

$$R-\overset{O}{\overset{\|}{C}}-OR' + Na^+OH^- \longrightarrow R-\overset{O}{\overset{\|}{C}}-O^-Na^+ + R'OH$$

g. reduction of esters (11.7d, 12.2c)

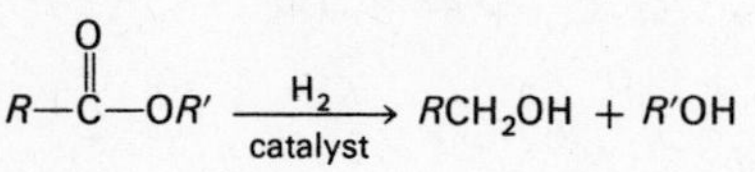

$$R-\overset{O}{\overset{\|}{C}}-OR' \xrightarrow[catalyst]{H_2} RCH_2OH + R'OH$$

h. diazotization of primary amines (13.4c)

$$RNH_2 + HONO \longrightarrow ROH + N_2 + H_2O$$

i. methanol from carbon monoxide and hydrogen (7.8)

$$CO + 2\,H_2 \xrightarrow{\text{catalyst}} CH_3OH$$

j. fermentation (7.8)

6. PHENOLS

a. from diazonium salts and base (13.5a)

$$ArN_2{}^+X^- + Na^+OH^- \xrightarrow[\text{warm}]{H_2O} Ar\!-\!OH + N_2 + Na^+X^-$$

b. from phenoxides and acid (7.4)

$$ArO^-Na^+ + H^+X^- \longrightarrow ArOH + Na^+X$$

c. substituted phenols from phenols (7.6c)

7. GLYCOLS

a. ring opening of epoxides (8.5)

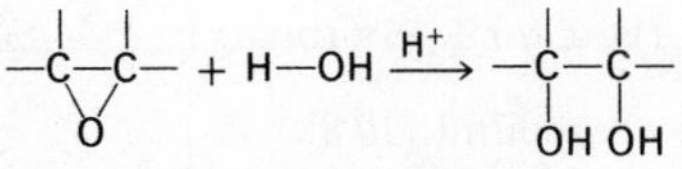

b. oxidation of alkenes (4.9b)

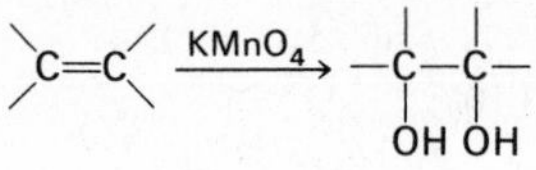

c. hydrolysis of fats and oils to give glycerol (12.1)

8. ETHERS AND EPOXIDES

a. from alkoxides and alkyl halides; Williamson synthesis (9.1a, 14.8)

$$RO^-Na^+ + R'X \longrightarrow R\!-\!OR' - Na^+X^-$$

or

$$ArO^-Na^+ + R'X \longrightarrow Ar\!-\!OR' + Na^+X^-$$

Best for $R' =$ 1° or 2°

b. alkenes and peracids (8.5)

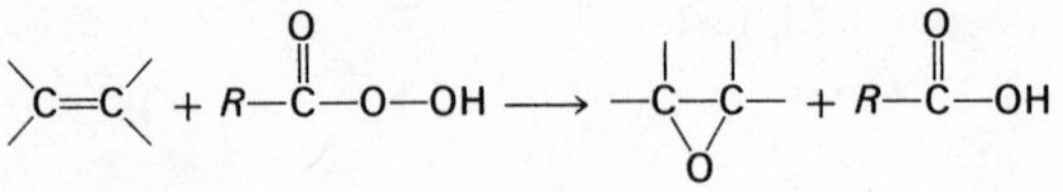

c. ethylene oxide from ethylene and air (8.5)

$$CH_2{=}CH_2 + O_2 \xrightarrow[\text{catalyst}]{\text{Ag}} CH_2{-}CH_2 \underset{O}{\diagdown\diagup}$$

9. ALKYL HALIDES

a. halogenation of alkanes (3.6b, 5.7)

$$-\underset{|}{\overset{|}{C}}-H + X_2 \xrightarrow[\text{light}]{\text{heat or}} -\underset{|}{\overset{|}{C}}-X + H{-}X$$

b. allylic halogenation of alkenes (4.9c)

$$\overset{\diagup}{\underset{\diagdown}{C}}{=}\underset{|}{\overset{|}{C}}{-}\underset{\underset{H}{|}}{\overset{|}{C}}{-} + X_2 \longrightarrow \overset{\diagup}{\underset{\diagdown}{C}}{=}\underset{|}{\overset{|}{C}}{-}\underset{\underset{X}{|}}{\overset{|}{C}}{-} + H{-}X$$

c. alkenes (or dienes) + hydrogen halides (4.6a, 4.6b, 4.7)

$$\overset{\diagdown}{\underset{\diagup}{C}}{=}\overset{\diagup}{\underset{\diagdown}{C}} + H{-}X \longrightarrow -\underset{\underset{H}{|}}{\overset{|}{C}}{-}\underset{\underset{X}{|}}{\overset{|}{C}}{-}$$

d. alcohols + hydrogen halides (7.5b)

$$R{-}OH + H{-}X \longrightarrow R{-}X + H_2O$$

(Catalysts such as ZnX_2 are required when R is primary.)

e. alcohols + thionyl chloride or phosphorus halides (7.5c)

$$R{-}OH + SOCl_2 \longrightarrow R{-}Cl + SO_2 + HCl$$
$$3R{-}OH + PX_3 \longrightarrow 3R{-}X + H_3PO_3$$

f. cleavage of ethers with hydrogen halides (8.3a)

$$R{-}O{-}R' + 2H{-}X \longrightarrow R{-}X + R'{-}X + H_2O$$

g. alkyl iodides from alkyl chlorides (9.1a)

$$R{-}Cl + NaI \xrightarrow{\text{acetone}} R{-}I + NaCl$$

10. POLYHALOGEN COMPOUNDS

a. halogenation of alkanes (3.6b)

b. addition of halogen to alkenes, dienes, polyenes, and alkynes (4.6, 4.6a, 4.7)

c. the haloform reaction (10.11c)

$$R{-}\overset{O}{\overset{\|}{C}}{-}CH_3 + 3X_2 + 4OH^- \longrightarrow R{-}\overset{O}{\overset{\|}{C}}{-}O^- + CHX_3 + 3X^- + 3H_2O$$

11. ALDEHYDES AND KETONES

a. oxidation of alcohols (7.5e, 10.13, 13.7)

$$H{-}\overset{\displaystyle |}{\underset{\displaystyle |}{C}}{-}OH \xrightarrow[H^+]{CrO_3} \;\; \overset{\diagup}{\underset{\diagdown}{C}}{=}O$$

b. hydration of alkynes (4.6a, 10.11a)

$$R{-}C{\equiv}C{-}H + H{-}OH \xrightarrow[H_2SO_4]{HgSO_4} R{-}\overset{\displaystyle O}{\overset{\displaystyle \|}{C}}{-}CH_3$$

c. hydrolysis of dihalides (10.4)

$$X{-}\overset{\displaystyle |}{\underset{\displaystyle |}{C}}{-}X \xrightarrow[NaOH]{H_2O} \;\; \overset{\diagup}{\underset{\diagdown}{C}}{=}O$$

d. ozonolysis of alkenes (4.9b)

$$\overset{\diagdown}{\underset{\diagup}{C}}{=}\overset{\diagup}{\underset{\diagdown}{C}} + O_3 \longrightarrow \overset{\diagdown}{\underset{\diagup}{C}}{=}O + O{=}\overset{\diagup}{\underset{\diagdown}{C}}$$

e. decarboxylation of β-ketoacids (11.11d)

$$-\overset{\displaystyle O}{\overset{\displaystyle \|}{C}}-\overset{\displaystyle |}{\underset{\displaystyle |}{C}}-\overset{\displaystyle O}{\overset{\displaystyle \|}{C}}-OH \xrightarrow{heat} -\overset{\displaystyle O}{\overset{\displaystyle \|}{C}}-\overset{\displaystyle |}{\underset{\displaystyle |}{C}}-H + CO_2$$

f. hydrolysis of acetals and ketals (10.7, 14.3a, 14.5)

$$\overset{\diagup}{\underset{\diagdown}{C}}\overset{\textstyle OR}{\underset{\textstyle OR}{}} + H_2O \xrightarrow{H^+} \overset{\diagup}{\underset{\diagdown}{C}}{=}O + 2\,ROH$$

g. β-hydroxycarbonyl compounds and α,β-unsaturated carbonyl compounds by way of the aldol condensation (10.12)

$$2-\overset{\displaystyle |}{\underset{\displaystyle H}{C}}-\overset{\displaystyle O}{\overset{\displaystyle \|}{C}}- \xrightarrow{OH^-} -\overset{\displaystyle OH}{\underset{\displaystyle |}{C}}-\overset{\displaystyle |}{\underset{\displaystyle H}{C}}-\overset{\displaystyle O}{\overset{\displaystyle \|}{C}}- \xrightarrow[H^+]{heat\ or} \overset{\diagdown}{\underset{\diagup}{C}}{=}\overset{\displaystyle |}{C}-\overset{\displaystyle O}{\overset{\displaystyle \|}{C}}-$$

an aldol

h. α-halocarbonyl compounds, by halogenation (10.11c)

$$-\overset{\displaystyle O}{\overset{\displaystyle \|}{C}}-\overset{\displaystyle |}{\underset{\displaystyle H}{C}}- \xrightarrow[OH^-]{X_2} -\overset{\displaystyle O}{\overset{\displaystyle \|}{C}}-\overset{\displaystyle |}{\underset{\displaystyle X}{C}}-$$

12. CARBOXYLIC ACIDS

a. hydrolysis of nitriles (cyanides) (9.1a, 11.4a)

$$R{-}C{\equiv}N \xrightarrow[\text{H}^+ \text{ or OH}^-]{\text{H}_2\text{O}} R{-}\overset{\displaystyle O}{\underset{\displaystyle OH}{C}} \quad (+ \text{ NH}_3 \text{ or NH}_4{}^+)$$

b. Grignard reagents + carbon dioxide (11.4b)

$$R{-}MgX + O{=}C{=}O \longrightarrow R{-}\overset{O}{\overset{\|}{C}}{-}OMgX \xrightarrow[\text{H}^+]{\text{H}_2\text{O}} R{-}\overset{O}{\overset{\|}{C}}{-}OH$$

c. oxidation of aromatic side chains (5.7, 5.8b)

$$Ar{-}CH_3 \xrightarrow[\text{H}^+]{\text{CrO}_3} Ar{-}\overset{O}{\overset{\|}{C}}{-}OH$$

d. oxidation of aldehydes (10.5, 14.7a)

$$R{-}CH{=}O \xrightarrow{\text{Ag}^+} R\overset{O}{\overset{\|}{C}}{-}OH$$

e. saponification of esters (11.7a)

$$R{-}\overset{O}{\overset{\|}{C}}{-}OR' + NaOH \longrightarrow R'OH + R{-}\overset{O}{\overset{\|}{C}}{-}O^-Na^+ \xrightarrow{\text{H}^+} R{-}\overset{O}{\overset{\|}{C}}{-}OH$$

f. hydrolysis of acid derivatives (11.10a, 13.8)

$$R{-}\overset{O}{\overset{\|}{C}}{-}Cl + H_2O \longrightarrow R{-}\overset{O}{\overset{\|}{C}}{-}OH + HCl$$

$$R{-}\overset{O}{\overset{\|}{C}}{-}NH_2 + H_2O \xrightarrow[\text{OH}^-]{\text{H}^+ \text{ or}} R{-}\overset{O}{\overset{\|}{C}}{-}OH + NH_3$$

g. haloform reaction (10.11c)

$$R{-}\overset{O}{\overset{\|}{C}}{-}CH_3 \xrightarrow[\text{OH}^-]{X_2} CHX_3 + R{-}\overset{O}{\overset{\|}{C}}{-}O^- \xrightarrow{\text{H}^+} R{-}\overset{O}{\overset{\|}{C}}{-}OH$$

h. hydroxyacids from cyanohydrins (10.8a)

$$RCH{=}O \xrightarrow{\text{HCN}} R{-}\overset{OH}{\overset{|}{CH}}{-}CN \xrightarrow[\text{H}^+]{\text{H}_2\text{O}} R{-}\overset{OH}{\overset{|}{CH}}{-}\overset{O}{\overset{\|}{C}}{-}OH$$

i. phenolic acids from phenols and carbon dioxide (11.11c)

13. ESTERS

a. from an alcohol and an acid (7.5d, 11.5, 15.5)

$$R-\overset{\overset{\displaystyle O}{\|}}{C}-OH + R'OH \xrightarrow{H^+} R-\overset{\overset{\displaystyle O}{\|}}{C}-OR' + H_2O$$

b. from an alcohol and an acid derivative (7.6a, 11.10a, 11.10b, 14.8)

$$R-\overset{\overset{\displaystyle O}{\|}}{C}-Cl + R'OH \longrightarrow R-\overset{\overset{\displaystyle O}{\|}}{C}-OR' + HCl$$

$$R-\overset{\overset{\displaystyle O}{\|}}{C}-O-\overset{\overset{\displaystyle O}{\|}}{C}-R + R'OH \longrightarrow R-\overset{\overset{\displaystyle O}{\|}}{C}-OR' + RCO_2H$$

c. transesterification (11.7b)

$$R-\overset{\overset{\displaystyle O}{\|}}{C}-OR' + R''OH \xrightarrow{H^+} R-\overset{\overset{\displaystyle O}{\|}}{C}-OR'' + R'OH$$

(R'OH boils lower than R''OH.)

d. salt + an alkyl halide (15.8)

$$R-\overset{\overset{\displaystyle O}{\|}}{C}-O^-Na^+ + R'X \longrightarrow R-\overset{\overset{\displaystyle O}{\|}}{C}-OR' + Na^+X^-$$

e. lactones from hydroxyacids (11.6)

$$\underset{OH}{\overset{}{C}}-C-C-\overset{\overset{\displaystyle O}{\|}}{C}-OH \xrightarrow{heat} \begin{matrix} C-C \\ | \\ C-C \end{matrix}\overset{\displaystyle O}{\underset{O}{\diagup}} + H_2O$$

f. alkyne + an acid (4.6a)

$$R-C\equiv C-R + HO\overset{\overset{\displaystyle O}{\|}}{C}R' \longrightarrow RCH=\underset{R}{\overset{}{C}}-O\overset{\overset{\displaystyle O}{\|}}{C}R'$$

g. β-ketoesters by way of the Claisen condensation (11.8)

$$2\ RCH_2\overset{\overset{\displaystyle O}{\|}}{C}-OR' \xrightarrow{base} RCH_2\overset{\overset{\displaystyle O}{\|}}{C}-\underset{R}{\overset{}{C}H}-\overset{\overset{\displaystyle O}{\|}}{C}-OR' + R'OH$$

14. OTHER CARBOXYLIC ACID DERIVATIVES

a. salts by neutralization of acids (11.2c)

$$R-\overset{\overset{\displaystyle O}{\|}}{C}-OH + NaOH \longrightarrow R-\overset{\overset{\displaystyle O}{\|}}{C}-O^-Na^+ + H_2O$$

b. acyl halides from acids (11.10a)

$$R-\overset{\overset{\displaystyle O}{\|}}{C}-OH \xrightarrow[\text{PCl}_5]{\text{SOCl}_2 \text{ or}} R-\overset{\overset{\displaystyle O}{\|}}{C}-Cl$$

c. anhydrides from diacids and heat (11.10b)

d. anhydrides from acyl halides and salts (11.10b)

$$R-\overset{\overset{\displaystyle O}{\|}}{C}-O^-Na^+ + R-\overset{\overset{\displaystyle O}{\|}}{C}-Cl \longrightarrow R-\overset{\overset{\displaystyle O}{\|}}{C}-O-\overset{\overset{\displaystyle O}{\|}}{C}-R + Na^+Cl^-$$

e. nitriles from alkyl halides and inorganic cyanides (9.1a)

$$R-X + Na^+CN^- \longrightarrow R-CN + Na^+X^- \ (R = 1° \text{ or } 2°)$$

f. nitriles from diazonium ions (13.5a)

$$Ar-N_2^+X^- + Cu_2(CN)_2 \longrightarrow Ar-CN + N_2 + Cu_2X_2$$

15. AMIDES

a. acyl halides + ammonia (or 1° or 2° amines) (11.10a, 13.4b, 15.8)

$$R-\overset{\overset{\displaystyle O}{\|}}{C}-Cl + H-N\overset{R'}{\underset{R''}{\big\langle}} \longrightarrow R-\overset{\overset{\displaystyle O}{\|}}{C}-N\overset{R'}{\underset{R''}{\big\langle}} + HCl$$

(R' and R'' = H, alkyl, or aryl)

b. esters and ammonia (or 1° or 2° amines) (11.7c)

$$R-\overset{\overset{\displaystyle O}{\|}}{C}-OR' + H-N\overset{R''}{\underset{R'''}{\big\langle}} \longrightarrow R-\overset{\overset{\displaystyle O}{\|}}{C}-N\overset{R''}{\underset{R'''}{\big\langle}} + R'OH$$

c. controlled hydrolysis of nitriles (11.4a)

$$R-C\equiv N + H_2O \xrightarrow{H^+} R-\overset{\overset{\displaystyle O}{\|}}{C}-NH_2$$

d. from acids and amines (11.2c, 15.5)

$$R-\overset{\overset{\displaystyle O}{\|}}{C}-OH + HNR_2' \xrightarrow{\text{heat}} R-\overset{\overset{\displaystyle O}{\|}}{C}-NR_2' + H_2O \quad (R' = H, \text{ alkyl})$$

16. AMINES AND RELATED COMPOUNDS

a. alkylation of ammonia or amines (9.1a, 13.4a)

$$2 \; \diagdown\!\!N\!\!-\!\!H + R\!\!-\!\!X \longrightarrow \diagdown\!\!N\!\!-\!\!R + \overset{\oplus}{\diagdown\!\!N\!\!\diagup}\!\!\overset{H}{\underset{H}{}} \; X^{\ominus}$$

b. reduction of nitriles (9.1a)

$$R\!\!-\!\!C\!\!\equiv\!\!N + 2\,H_2 \xrightarrow{\text{catalyst}} RCH_2NH_2$$

c. reduction of nitro compounds (13.5)

$$Ar\!\!-\!\!NO_2 \xrightarrow[\text{HCl}]{\text{Fe}} Ar\!\!-\!\!NH_2 \, (+2\,H_2O)$$

d. hydrolysis of amides (13.8)

$$R\!\!-\!\!\overset{\overset{\displaystyle O}{\|}}{C}\!\!-\!\!N\overset{R'}{\underset{R''}{\diagup}} + H_2O \xrightarrow{OH^-} R\!\!-\!\!\overset{\overset{\displaystyle O}{\|}}{C}\!\!-\!\!O^- + R'\!\!-\!\!\overset{\overset{\displaystyle H}{|}}{N}\!\!-\!\!R''$$

(R′ and R″ = alkyl or aryl)

e. from certain aryl halides and ammonia (or 1° or 2° amines) (9.3, 15.7a)

$$O_2N\!\!-\!\!\underset{}{\bigcirc}\overset{NO_2}{}\!\!-\!\!X \xrightarrow{RNH_2} O_2N\!\!-\!\!\underset{}{\bigcirc}\overset{NO_2}{}\!\!-\!\!NHR$$

17. MISCELLANEOUS NITROGEN COMPOUNDS

a. oximes, hydrazones, osazones, and imines from carbonyl compounds and ammonia derivatives (10.9, 14.7b, 15.3)

$$\diagdown\!\!C\!\!=\!\!O + H_2N\!\!- \longrightarrow \diagdown\!\!C\!\!=\!\!N\diagup + H_2O$$

b. cyanohydrins from carbonyl compounds and cyanide (10.8a)

$$\diagdown\!\!C\!\!=\!\!O + HCN \longrightarrow \diagdown\!\!C\overset{OH}{\underset{CN}{\diagup}}$$

c. diazonium compounds from primary aromatic amines and nitrous acid (13.5)

$$Ar\!\!-\!\!NH_2 + HONO + HX \longrightarrow ArN_2^+X^- + 2\,H_2O$$

d. azo compounds, by coupling reactions (13.5b)

$$ArN_2^+X^- + \bigcirc\!\!-\!\!OH \text{ (or } NR_2) \longrightarrow Ar\!\!-\!\!N\!\!=\!\!N\!\!-\!\!\bigcirc\!\!-\!\!OH \text{ (or } NR_2)$$

e. quaternary ammonium salts (13.4a, 13.7)

$$\underset{\underset{R''}{|}}{R-\overset{..}{N}-R'} + R'''-X \longrightarrow \underset{\underset{R''}{|}}{R-\overset{\overset{R'''}{|}}{N}^{\oplus}-R'} \quad X^{\ominus}$$

18. ORGANIC SULFUR COMPOUNDS

a. thiols from alkyl halides and sodium hydrosulfide (9.1a)

$$R-X + Na^+SH^- \longrightarrow R-SH + Na^+X^- \quad \text{(best when } R \text{ is } 1°)$$

b. thiols from alkenes and H_2S (4.8)

$$\underset{}{>}C=C\underset{}{<} + H_2S \longrightarrow \underset{\underset{H}{|}\ \underset{SH}{|}}{-\overset{|}{C}-\overset{|}{C}-}$$

c. thioethers from alkyl halides and sodium mercaptides (9.1a)

$$R-X + Na^{+-}SR' \longrightarrow R-S-R' + Na^+X^- \quad \text{(best when } R \text{ is } 1°)$$

d. disulfides from thiols (7.10)

$$2R-SH \xrightarrow{\text{oxid}} R-S-S-R$$

e. sulfoxides and sulfones, by oxidation of sulfides (8.7)

$$R-S-R' \xrightarrow{H_2O_2} R-\overset{\overset{O}{\|}}{S}-R' \xrightarrow{H_2O_2} R-\overset{\overset{O}{\|}}{\underset{\underset{O}{\|}}{S}}-R'$$

f. thioesters (11.10d, 12.5a)

g. alkyl hydrogen sulfates from alcohols (7.5d, 12.4d) or from alkenes (4.6a, 4.6b)

$$R-OH + HOSO_3H \xrightarrow{\text{cold}} ROSO_3H + H_2O$$

$$\underset{}{>}C=C\underset{}{<} + HOSO_3H \xrightarrow{\text{cold}} \underset{\underset{H}{|}\ \underset{OSO_3H}{|}}{-\overset{|}{C}-\overset{|}{C}-}$$

h. sulfonamides from sulfonyl halides and amines (13.4b)

$$ArSO_2Cl + H-N\underset{\underset{R'}{}}{\overset{\overset{R}{}}{}} \longrightarrow ArSO_2N\underset{\underset{R'}{}}{\overset{\overset{R}{}}{}}$$

19. MISCELLANEOUS CLASSES OF COMPOUNDS

a. Grignard reagents (9.6a)

$$R-X + Mg \xrightarrow{\text{ether}} RMgX$$

b. alkoxides and phenoxides (1.6b, 2.1, 7.4)

$$2ROH + 2\,Na \longrightarrow 2RO^-Na^+ + H_2$$
$$ArOH + Na^+OH^- \longrightarrow ArO^-Na^+ + H_2O$$

c. hemiacetals and acetals (10.7, 14.3a, 14.5)

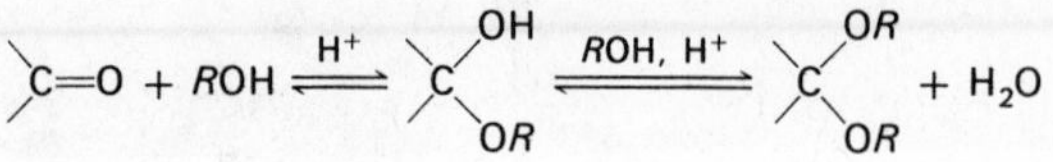

d. quinones (7.7)

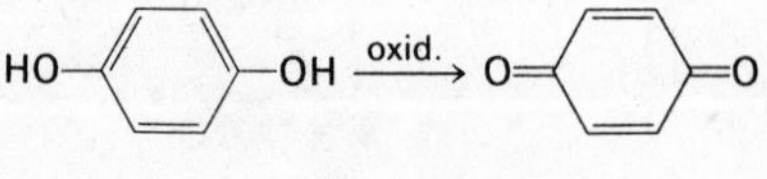

e. organic nitrates and phosphates (7.5d, 9.1c)

$$ROH + HONO_2 \longrightarrow RONO_2 + H_2O$$

$$ROH + ATP \xrightarrow{\text{enzyme}} RO\,\textcircled{P} + ADP$$

REACTION MECHANISMS

1. SUBSTITUTION

a. free-radical chain reaction (3.6b, 4.9c)

$$X_2 \longrightarrow 2X\cdot \quad \text{initiation}$$

$$\left.\begin{array}{l} X\cdot + R{-}H \longrightarrow X{-}H + R\cdot \\ R\cdot + X_2 \longrightarrow R{-}X + X\cdot \end{array}\right\} \text{propagation}$$

$$\left.\begin{array}{l} R\cdot + X\cdot \longrightarrow R{-}X \\ 2R\cdot \longrightarrow R{-}R \\ 2X\cdot \longrightarrow X_2 \end{array}\right\} \text{termination}$$

b. electrophilic aromatic (5.5b, 5.5c)

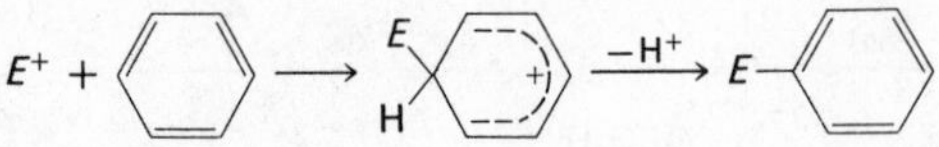

c. nucleophilic aromatic substitution (9.3)

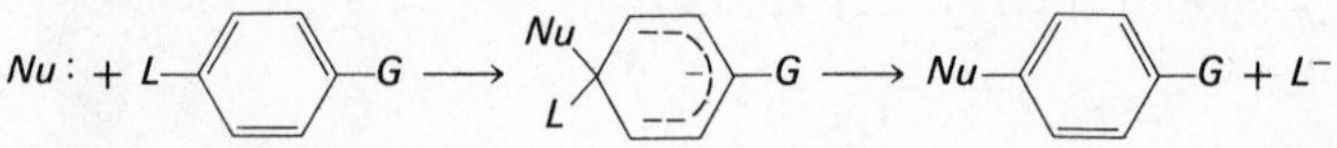

(G is an electron-withdrawing group that can stabilize carbanions, and L is a leaving group such as halide ion.)

d. nucleophilic aliphatic substitution (7.5b, 8.3b, 8.5b, 9.1b, 9.6b, 13.4a)

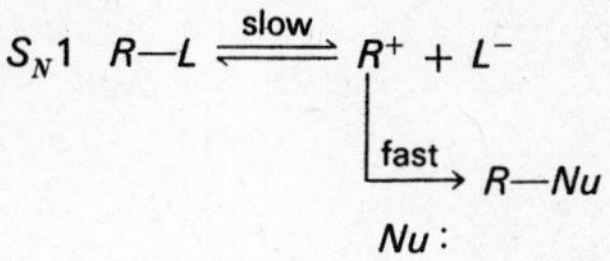

$$S_N1 \quad R{-}L \xrightleftharpoons[\text{slow}]{} R^+ + L^-$$

$$\xrightarrow[\text{fast}]{} R{-}Nu$$

$$Nu:$$

R^+ is a carbocation; best when R is tertiary, allylic, or benzylic.

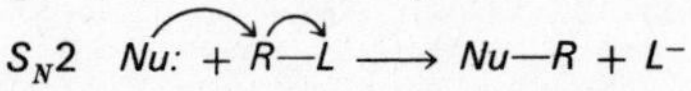

$$S_N2 \quad Nu: + \overset{\frown}{R{-}L} \longrightarrow Nu{-}R + L^-$$

A one-step, direct displacement that is best when R is primary or secondary.

2. ADDITION

    a. electrophilic addition to C=C and C≡C (4.6c, 4.7)

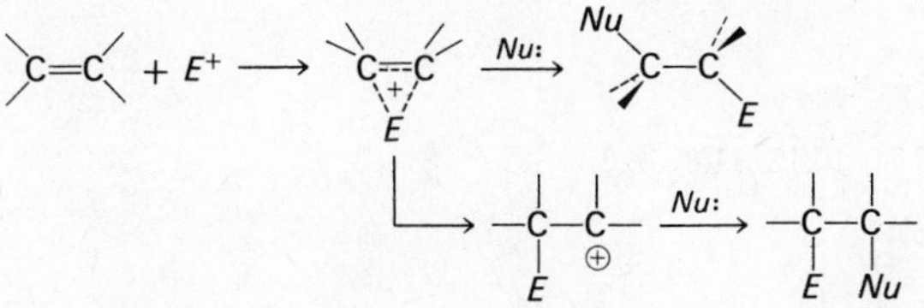

    b. free-radical addition to C=C (4.8)

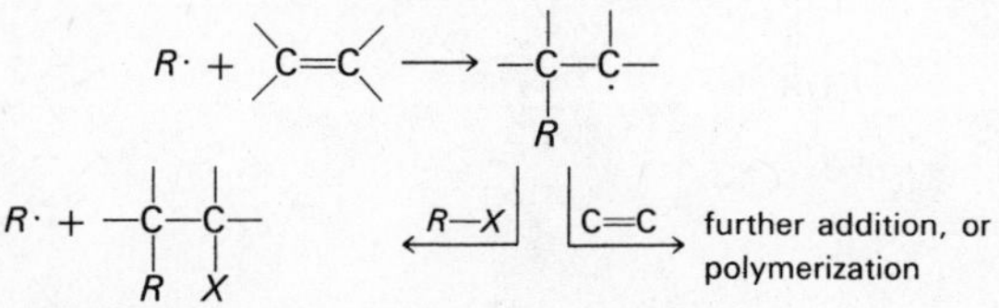

       a radical abstraction to continue
       the chain reaction by producing
       another $R\cdot$

    c. nucleophilic addition

       to C=O (10.6, 10.7, 10.8, 10.9, 10.10, 10.12, 11.4b, 11.5, 11.7, 11.10, 13.4b, 14.3a)

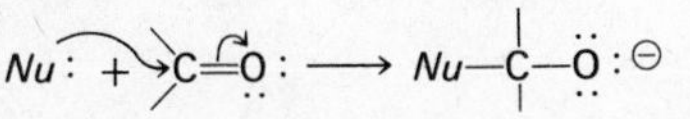

       to C≡N (11.4a)

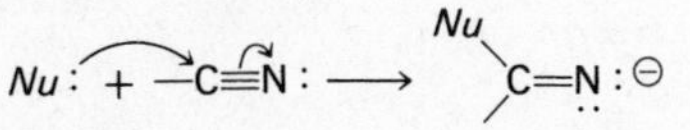

       to N=O (13.4c)

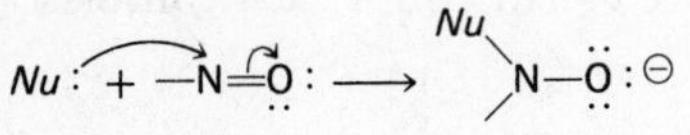

3. ELIMINATION (7.5a, 9.2)

$$E1 \quad \underset{}{>}CH-\underset{|}{\overset{|}{C}}-L \rightleftharpoons \underset{}{>}CH-\underset{|}{\overset{|}{C}}\oplus + L\ominus$$

$$\xrightarrow[\text{fast}]{-H^+} \quad >C=C<$$

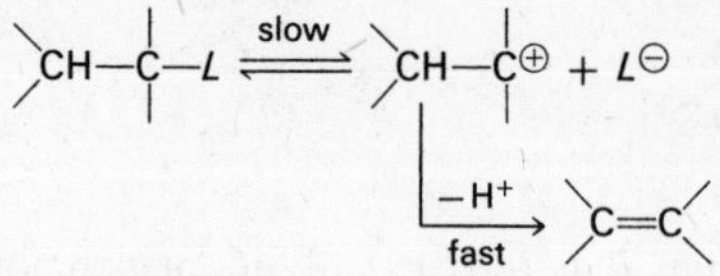

Competes with S_N1

$$E2 \quad B: \quad \overset{H}{\underset{L}{>C-C<}} \longrightarrow BH^+ + >C=C< + L^-$$

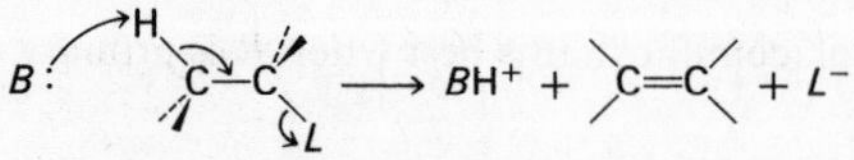

A one-step process; competes with S_N2

4. FREE-RADICAL COUPLING REACTIONS (7.6b, 7.10)

$$2R\cdot \longrightarrow R-R$$

5. ENOLIZATION (10.11, 10.12, 11.8, 16.2)

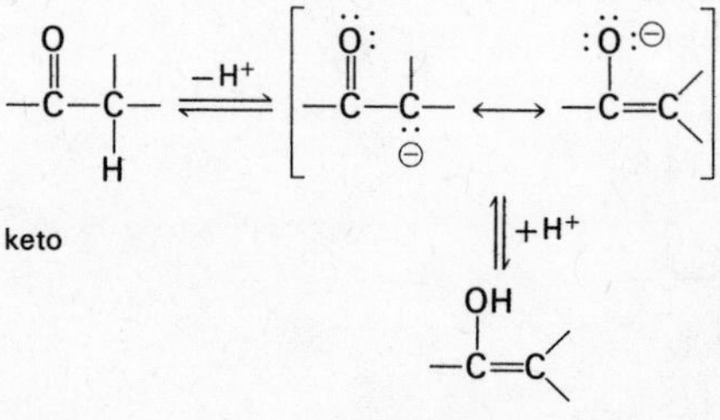

$$-\overset{O}{\overset{||}{C}}-\underset{H}{\overset{|}{C}}- \rightleftharpoons \left[-\overset{\overset{\cdot\cdot}{O}:}{\overset{||}{C}}-\overset{\ominus}{\underset{\cdot\cdot}{C}}- \longleftrightarrow -\overset{:\overset{\cdot\cdot}{O}:\ominus}{C}=C< \right]$$

keto

$$\Big\Updownarrow +H^+$$

$$-\overset{OH}{\overset{|}{C}}=C<$$

enol

For definitions of nucleophile, electrophile, carbanion, free radical, and carbocation see Section 3.6a and 9.1.

REVIEW PROBLEMS ON SYNTHESIS

SR.1. Show how each of the following can be prepared from propene:

    a. propane

    b. 2-bromopropane

    c. 1,2-dichloropropane

    d. 2-propanol

    e. 2-propyl hydrogen sulfate

SR.2. Each of the following conversions requires the combination, in the proper sequence, of two reactions. Write equations for each conversion.

a. n-propyl bromide to propene to 1,2-dibromopropane

b. isopropyl alcohol to propene to 2-iodopropane

c. 1-bromobutane to 2-chlorobutane

d. 2-butanol to butane

e. bromocyclopentane to 1,2-dibromocyclopentane

SR.3. Starting with acetylene, write equations for the preparation of:

a. ethane   e. 2,2-dibromobutane

b. ethyl iodide   f. 3-hexyne

c. 1-butyne   g. 1,1,2,2-tetrabromoethane

d. 1,1-diiodoethane   h. 3-hexene

SR.4. Write equations for each of the following conversions:

a. 2-butene to 1,3-butadiene (two steps)

b. 2-propanol to propyne (three steps)

c. 1-bromopropane to 2,2-dichloropropane

d. 1,3-butadiene to 1,4-dibromobutane

SR.5. Using benzene or toluene as the only organic starting materials, devise a synthesis for each of the following:

a. m-chlorobenzenesulfonic acid   d. —CH$_2$D

b. 2,4,6-tribromotoluene

c. benzyl alcohol   e. 2,4,6-trinitrophenol (picric acid)

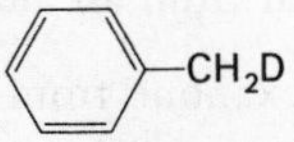

SR.6. Write equations for the preparation of

a. 1-phenylethanol from styrene

b. 1-butanol from 1-bromobutane

c. allyl alcohol from propene

d. sodium 2-butoxide from 1-butene

e. 1-butanethiol from 1-butanol

f. 2,4,6-tribromobenzoic acid from toluene

g. ethyl cyclohexyl ether from ethanol and phenol

h. n-butyl ether from 1-butanol

SR.7. Write equations that show how 2-propanol can be converted to each of the following:

a. isopropyl chloride

b. allyl chloride

c. 1,2-dibromopropane

d. 2-methoxypropane

e. isopropylbenzene

SR.8. 2-Bromobutane can be obtained in one step from each of the following precursors: butane, 2-butanol, 1-butene, and 2-butene. Write an equation for each method. Describe the advantages or disadvantages of each.

SR.9. Starting with an unsaturated hydrocarbon, show how each of the following can be prepared:

a. 1,2-dibromobutane

b. 1,1-dichloroethane

c. 1,2,3,4-tetrabromobutane

d. cyclohexyl iodide

e. 1,4-dibromo-2-butene

f. 1,1,2,2-tetrachloropropane

g. 1-bromo-1-phenylethane

h. 1,2,5,6-tetrabromocyclooctane

SR.10. Give equations for the preparation of the following carbonyl compounds:

a. 2-pentanone from an alcohol

b. pentanal from an alcohol

c. cyclohexanone from phenol (two steps)

d. acetone from propyne

e. *p*-chlorobenzaldehyde from toluene

SR.11. Complete each of the following equations, giving the structures and names of the main organic products:

a. benzoic acid + ethylene glycol + H$^+$

b. C$_6$H$_5$CH$_2$MgBr + CO$_2$, followed by H$_3$O$^+$

c. *p*-nitrobenzoyl chloride + sodium acetate

d. *p*-hydroxybenzoic acid + acetic anhydride

e. *n*-propylbenzene + K$_2$Cr$_2$O$_7$ + H$^+$

f. phthalic anhydride + methanol + H$^+$

g. pentanedioic acid + thionyl chloride

h. cyclopropanecarboxylic acid + NH$_4$OH, then heat

i. methyl 3-butenoate + LiAlH$_4$

SR.12. Show how each of the following conversions can be accomplished:

a. n-butyryl chloride to methyl n-butyrate

b. propionic anhydride to propionamide

c. butanoic acid to 1-butanol

d. 1-pentanol to pentanoic acid

e. propionyl bromide to propionamide

f. acetyl chloride to acetic anhydride

g. acetic anhydride to acetyl hydrazide

h. oxalic acid to diethyl oxalate

i. urea to ammonia and CO_2

j. benzoyl chloride to N-methylbenzamide

SR.13. Show how each of the following compounds can be prepared from the appropriate acid:

a. propionyl bromide

b. ethyl pentanoate

c. n-butyramide

d. phthalic anhydride

e. calcium oxalate

f. phenylacetamide

g. pentanoic anhydride

h. isopropyl benzoate

i. m-nitrobenzoyl chloride

j. formamide

SR.14. Write equations to describe how each of the following conversions might be accomplished:

a. n-butyl chloride to n-butyltrimethylammonium chloride

b. o-toluidine to o-toluic acid

c. o-toluidine to o-bromobenzoic acid

d. 1-butene to 2-methyl-1-aminobutane

SR.15. Starting with benzene, toluene, or any alcohol with four carbon atoms or fewer, and any essential inorganic reagents, outline steps of the synthesis of

a. n-butylamine

b. p-toluidine

c. 1-aminopentane

d. N-ethylaniline

e. m-aminobenzoic acid

f. tri-n-butylamine

g. 1,4-diaminobutane

SOLUTIONS TO THE STUDY REVIEW PROBLEMS

The best technique to follow in solving a multistep synthetic problem is to work backward from the final synthetic goal. Keep in mind the structure of the available starting material, however, so that eventually you can link the starting material with the product. The other constraint on synthesis problems is that you *must* use combinations of known reactions to achieve your ultimate goal. Although research chemists do try to discover and develop new reactions, you cannot afford that luxury until you have already mastered known reactions.

SR.1. a. $CH_2\!\!=\!\!CHCH_3 + H_2 \xrightarrow[\text{catalyst}]{\text{Pt}} CH_3CH_2CH_3$ (Eq. 4.14)

b. $CH_2\!\!=\!\!CHCH_3 + HBr \xrightarrow[\text{peroxides}]{\text{no}} CH_3CHCH_3$ (Eq. 4.24)
$\qquad\qquad\qquad\qquad\qquad\qquad\quad |$
$\qquad\qquad\qquad\qquad\qquad\qquad\;\; Br$

c. $CH_2\!\!=\!\!CHCH_3 + Cl_2 \longrightarrow CH_2\!\!-\!\!CHCH_3$ (Eq. 4.12)
$\qquad\qquad\qquad\qquad\qquad\qquad\;\; | \quad\;\; |$
$\qquad\qquad\qquad\qquad\qquad\qquad\; Cl \quad Cl$

d. $CH_2\!\!=\!\!CHCH_3 + H\!\!-\!\!OH \xrightarrow{H^+} CH_3CHCH_3$ (Eq. 4.9)
$\qquad\qquad\qquad\qquad\qquad\qquad\qquad\qquad |$
$\qquad\qquad\qquad\qquad\qquad\qquad\qquad\; OH$

e. $CH_2\!\!=\!\!CHCH_3 + H\!\!-\!\!OSO_3H \longrightarrow CH_3\!\!-\!\!CH\!\!-\!\!CH_3$ (Eq. 4.19)
$\qquad\qquad\qquad\qquad\qquad\qquad\qquad\qquad\qquad\;\; |$
$\qquad\qquad\qquad\qquad\qquad\qquad\qquad\qquad\; OSO_3H$

SR.2. a. $CH_3CH_2CH_2Br \xrightarrow[\text{KOH}]{\text{alc.}} CH_3CH\!\!=\!\!CH_2 \xrightarrow[\text{Eq. 4.3}]{Br_2} CH_2\!\!-\!\!CHCH_3$
$\qquad\qquad\qquad\qquad\quad \text{Eq. 9.32} \qquad\qquad\qquad\qquad\qquad\quad | \quad\; |$
$\qquad\qquad\qquad\qquad\qquad\qquad\qquad\qquad\qquad\qquad\quad Br \;\; Br$

b. $CH_3CHCH_3 \xrightarrow[\text{Eq. 7.8}]{H_2SO_4,\ heat} CH_2\!\!=\!\!CHCH_3 \xrightarrow[\text{Eq. 4.21}]{HI} CH_3CHCH_3$
$\qquad\; |$
$\qquad OH$

c. $CH_3CH_2CH_2CH_2Br \xrightarrow[\text{KOH}]{\text{alc.}} CH_3CH_2CH\!\!=\!\!CH_2 \xrightarrow[\text{Eq. 4.21}]{HCl} CH_3CH_2CHCH_3$
$\qquad\qquad\qquad\qquad\quad\; \text{Eq. 9.32} \qquad\qquad\qquad\qquad\qquad\qquad\qquad\quad |$
$\qquad\qquad\qquad\qquad\qquad\qquad\qquad\qquad\qquad\qquad\qquad\qquad\; Cl$

d. $CH_3CH_2CHCH_3 \xrightarrow[\text{Eq. 7.8}]{H^+} \begin{matrix} CH_3CH\!\!=\!\!CHCH_3 \\ + \\ CH_3CH_2CH\!\!=\!\!CH_2 \end{matrix} \Bigg] \xrightarrow[\text{Eq. 4.14}]{H_2 \atop \text{Pt}} CH_3CH_2CH_2CH_3$
$\qquad\qquad |$
$\qquad\quad OH$

e. $\xrightarrow[\text{KOH}]{\text{alc.}} $ $\xrightarrow[\text{Eq. 4.3}]{Br_2}$
$\qquad\qquad\quad \text{Eq. 9.32}$

SR.3. a. $HC\!\!\equiv\!\!CH + 2H_2 \xrightarrow{\text{Pt}} CH_3\!\!-\!\!CH_3$ (analogous to **Eq. 4.14**)

b. $HC\!\!\equiv\!\!CH + H_2 \xrightarrow[\text{Eq. 4.17}]{\text{Pd/Lindlar}} CH_2\!\!=\!\!CH_2 \xrightarrow[\text{Eq. 4.6}]{HI} CH_3CH_2I$

c. $HC\!\!\equiv\!\!CH + NaNH_2 \xrightarrow[\text{Eq. 4.52}]{NH_3} HC\!\!\equiv\!\!C^-Na^+ \xrightarrow[\substack{\text{(from part b)} \\ \text{Eq. 4.53}}]{CH_3CH_2I} HC\!\!\equiv\!\!CCH_2CH_3$

d. $HC\!\!\equiv\!\!CH + 2HI \longrightarrow CH_3CHI_2$ (Eq. 4.6)

e. $HC\!\!\equiv\!\!CCH_2CH_3$ (from part c) $+ 2HBr \longrightarrow CH_3CBr_2CH_2CH_3$ (Eq. 4.6)

f. $HC{\equiv}CCH_2CH_3$ (from part c) + $Na^+NH_2^-$ $\xrightarrow[\text{Eq. 4.52}]{NH_3}$

$CH_3CH_2C{\equiv}C^-Na^+$ $\xrightarrow[\text{from part b}]{CH_3CH_2I}$ $CH_3CH_2C{\equiv}CCH_2CH_3$ + Na^+I^-
Eq. 4.53

g. $HC{\equiv}CH$ + $2Br_2$ $\longrightarrow$ $CHBr_2CHBr_2$ **(Eq. 4.3)**

h. $CH_3CH_2C{\equiv}CCH_2CH_3$ (from part f) + H_2 $\xrightarrow[\text{Eq. 4.17}]{Pd/Lindlar}$ $CH_3CH_2CH{=}CHCH_2CH_3$
cis isomer

SR.4. In problems of this type, carefully examine the structures of the starting material and the final product. Seek out similarities and differences. Note the types of bonds that must be made or broken in order to go from one structure to the other. Sometimes it is profitable to work backward from the product, and forward from the starting material simultaneously, hoping to arrive at a common intermediate.

a. $CH_3CH{=}CHCH_3$ $\xrightarrow[\text{Eq. 4.3}]{Br_2}$ $CH_3\underset{Br}{CH}{-}\underset{Br}{CH}CH_3$ $\xrightarrow[\text{Eq. 9.32}]{\underset{\text{in alcohol}}{KOH}}$ $CH_2{=}CH{-}CH{=}CH_2$

(Possible by-products in the second step include $CH_3C{\equiv}CCH_3$ and $CH_2{=}C{=}CHCH_3$.)

b. $CH_3\underset{OH}{CH}CH_3$ $\xrightarrow[\substack{\text{heat} \\ \text{Eq. 7.8}}]{H^+}$ $CH_2{=}CHCH_3$ $\xrightarrow[\text{Eq. 4.3}]{Br_2}$ $\underset{Br}{CH_2}{-}\underset{Br}{CH}{-}CH_3$ $\xrightarrow[\substack{\text{in alcohol} \\ \text{Eq. 9.32}}]{KOH}$ $HC{\equiv}CCH_3$

(A possible by-product in the last step is $CH_2{=}C{=}CH_2$.)

c. $CH_3CH_2CH_2Br$ $\xrightarrow[\substack{\text{in alcohol} \\ \text{Eq. 9.32}}]{KOH}$ $CH_3CH{=}CH_2$ $\xrightarrow[\text{part } b]{\text{as in}}$ $CH_3C{\equiv}CH$ $\xrightarrow[\text{Eq. 4.21}]{2\,HCl}$ $CH_3\underset{Cl}{\overset{Cl}{C}}{-}CH_3$

d. $CH_2{=}CH{-}CH{=}CH_2$ $\xrightarrow[\text{Eq. 4.27}]{Br_2}$ $\underset{Br}{CH_2}{-}CH{=}CH{-}\underset{Br}{CH_2}$ $\xrightarrow[\substack{\text{Pt} \\ \text{Eq. 4.14}}]{H_2}$ $\underset{Br}{CH_2}CH_2CH_2\underset{Br}{CH_2}$

A possible by-product in the first step is

$\underset{Br}{CH_2}{-}\underset{Br}{CH}{-}CH{=}CH_2$

SR.5. a.

         (Eq. 5.7)

Sulfonation must precede chlorination, since the SO_3H group is meta-directing whereas the Cl group is ortho-para directing (Section 5.5c).

b.

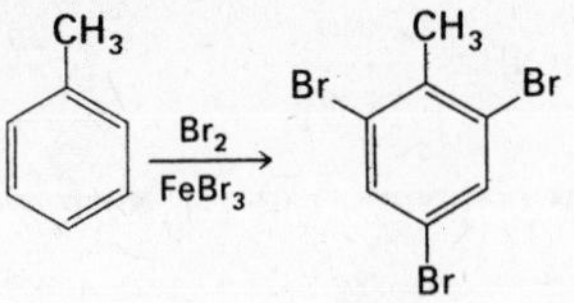

(Eq. 5.7)

The methyl group is ortho-para directing. We must use an $FeBr_3$ catalyst to ensure that electrophilic (on the ring) and not free-radical (on the side chain) bromination occurs.

c.

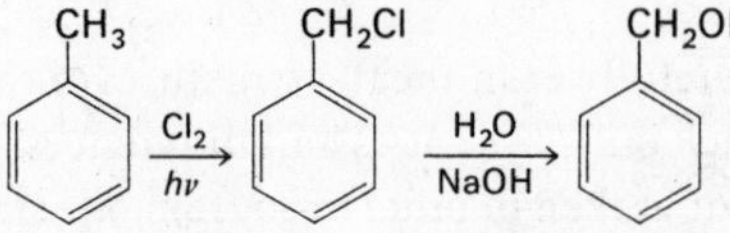

The first step is a free-radical reaction (Eq. 5.17). The second step is the hydrolysis of an alkyl halide (Eq. 9.2).

d.

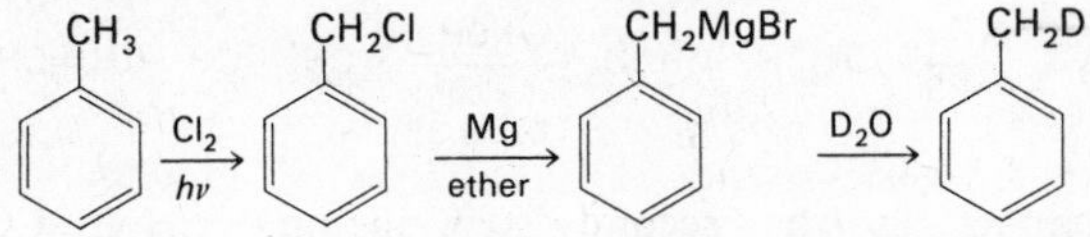

The first step is as in part c. The second is the formation of a Grignard reagent (Eq. 9.41) and its reaction with heavy water (Eq. 9.45).

e.

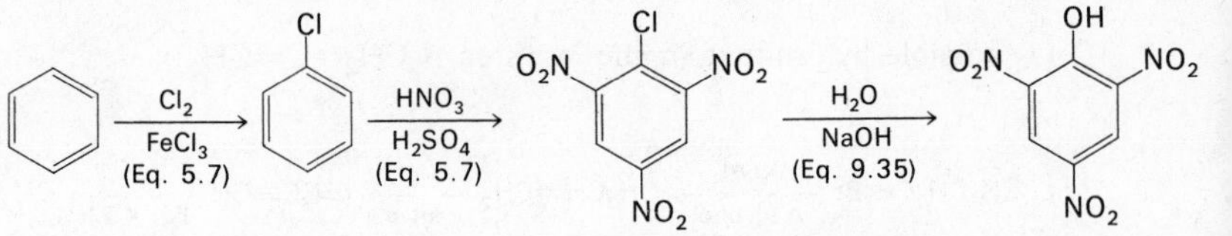

The first two steps involve electrophilic aromatic substitution; the Cl substituent is o/p directing. The final step is a nucleophilic aromatic substitution (Section 9.3).

SR.6. a.

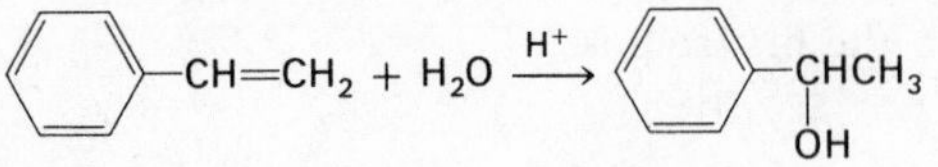

(Eq. 4.20)

b. $CH_3CH_2CH_2CH_2Br \xrightarrow[OH^-]{aqueous} CH_3CH_2CH_2CH_2OH$ (Eq. 9.2)

c. $CH_3CH{=}CH_2 \xrightarrow[\substack{heat \\ Eq.\ 4.46}]{Cl_2,} CH_2CH{=}CH_2 \xrightarrow[\substack{OH^- \\ Eq.\ 9.2}]{aqueous} CH_2CH{=}CH_2$

(with Cl and OH substituents shown)

d. $CH_2{=}CHCH_2CH_3 \xrightarrow[\substack{H^+ \\ Eq.\ 4.20}]{H_2O} CH_3CHCH_2CH_3 \xrightarrow[Eq.\ 7.2]{Na} CH_3CHCH_2CH_3 + H_2$

(with OH and O⁻Na⁺ substituents shown)

e. $CH_3CH_2CH_2CH_2OH \xrightarrow[\substack{ZnBr_2 \\ Eq.\ 7.15}]{HBr} CH_3CH_2CH_2CH_2Br \xrightarrow[Eq.\ 9.8]{NaSH} CH_3CH_2CH_2CH_2SH$

f.

$\xrightarrow[\substack{FeBr_3 \\ Eq.\ 5.7}]{Br_2}$ $\xrightarrow[Eq.\ 5.18]{KMnO_4}$

g.

$\xrightarrow[Eq.\ 7.4]{NaOH}$ $\xrightarrow{Eq.\ 9.5}$ $\xrightarrow[]{Eq.\ 5.16}$ H_2, Pt

$CH_3CH_2OH \xrightarrow[\substack{ZnBr_2 \\ Eq.\ 7.15}]{HBr} CH_3CH_2Br$

Alternatively, the phenol could have been reduced to cyclohexanol (Eq. 5.16), converted with sodium to its alkoxide (Eq. 7.2), and then treated with ethyl bromide to give the desired product.

h. $CH_3CH_2CH_2CH_2OH \xrightarrow[\substack{cold \\ Eq.\ 7.22}]{H_2SO_4} CH_3CH_2CH_2CH_2OSO_3H$

$\begin{array}{l} CH_3CH_2CH_2CH_2OH,\ heat \\ Eq.\ 9.4\ (X = OSO_3H) \end{array}$

$(CH_3CH_2CH_2CH_2)_2O + H_2SO_4 \longleftarrow$

The Williamson synthesis can also be used:

$CH_3CH_2CH_2CH_2OH \xrightarrow[Eq.\ 7.2]{Na} CH_3CH_2CH_2CH_2O^-Na^+$

Eq. 7.15 | HBr | Eq. 9.5

$CH_3CH_2CH_2CH_2Br \longrightarrow (CH_3CH_2CH_2CH_2)_2O$

SR.7. a. $CH_3\underset{OH}{CH}CH_3 + HCl \xrightarrow[(conc)]{ZnCl_2} CH_3\underset{Cl}{CH}CH_3 + H_2O$ **(Eq. 7.15)**

b. $CH_3\underset{OH}{CH}CH_3 \xrightarrow[heat]{H^+} CH_3CH=CH_2 \xrightarrow[400°]{Cl_2} \underset{Cl}{CH_2}CH=CH_2$

(Eq. 7.8)   (Eq. 4.46)

c. $CH_3CH=CH_2 + Br_2 \xrightarrow{(Eq.\ 4.3)} CH_3\underset{Br}{CH}-\underset{Br}{CH_2}$

(from b)

d. $2\ CH_3\underset{OH}{CH}CH_3 + 2\ Na \xrightarrow{(Eq.\ 7.2)} 2\ CH_3\underset{O^-Na^+}{CH}CH_3 + H_2$

$CH_3\underset{O^-Na^+}{CH}CH_3 + CH_3I \xrightarrow{(Eq.\ 9.5)} CH_3\underset{OCH_3}{CH}CH_3 + Na^+I^-$

e. $CH_3\underset{\underset{Cl}{|}}{C}HCH_3 +$ $\xrightarrow[\substack{\text{Friedel–}\\\text{Crafts}\\\text{alkylation}\\\text{(Eq. 5.7)}}]{AlCl_3}$ $+ HCl$

(from *a*) $CH(CH_3)_2$

SR.8. a. $CH_3CH_2CH_2CH_3 + Br_2 \xrightarrow[\substack{\text{or}\\\text{light}}]{\text{heat}} CH_3\underset{\underset{Br}{|}}{C}HCH_2CH_3 + HBr$

The product is contaminated with l-bromobutane, as well as with di-, tri-, and so on bromobutanes.

b. $CH_3\underset{\underset{OH}{|}}{C}HCH_2CH_3 + HBr \xrightarrow{ZnBr_2} CH_3\underset{\underset{Br}{|}}{C}HCH_2CH_3$ **(Eq. 7.15)**

One can also use PBr_3 as the reagent. This method gives a good yield and is unlikely to give isomers.

c. $CH_2{=}CHCH_2CH_3 + HBr \longrightarrow CH_3\underset{\underset{Br}{|}}{C}HCH_2CH_3$

Addition follows Markownikoff's rule (Section 4.6b) and mainly gives the desired isomer.

d. $CH_3CH{=}CHCH_3 + HBr \longrightarrow CH_3\underset{\underset{Br}{|}}{C}HCH_2CH_3$

The alkene is symmetric and can give only one addition product.

SR.9. In each case, write the structural formula of the desired product, note the positions of the halogens, and select the desired alkene, alkyne, or diene accordingly.

a. $CH_2{=}CHCH_2CH_3 + Br_2 \longrightarrow \underset{\underset{Br}{|}}{C}H_2{-}\underset{\underset{Br}{|}}{C}HCH_2CH_3$

b. $HC{\equiv}CH \xrightarrow{HCl} CH_2{=}CHCl \xrightarrow{HCl} CH_3CHCl_2$

c. $CH_2{=}CH{-}CH{=}CH_2 + 2\ Br_2 \longrightarrow \underset{\underset{Br}{|}}{C}H_2\underset{\underset{Br}{|}}{C}H{-}\underset{\underset{Br}{|}}{C}H{-}\underset{\underset{Br}{|}}{C}H_2$

d. $+ HI \longrightarrow$ $-I$

e. $CH_2{=}CH{-}CH{=}CH_2 + Br_2 \longrightarrow \underset{\underset{Br}{|}}{C}H_2{-}CH{=}CH{-}\underset{\underset{Br}{|}}{C}H_2$

f. $HC{\equiv}C{-}CH_3 + 2\ Cl_2 \longrightarrow \underset{\underset{Cl}{|}}{\overset{\overset{Cl}{|}}{H}}C{-}\underset{\underset{Cl}{|}}{\overset{\overset{Cl}{|}}{C}}{-}CH_3$

g. 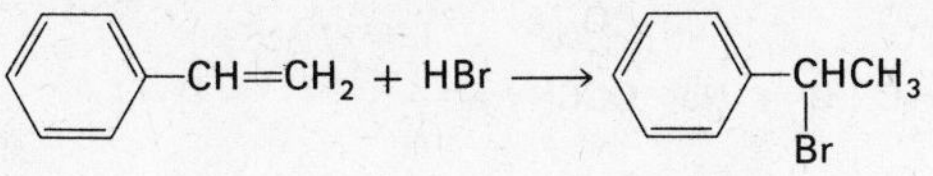

h. 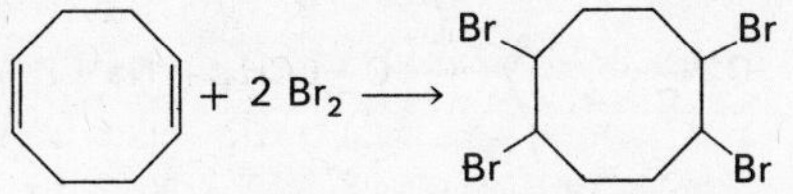

SR.10. a. $CH_3CH(OH)CH_2CH_2CH_3 \xrightarrow[H^+ \text{ heat}]{CrO_3} CH_3C(=O)CH_2CH_2CH_3$ **(Eqs. 7.27 and 7.30)**

b. $CH_3CH_2CH_2CH_2CH_2OH \xrightarrow[\text{heat}]{CrO_3,\ H^+} CH_3CH_2CH_2CH_2CHO$ **(Eq. 7.26)**

c. 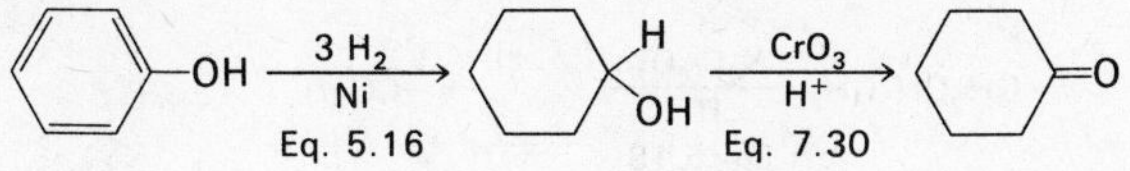

d. $CH_3C{\equiv}CH + 2\ HCl \xrightarrow[\text{and Eq. 4.6}]{\text{Eq. 4.8}} CH_3CCl_2CH_3 \xrightarrow[H_2O]{OH^-} CH_3C(=O)CH_3$ **(Eq. 10.2)**

or

$CH_3C{\equiv}CH + H_2O \xrightarrow[H_2SO_4]{HgSO_4} CH_3C(=O)CH_3$ **(Eq. 4.11)**

e. 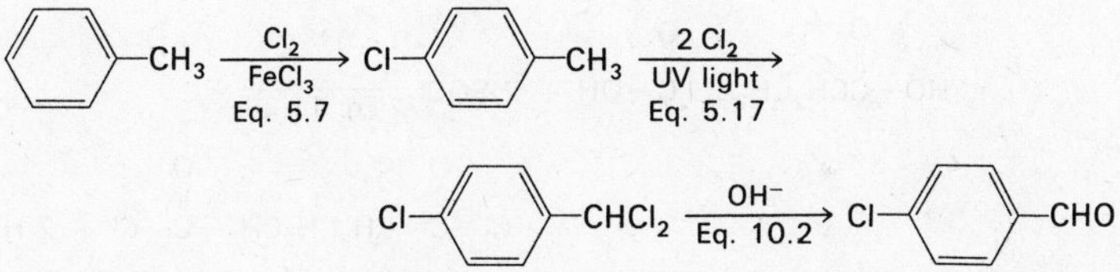

SR.11. a. 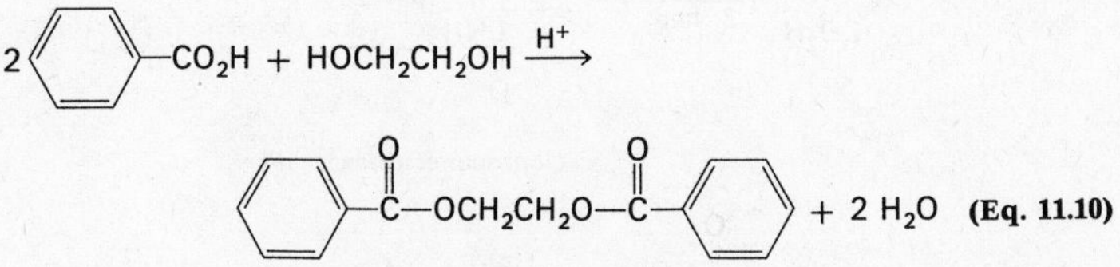

ethylene glycol dibenzoate

b. 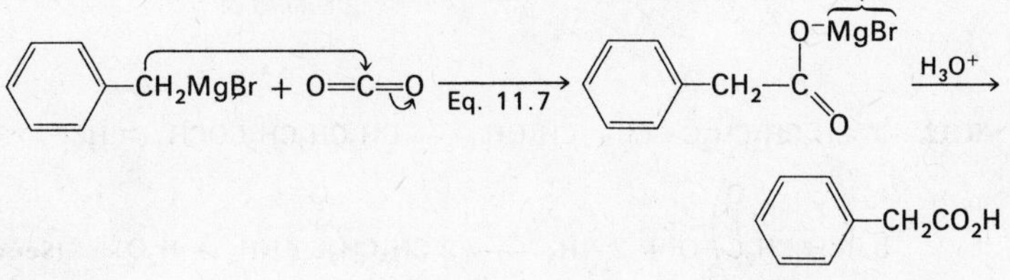

phenylacetic acid

c. O_2N—⟨benzene ring⟩—$\overset{\displaystyle O}{\overset{\|}{C}}$—Cl + Na$^+$ $^-\overset{\displaystyle O}{\overset{\|}{O}}CCH_3$ ⟶

O_2N—⟨benzene ring⟩—$\overset{\displaystyle O}{\overset{\|}{C}}$—O—$\overset{\displaystyle O}{\overset{\|}{C}}CH_3$ + Na$^+$Cl$^-$ **(Eq. 11.35)**

acetic *p*-nitrobenzoic anhydride

d. HO—$\overset{\displaystyle O}{\overset{\|}{C}}$—⟨benzene ring⟩—OH + $CH_3\overset{\displaystyle O}{\overset{\|}{C}}\overset{\displaystyle O}{\overset{\|}{O}}CCH_3$ ⟶

HO$\overset{\displaystyle O}{\overset{\|}{C}}$—⟨benzene ring⟩—O—$\overset{\displaystyle O}{\overset{\|}{C}}CH_3$ + CH_3CO_2H **(Eq. 11.46)**

e. ⟨benzene ring⟩—$CH_2CH_2CH_3$ $\xrightarrow[\text{Eq. 5.18}]{\frac{K_2Cr_2O_7}{H^+}}$ ⟨benzene ring⟩—CO_2H

benzoic acid

f. ⟨phthalic anhydride⟩ + 2 CH_3OH $\xrightarrow[\text{Eq. 11.36}]{H^+}$ ⟨benzene ring⟩$\overset{\displaystyle CO_2CH_3}{\underset{\displaystyle CO_2CH_3}{}}$ + H_2O

dimethyl phthalate

g. HO—$\overset{\displaystyle O}{\overset{\|}{C}}CH_2CH_2CH_2\overset{\displaystyle O}{\overset{\|}{C}}$—OH + 2 $SOCl_2$ $\xrightarrow[\text{Eq. 11.29}]{}$

Cl—$\overset{\displaystyle O}{\overset{\|}{C}}$—$CH_2CH_2CH_2$—$\overset{\displaystyle O}{\overset{\|}{C}}$—Cl + 2 HCl + 2 SO_2

h. ⟨cyclopropane⟩$\overset{\displaystyle H}{\underset{\displaystyle CO_2H}{}}$ $\xrightarrow[\text{2. heat}]{\text{1. } NH_4OH}$ ⟨cyclopropane⟩$\overset{\displaystyle H}{\underset{\displaystyle \overset{\displaystyle CNH_2}{\underset{\displaystyle \|}{}O}}{}}$ **(Eq. 11.3)**

cyclopropanecarboxamide

i. CH_2=CH—$CH_2\overset{\displaystyle O}{\overset{\|}{C}}$—$OCH_3$ $\xrightarrow[\text{Eq. 11.21}]{LiAlH_4}$ CH_2=$CHCH_2CH_2OH$ + CH_3OH

3-buten-1-ol

SR.12. a. $CH_3CH_2CH_2\overset{\displaystyle O}{\overset{\|}{C}}$—Cl + CH_3OH ⟶ $CH_3CH_2CH_2\overset{\displaystyle O}{\overset{\|}{C}}OCH_3$ + HCl **(Eq. 11.31)**

b. $\left(CH_3CH_2\overset{\displaystyle O}{\overset{\|}{C}}\right)_2O$ + 2 NH_3 ⟶ 2 $CH_3CH_2\overset{\displaystyle O}{\overset{\|}{C}}$—$NH_2$ + H_2O **(Section 11.10b)**

c. $CH_3CH_2CH_2CO_2H \xrightarrow[H^+]{CH_3OH} CH_3CH_2CH_2CO_2CH_3 \xrightarrow[Eq.\ 11.21]{LiAlH_4}$
Eq. 11.10

$$CH_3CH_2CH_2CH_2OH + CH_3OH$$

The two alcohols can be separated by fractional distillation.

d. $CH_3CH_2CH_2CH_2CH_2OH \xrightarrow{Na_2Cr_2O_7} CH_3CH_2CH_2CH_2CO_2H$ **(Eqs. 7.26 and 10.3)**

e. $CH_3CH_2\overset{\text{O}}{\overset{\|}{C}}Br + 2\ NH_3 \longrightarrow CH_3CH_2\overset{\text{O}}{\overset{\|}{C}}NH_2 + NH_4^+Br^-$ **(Eq. 11.32)**

f. $CH_3\overset{\text{O}}{\overset{\|}{C}}Cl + CH_3\overset{\text{O}}{\overset{\|}{C}}O^-Na^+ \xrightarrow{heat} CH_3\overset{\text{O}}{\overset{\|}{C}}O\overset{\text{O}}{\overset{\|}{C}}CH_3 + Na^+Cl^-$ **(Eq. 11.35)**

g. $CH_3\overset{\text{O}}{\overset{\|}{C}}O\overset{\text{O}}{\overset{\|}{C}}CH_3 + H_2NNH_2 \longrightarrow CH_3\overset{\text{O}}{\overset{\|}{C}}NHNH_2 + CH_3CO_2H$ **(Eq. 11.20)**

h. $HO-\overset{\text{O}}{\overset{\|}{C}}-\overset{\text{O}}{\overset{\|}{C}}-OH + 2\ CH_3CH_2OH \xrightarrow{H^+} CH_3CH_2O-\overset{\text{O}}{\overset{\|}{C}}-\overset{\text{O}}{\overset{\|}{C}}-OCH_2CH_3$
diethyl oxalate **(Eq. 11.10)**

i. $H_2N\overset{\text{O}}{\overset{\|}{C}}NH_2 + H_2O \longrightarrow 2\ NH_3 + CO_2$ (Section 13.8, reverse of Eq. 13.38)

j. $\bigcirc\!\!-\overset{\text{O}}{\overset{\|}{C}}Cl + 2\ CH_3NH_2 \longrightarrow \bigcirc\!\!-\overset{\text{O}}{\overset{\|}{C}}-NHCH_3 + CH_3NH_3^+Cl^-$
(Eq. 11.32)

SR.13. a. $CH_3CH_2CO_2H \xrightarrow{PBr_3} CH_3CH_2\overset{\text{O}}{\overset{\|}{C}}-Br$ (compare with Eq. 11.28)

b. $CH_3CH_2CH_2CH_2CO_2H + CH_3CH_2OH \xrightarrow[heat]{H^+}$

$$CH_3CH_2CH_2CH_2\overset{\text{O}}{\overset{\|}{C}}-OCH_2CH_3 + H_2O$$ **(Eq. 11.10)**

c. $CH_3CH_2CH_2CO_2H + NH_4OH \xrightarrow{heat} CH_3CH_2CH_2\overset{\text{O}}{\overset{\|}{C}}NH_2 + 2\ H_2O$ **(Eq. 11.3)**

d. $\bigcirc\!\!\overset{CO_2H}{\underset{CO_2H}{\Big\langle}} \xrightarrow{heat} \bigcirc\!\!\Big\langle{}_O^O + H_2O$ **(Eq. 11.33)**

e. $HO_2C-CO_2H + Ca(OH)_2 \longrightarrow (^-O_2C-CO_2^-)Ca^{2+} + 2\ H_2O$ **(Eq. 11.2)**

f. $\bigcirc\!\!-CH_2CO_2H + NH_3 \xrightarrow{heat} \bigcirc\!\!-CH_2\overset{\text{O}}{\overset{\|}{C}}-NH_2 + H_2O$ **(Eq. 11.3)**

g. $CH_3CH_2CH_2CH_2CO_2H \xrightarrow{PCl_5} CH_3CH_2CH_2CH_2\overset{\displaystyle O}{\overset{\|}{C}}-Cl$ **(Eq. 11.28)**

$CH_3CH_2CH_2CH_2CO_2H \xrightarrow{NaOH} CH_3CH_2CH_2CH_2CO_2^-Na^+$ **(Eq. 11.2)**

$CH_3CH_2CH_2CH_2\overset{\displaystyle O}{\overset{\|}{C}}-Cl + CH_3CH_2CH_2CH_2CO_2^-Na^+ \xrightarrow{heat}$

$CH_3CH_2CH_2CH_2\overset{\displaystyle O}{\overset{\|}{C}}-O-\overset{\displaystyle O}{\overset{\|}{C}}CH_2CH_2CH_2CH_3 + Na^+Cl^-$ **(Eq. 11.35)**

h. 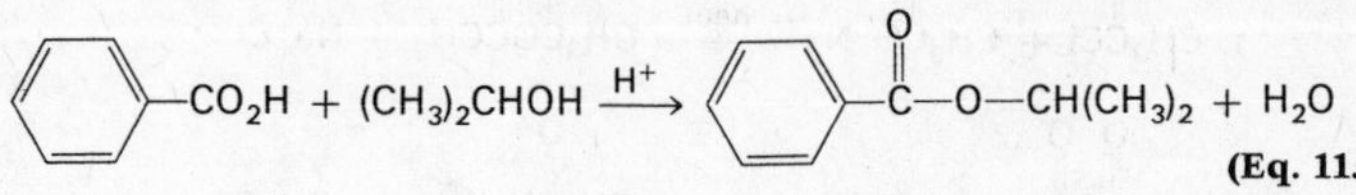 $-CO_2H + (CH_3)_2CHOH \xrightarrow{H^+}$ $\overset{\displaystyle O}{\overset{\|}{C}}-O-CH(CH_3)_2 + H_2O$

     (Eq. 11.10)

i. 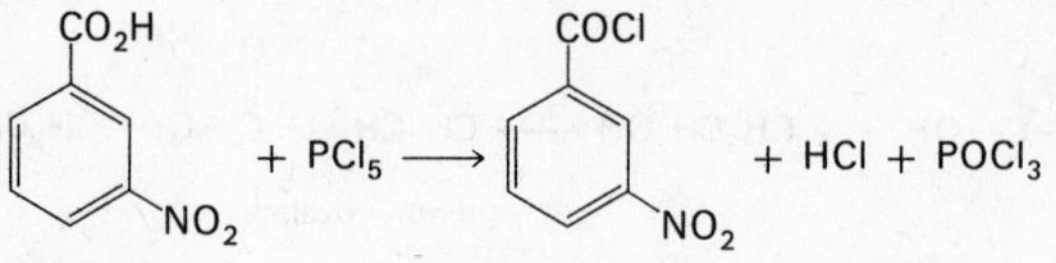 $+ PCl_5 \longrightarrow$ $+ HCl + POCl_3$ **(Eq. 11.28)**

j. $H\overset{\displaystyle O}{\overset{\|}{C}}-OH + NH_3 \xrightarrow{heat} H\overset{\displaystyle O}{\overset{\|}{C}}-NH_2 + H_2O$ **(Eq. 11.3)**

SR.14.   a. $CH_3CH_2CH_2CH_2Cl + (CH_3)_3N \xrightarrow[Eq.\ 13.10]{} (CH_3)_3\overset{+}{N}CH_2CH_2CH_2CH_3$ Cl^-

b. Advantage is taken, in parts b and c, of the displacement reactions that aryl diazonium salts undergo.

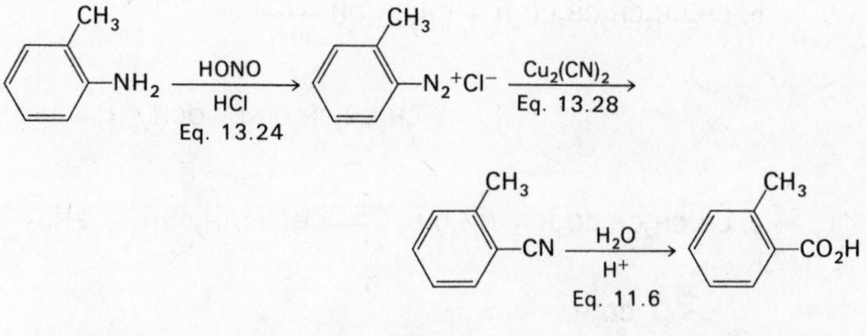

c.

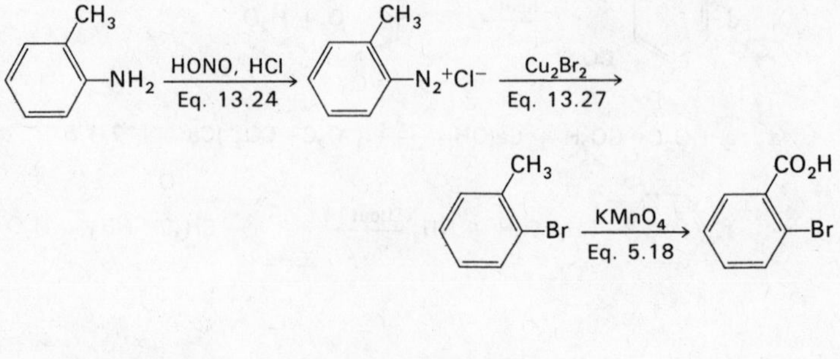

d. $CH_2{=}CHCH_2CH_3 + HBr \xrightarrow[\text{Eq. 4.21}]{} CH_3\overset{|}{\underset{Br}{C}}HCH_2CH_3$

Eq. 9.14 $\Big\downarrow$ NaCN

$CH_3\overset{|}{\underset{CH_2NH_2}{C}}HCH_2CH_3 \xleftarrow[\text{Eq. 9.15}]{\overset{H_2}{\underset{Pt}{}}} CH_3\overset{|}{\underset{CN}{C}}HCH_2CH_3$

SR.15. a. We can start with a three-carbon alcohol and add the fourth carbon by way of the nitrile:

$CH_3CH_2CH_2OH \xrightarrow[\text{Eq. 7.20}]{PBr_3} CH_3CH_2CH_2Br \xrightarrow[\text{Eq. 9.14}]{NaCN}$

$CH_3CH_2CH_2CN \xrightarrow[\text{Ni}]{H_2} CH_3CH_2CH_2CH_2NH_2$

Eq. 9.15

Alternatively, we can start with a four-carbon alcohol:

$CH_3CH_2CH_2CH_2OH \xrightarrow[\text{ZnBr}_2]{HBr} CH_3CH_2CH_2CH_2Br \xrightarrow[\substack{\text{(excess)}}]{NH_3}$

Eq. 7.15   Eqs. 9.10
and 9.11

$CH_3CH_2CH_2CH_2NH_2$

b. $CH_3{-}\langle\hspace{-4pt}\bigcirc\hspace{-4pt}\rangle \xrightarrow[\text{Eq. 5.7}]{HONO_2} CH_3{-}\langle\hspace{-4pt}\bigcirc\hspace{-4pt}\rangle{-}NO_2 \xrightarrow[\text{HCl}]{Sn} CH_3{-}\langle\hspace{-4pt}\bigcirc\hspace{-4pt}\rangle{-}NH_2$

Eq. 13.25

c. Repeat the first method used in part a, but start with 1-butanol.

d. $\langle\hspace{-4pt}\bigcirc\hspace{-4pt}\rangle \xrightarrow[\substack{\text{2. H}_2/\text{Pt}}]{\text{1. HONO}_2} \langle\hspace{-4pt}\bigcirc\hspace{-4pt}\rangle{-}NH_2 \xrightarrow[\text{Eq. 13.8}]{CH_3CH_2Br} \langle\hspace{-4pt}\bigcirc\hspace{-4pt}\rangle{-}NHCH_2CH_3$

Eqs. 5.7 and
13.25

e. $\langle\hspace{-4pt}\bigcirc\hspace{-4pt}\rangle{-}CH_3 \xrightarrow[\text{Eq. 5.18}]{KMnO_4} \langle\hspace{-4pt}\bigcirc\hspace{-4pt}\rangle{-}CO_2H \xrightarrow[\text{H}^+]{HONO_2}$

Eq. 5.7

$O_2N{-}\langle\hspace{-4pt}\bigcirc\hspace{-4pt}\rangle{-}CO_2H \xrightarrow[\text{Eq. 13.25}]{H_2/Pt} H_2N{-}\langle\hspace{-4pt}\bigcirc\hspace{-4pt}\rangle{-}CO_2H$

The carboxyl group is meta directing; thus it is better to nitrate the benzoic acid rather than the toluene, which would give mainly the ortho and para isomers.

f. $CH_3CH_2CH_2CH_2OH \xrightarrow[\text{Eq. 7.20}]{PBr_3} CH_3CH_2CH_2CH_2Br \xrightarrow[\text{Eqs. 9.10 and 9.11}]{NH_3}$

$(CH_3CH_2CH_2CH_2)_3N$

In the second step, use an excess of *n*-butyl bromide.

g. $CH_3CH_2OH \xrightarrow[\text{heat}]{H^+} CH_2{=}CH_2 \xrightarrow[\text{Eq. 4.3}]{Br_2} \underset{\underset{Br}{|}}{CH_2}{-}\underset{\underset{Br}{|}}{CH_2} \xrightarrow[\text{Eq. 9.14}]{2\,Na^+CN^-}$
Eq. 7.8

$\underset{\underset{CN}{|}}{CH_2}{-}\underset{\underset{CN}{|}}{CH_2} \xrightarrow[\text{Pt}]{4\,H_2} H_2NCH_2CH_2CH_2CH_2NH_2$
Eq. 9.15

BCDEFGHIJ-A-79